Mark Marshaw
12/7/85
N.Y.C.

1000

**HOME ENERGY
FOR THE EIGHTIES**

# HOME ENERGY
# FOR THE EIGHTIES

**Ralph Wolfe and Peter Clegg**

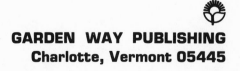

**GARDEN WAY PUBLISHING**
**Charlotte, Vermont 05445**

*Text Illustrations by Ralph Wolfe, except as otherwise credited*
*Catalog illustrations courtesy of product manufacturers*

*Catalog sections researched and compiled by Kathy Smith,*
*Martha Hess, and Georgene Grover*

*Printed in the United States*
*Second Printing, October 1979*

**Library of Congress Cataloging in Publication Data**

Wolfe, Ralph, 1949–
  Home energy for the eighties.

Includes bibliographical references and index.
  1. Dwellings—Energy conservation.  2. Solar energy.
3. Wind power.  4. Water power.  I. Clegg, Peter,
joint author.  II. Title.
TJ163.5.D86W64    696    79-9412
ISBN 0-88266-158-2
ISBN 0-88266-165-5

# Contents

# 3

# Wind Power 125

# 4

# Water Power 165

# 5

# Wood Heat 195

# Introduction

Energy is the hot topic of the decade, and with good reason: it is becoming scarcer and more expensive annually, as conventional fuels dry up. Politicians argue, newspapers probe, while homeowners feel the squeeze of the Great Energy Crisis. Everyone looks forward to that distant day when solar power becomes available, and we can reduce our dependence on Saudi Arabia, Standard Oil and United Nuclear. *Time* magazine tells us, however, that such alternative energy sources are costly, experimental, and still many years away from practical reality.

Don't believe it. *Alternative energy is already available.* And it is cheaper and simpler than we have been led to expect.

There is more to *solar energy* than rooftop collectors and expensive plumbing. Or perhaps we should say there is *less*: solar energy may be no more complex than a few well-placed windows to admit the sunlight, and a masonry floor to retain its heat. A house that is carefully planned according to passive solar heating principles may receive up to 100 percent of its warmth from the sun, and cost no more than a conventionally-heated house.

*Wind energy*, too, is becoming simpler and cheaper. Modern windmills are able to extract more power from the wind more efficiently. New electronic hardware is available that can eliminate the need for expensive battery banks to store electric power. Instead, excess power can be sold back to the utility company, running the meter backwards!

New equipment also has placed *water power* within the grasp of rural homeowners who wish to take advantage of the available energy in small streams and rivers. Once installed, a home hydro-electric plant will provide low-cost electric power for twenty years or more, immune to blackouts, oil crises or rate increases.

As fuel costs spiral upward, *wood heat* becomes more and more attractive as an alternative energy source—particularly for those who can cut their own. Furnaces are now available that can accept oil, coal or wood to heat the house. Automatic-feed systems eliminate the need for constant fire tending. And the new stoves and heat-extracting fireplace devices squeeze more heat out of each log.

Home *energy conservation* hardly seems in the same category with these other more "glamorous" power sources. But conservation really is the cornerstone of alternative energy consciousness. It is senseless to pursue new sources before reducing waste to an absolute minimum. And conservation is the best energy investment of all: house heating, cooling and electric bills could be reduced by *50 percent or more* by a few simple and inexpensive measures.

This book is an attempt to de-mystify the new energy hocus-pocus, and to make alternative energy ideas available to the homeowner in a simple but comprehensive treatment. Complex formulas have been reduced to simple rules-of-thumb. Practical explanations are supplemented by a list of references that contain more elaborate technical data. Up-to-date prices are featured throughout. And a complete catalog of available equipment follows each chapter, so that the homeowner can see:

- how it works
- what it looks like
- how much it costs
- and where to get it

But please note: this book is not a ticket to a free lunch. Solar power is not free; nor is wind, water or wood. They all entail the purchase and installation of expensive equipment. Carefully planned and installed, the equipment will work well, and it will quickly pay for itself in reduced fuel bills. Like any other good investment, money well spent will produce a profitable "income" of energy savings over the years. This is the principle of *life-cycle costing*, fundamental to the economics of alternative energy.

Most developers and builders install cheap heating systems and minimal insulation in new houses to keep the purchase price as low and attractive as possible. Purchasers later discover that they have been penalized many times over for this apparent "saving." If life-cycle costing were considered, homebuyers would realize that "luxuries" like extra insulation, solar heating, or even a windmill can be a financial bargain. An extra $1200 for the down payment on a $40,000 house could result in a saving of $300 to $800 or more *per year* of total owning and operating expenses.

The key to wise energy investment is threefold: (1) thoughtful reduction of your present energy consumption, (2) assessment of the locally available alternatives (sun, wind, water and wood), and (3) selection of appropriate strategies to make best use of them. This book will not transform you into an energy expert. But it will arm you with a background of principles, an outline of economics, and a sourcebook of hardware for the war on energy.

## A WORD ABOUT PRICES

To make this book as useful as possible, we have tried to list current prices and approximate costs for most of the products described.

Many manufacturers balk at naming specific prices, because they expect the price to rise and don't want to be out-of-date. But inflation is now a common fact of life; we trust that the reader understands this, and will anticipate general price increases of about 10 percent per year. At this rate, prices (and wages) can be expected to double in about eight years.

There will be exceptions: foreign-made products will vary in price with the fluctuating world currency market. Petroleum-based goods, like plastic, will rise as oil costs rise. And some products may actually drop in price, as mass production and technological improvements continue to make alternative energy sources more and more economical.

## About the Authors

RALPH WOLFE, a native of Burnt Hills, New York, worked as a carpenter for several years before attending Yale University's School of Architecture, where he was awarded the Alpha Rho Chi Medal upon graduation in 1978. He has worked for Cambridge Seven Associates and the Hartford Design Group, and is currently a partner in the firm of Lipkin/Wolfe Design/Build. A writer, lecturer and designer of energy alternatives, Mr. Wolfe resides in Cambridge, Massachusetts.

PETER CLEGG, a native of the Yorkshire village of Saxton in England, studied architecture at Cambridge University. He came to the United States on a Mellon fellowship, attending Yale University in the environmental design program. In 1974, Peter shared an American Institute of Architects (AIA) award for his work in energy conservation and building design. He is presently a practicing architect in Bath, England, specializing in solar applications.

# 1

# Energy Conservation

Passive energy house, Hinesburg, Vermont. Designed by Parallax, Inc., it uses panels of double-skinned acrylic, a wall storage unit, and heavy insulation to reduce heating costs.

mericans waste energy. Since 1973, this unfortunate fact has become painfully clear. With only 6 percent of the world's population, the United States uses over 30 percent of the world's energy. This imbalance is more than simply a reflection of our high standard of living: Denmark, with a per capita GNP equal to that of the United States, consumes *half* the per capita energy, achieving the same high standards of living without deprivation or discomfort.

The Danes, and other energy-enlightened societies, have learned to tap one of the world's richest "hidden" energy supplies—conservation, a potential energy "source" equivalent to trillions of barrels of oil. Energy experts assert that through conservation a 30 to 40 percent reduction in national energy use is entirely feasible. One study estimates that nearly half of U.S. energy consumption can be saved by a comprehensive energy conservation effort—an amount equivalent to the electrical output of 680 nuclear reactors.

Much of this saving can be accomplished through the individual, small-scale efforts of home owners. Houses consume one-fifth of America's energy (Figure 1-1). But less than 2 percent of American homes are well-insulated. If your house is an energy hog, a thorough conservation effort could reduce your fuel bills by half. Any study of energy alternatives must begin here, with some guidelines for belt-tightening.

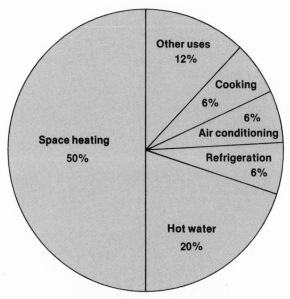

**Figure 1-1. Energy use in United States homes.**

# Energy Fundamentals

Heat flows from warm objects to colder objects. This flow of energy is measured in British Thermal Units, or Btu. (One Btu is the energy required to heat one pound of water by 1° Fahrenheit. See Table 1-2.) The rate of flow depends upon two things: the *temperature difference*, or $\Delta T$, and the *resistance to heat flow*, or R-value. Materials with high R-values retard the flow of

**Table 1-2. Heat Produced by Various Sources.**

| | |
|---|---|
| A 100-watt lightbulb | 341 Btu/hour |
| A couple dancing | 1700 Btu/hour |
| Sunlight through a window | 3000 Btu/hour |
| Typical house furnace | 60,000 Btu/hour |

heat better than materials with low R-values. Typical R-values of some common materials are given in Table 1-3.

When building materials of different R-values are combined to construct a wall or roof, their combined insulation effectiveness is given by the *U-factor*. (See Table 1-4.) U and R are inversely related; good insulation has a *high* R-value, and a

**Table 1-3. R-Values of Common Insulators.**

| Insulation Material | For One Inch | In 2 × 4 Wall* | In 2 × 6 Wall* |
|---|---|---|---|
| Mineral wool | 3.0 | 13.7 | 19.7 |
| Fiber glass | 3.5 | 15.5 | 22.4 |
| Polystyrene | 4.0 | 17.2 | 25.2 |
| Urethane | 6.5 | 25.9 | 38.9 |
| Vermiculite | 2.5 | 11.9 | 16.9 |
| Cellulose | 4.5 | 18.9 | 27.9 |
| Urea formaldehyde | 5.5 | 22.5 | 33.4 |

* Includes siding, sheathing, insulation and air films.
*Source*: E. Eccli, *Low-Cost Energy-Efficient Shelter for the Owner and Builder* (Emmaus, Pa.: Rodale Press, 1976).

**Table 1–4. U Factors in Building Construction.**

| Material | U Factor |
| --- | --- |
| Single glass | 1.13 Btu/hr/ft²/°F. |
| Double glass | 0.56 |
| Triple glass | 0.41 |
| Single plastic sheet | 1.09 |
| 8″ brick wall with gypsum wallboard | 0.29 |
| 2 × 4 stud wall with siding, sheathing, fiberglass insulation | 0.06 |
| 2 × 6 stud wall with siding, sheathing, fiberglass insulation | 0.04 |

*low* U-factor. Heat loss through a surface can be calculated from the U-factor:

$$\text{Heat loss (Btu/hr)} = U \times \text{Area (sq. ft.)} \times \Delta T\ (°\text{F.})$$

$$\text{and } U = \frac{1}{R_1 + R_2 + R_3 + \dots}$$

where $R_1$, $R_2$, $R_3$ are the R-values of the component layers in the wall (clapboard, insulation, plaster, etc.)

**Design heat loss.** The design heat loss is an estimate of the maximum hourly energy consumption of a house, under the most severe conditions to be expected. This figure is used to calculate the size of the house heating and cooling system. A poorly insulated, leaky house in a cold climate might have a design heat loss of about 60 Btu/hr per square foot of living area. A tight, well-insulated house might have a design heat loss of 20 Btu/hr/sq. ft. in the same climate.

**Annual energy use.** You can estimate the current energy consumption of your house from last year's fuel bills. Use Table 1–19 at the end of this section to calculate your total Btu consumption last year. A poorly insulated house in a cold

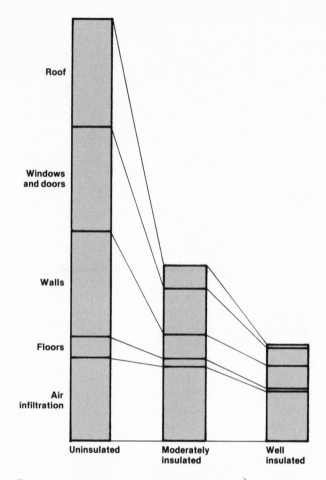

**Figure 1–5. Heat losses from typical houses.** \

climate might use approximately 130,000 Btu/year per square foot of living area (Figure 1–5). The tight, well-insulated house next door might consume only 40,000 Btu/year per square foot. This represents a saving of *70 percent* on fuel bills. Such dramatic savings are not possible for every house. Nonetheless, a careful inspection of the strengths and weaknesses of your house should reveal some ways that you can substantially reduce energy waste.

# Insulating

TYPES OF INSULATION

**Fiber glass.** Inexpensive, widely available and easy to install, fiber glass is the most commonly used insulation. It is available in rolls, batts, loose fill and rigid boards, with or without a vapor

---

> ### ESTIMATING THE DESIGN HEAT LOSS OF YOUR HOUSE
>
> Using Table 1–19 and last year's fuel bills, calculate Q, your yearly consumption of energy (MBtu/yr.) Examine the map and table on page 20 to estimate $\Delta T$, your local Design Temperature and Degree Days for your area.
>
> $$\text{Design Heat Loss} = \frac{Q \times \Delta T}{24\ \text{hr/day} \times \text{Degree Days}}$$

barrier. Fiber glass is fire-resistant and moisture-resistant. But it may be carcinogenic, so always wear gloves, long-sleeved shirt and a respirator when working with fiber glass. See Figure 1-7 for illustrations of various kinds of insulation.

**Rock wool.** This is the predecessor of fiber glass, and is a fibrous blanket made from rock or slag. It has properties similar to fiber glass, and is available in blankets, batts or loose fill.

**Cellulose.** Shredded paper, treated to be fire-retardant. It is an excellent insulator and quite cheap. Rodents like it, however, and moisture may rot it. Make sure it meets federal specs for fire-retardancy. Available as loose fill.

**Vermiculite.** Pellets of light, expanded mineral material, more familiar as a potting material for house plants. Cheap and easy, but with the same problems of moisture retention and settlement. Loose fill.

**Perlite.** Similar to vermiculite.

**Polystyrene.** Beads of expanded plastic, either loose or formed into boards. Moisture-resistant—but *not* a vapor barrier. Very flammable, so polystyrene must be enclosed or faced with a fire-resistant substance, such as wallboard.

**Polyurethane.** In rigid boards or foamed in place, polyurethane is one of the best insulators available. But it is expensive, and highly flammable, emitting cyanide gas when it burns. It cannot be foamed into a cavity wall, as it will expand and rupture the wall. It shrinks somewhat as it cures. Also, unless it is protected sunlight will degrade and destroy it.

**Isocyanurate.** The most effective insulating material available, with an R-value of 9.0 per inch. But like polyurethane, it is highly flammable and gives off cyanide gas when it burns. It is quite expensive, moisture resistant and serves as a vapor barrier. Available in rigid boards.

**Urea-formaldehyde.** This plastic foam has the consistency of shaving cream as it is squirted through holes into wall cavities or between ceiling rafters. It quickly hardens into a styrofoam-like substance. Urea-formaldehyde is water absorptive and needs a vapor barrier. It is flammable. There are many reports that the formaldehyde gas emitted as the foam cures may be hazardous to health.

**Urea-tripolymer.** This product, while similar to urea-formaldehyde, contains no formaldehyde to cause unpleasant odors or health problems. It does not absorb water. Tripolymer foam provides

Table 1-6. Economic Comparison of Insulation.

| Insulation | R per Inch | Cost per Board Ft. | Cost per Board Ft., Installed | Insulation | R per Inch | Cost per Board Ft. | Cost per Board Ft., Installed |
|---|---|---|---|---|---|---|---|
| **ROLLS & BATTS** | | | | **RIGID BOARDS** | | | |
| Fiber glass | 3.2 | $0.04 | $0.10 | Foam board (extruded polystyrene) | 5.0 | $0.26 | $0.50 |
| Rock wool | 3.2 | 0.04 | 0.10 | Urethane | 5.9 | 0.24 | 0.44 |
| **LOOSE FILL** | | | | Fiber glass | 4.0 | 0.30 | 0.43 |
| Fiber glass | 3.0 | 0.03 | 0.09 | Celotex or homosote | 2.0 | 0.12 | 0.30 |
| Rock wool | 3.1 | 0.03 | 0.09 | Isocyanurate | 9.0 | 0.50 | 0.73 |
| Cellulose fiber | 3.7 | 0.04 | 0.11 | | | | |
| Vermiculite | 2.3 | 0.06 | 0.12 | **FOAM-IN-PLACE** | | | |
| Perlite | 2.7 | 0.06 | 0.12 | Urea-formaldehyde | 4.8 | — | 0.25 |
| Polystyrene | 3.0 | 0.10 | 0.17 | Urea-tripolymer | 4.5 | — | 0.25 |
| | | | | easy installation | | | 0.13 |
| **RIGID BOARDS** | | | | open side walls | | | |
| Bead board (expanded polystyrene) | 3.6 | 0.20 | 0.40 | (with poly film) | | | 0.20 |
| | | | | Polyurethane | 7.7 | — | 1.00 |

a fair vapor barrier, though an additional barrier is recommended. It is a fairly low fire hazard. Both tripolymer and urea-formaldehyde foams tend to shrink in curing, reducing their insulative effectiveness.

## FORMS OF INSULATION

**Rolls.** Best for walls or floors with standard 16 inch or 24 inch stud spacing, relatively unobstructed by blocking, plumbing or wiring, and where all areas are easily accessible. Available with or without a vapor barrier.

**Batts.** Semi-rigid sections of fiber glass or rock wool, 4 or 8 feet long, designed for inserting between studs spaced 16 or 24 inches. Somewhat easier to handle than long rolls of insulation. Available with or without vapor barrier.

**Loose fill.** Either poured or blown in, loose fill is useful for placing insulation in construction of irregular or nonstandard spacing, or for getting it down into enclosed wall cavities. Make sure that obstructions are not preventing the insulation from completely filling the cavity. Loose fill has a tendency to settle, reducing its effectiveness.

**Rigid boards.** Useful for insulating basement or foundation walls, or sandwiched into wall or roof constructions. Some rigid insulation, reinforced with fiber glass, can be used as sheathing in new construction. Also available is rigid insulation bonded to gypsum wallboard, ready to be installed on the inside of an existing wall or ceiling. Some types of plastic are effective vapor barriers; others have an aluminum layer bonded to one surface.

**Foam-in-place.** Like loose fill, this method is useful for irregular spaces or for getting into enclosed cavities or inaccessible areas. Because the foam hardens in place, settlement is not a problem. More likely is shrinkage. Foaming is a tricky process using expensive equipment; it must be done by a reputable contractor willing to guarantee his or her work.

**Figure 1-7. Forms of insulation.**

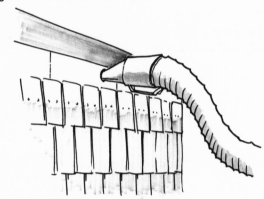

Foamed-in-place

Loose fill

Rolls

Batts

Rigid boards

## VAPOR BARRIERS

During the heating season, humidity within the house is usually higher than humidity outside. This water vapor, emitted by people, plants, kitchens and bathrooms, tries to migrate through the wall. The cold temperatures cause the vapor to condense inside the wall, damaging insulation and structural members. To prevent this possible damage, a vapor barrier is recommended whenever insulation is added to a previously uninsulated structure. The vapor barrier should always be on the *warm* side of the insulation—that is, the side nearest the inside of the house. (See Figure 1-8.)

The best vapor barrier is a continuous sheet of polyethylene film, taped at all seams. Some forms of insulation come with integral vapor barrier of aluminum foil. But in retrofit installations, it may not be possible to place such a barrier. In such cases, *vapor-proof paint* is recommended for the inside surface. At least two careful coats are needed to seal the wall. Vapor-proof, vinyl-base wallpaper is another option. Extruded polystyrene, urethane or isocyanurate act as their own vapor barriers.

Attic vents should be installed *above* the insul-

**Figure 1-8. To prevent condensation damage, always place vapor barrier on the *warm* side of the insulation.**

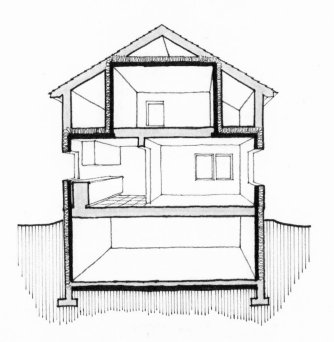

**Table 1-9. Recommended Insulation Levels.**

| Area of House | Thickness of Existing Insulation | How Much to Add | How Much to Add if Electric Heat or Cold Climate | How Much to Add if Electric Heat **and** Cold Climate |
|---|---|---|---|---|
| Ceiling or attic | 0 | R-30 | R-38 | R-38 |
| | 0-2″ | R-22 | R-30 | R-38 |
| | 2-4″ | R-11 | R-19 | R-22 |
| | 4-6″ | R-11 | R-11 | R-19 |
| Walls | 0 | R-11 | R-11 | R-19 |
| Below-grade walls | 0 | | R-11 | R-11 |

ation to allow moisture to escape. Vents should be located at the eaves, on the gable ends, or both. Enclosed crawl spaces should also allow ventilation *below* the insulation. Small vents or grills in the skirt board will prevent condensation or rot from ground moisture. In addition, polyethylene film should be placed on the ground under the crawl space to block moisture from the earth below.

## ATTIC INSULATION

This is the most important place to insulate. An investment of $300 to $500 can give a saving of $75 to $125 per year or more, plus additional savings if your house is air conditioned. If the attic is unfinished, with no floor, you can fit batts, blankets or loose fill between the joists. (See Tables 1-9 and 1-10.) If the floor is finished, fit insulation between rafters and between the end-wall studs. Or hire a contractor to blow loose fill or foam insulation under the floorboards, filling the cavity.

## BASEMENT INSULATION

If your basement or crawlspace is unheated, insulate the floor above to R-22, with a vapor barrier *above* the insulation. Insulate all ductwork and pipes with 2-inch foil-backed insulation, with the foil outside. Also, seal the ducts themselves with silver duct tape, to prevent air spillage.

If the basement is heated, do *not* insulate the floor above. *Do*, however, insulate pipes and ducts. Insulate the walls with studs and 3½-inch

**Table 1-10. How Much To Add.**

| | Batts or Blankets | | Loose Fill (Poured in) | | | Foam-in-Place | |
| | Glass | Rock Wool | Glass | Rock Wool | Cellulose | Ureatri-polymer | Poly-urethane |
|---|---|---|---|---|---|---|---|
| R-11 | 3¾″ | 3″ | 5″ | 4″ | 3″ | 2½″ | 1½″ |
| R-19 | 6¼″ | 5¼″ | 8½″ | 6½″ | 5″ | 4¼″ | 2½″ |
| R-22 | 6½″ | 6″ | 10″ | 7½″ | 6″ | 4⅞″ | 2⅞″ |
| R-30 | 10″ | 9″ | 13½″ | 10½″ | 8″ | 6⅝″ | 3⅞″ |
| R-38 | 12½″ | 10½″ | 17½″ | 13½″ | 10½″ | 8½″ | 4⅞″ |

fiber glass, or with 1-inch rigid board insulation attached with furring strips. Cover the insulation with gypsum wallboard or other wall covering.

## INSULATING THE FURNACE AND HOT WATER TANK

Use 2-inch foil-backed duct insulation, foil-side out, sealed carefully with duct tape. (Note: avoid placing insulation in contact with the flue pipe, as it gets very hot and a fire hazard might be created. Avoid blocking the combustion-air intake at the bottom of the unit.)

Insulating the hot water tank is very cost-effective, producing a saving of about 25 percent on hot water bills (approximately $35 per year for an electric heater, $20 per year for a gas heater).

## INSULATING A CONCRETE SLAB

Much heat is lost at the edge of an exposed concrete slab. In addition, this heat flow makes the floor uncomfortably cold. Remedy: Dig a trench around the house, apply waterproofing to the slab edge, insert 1- to 2-inch rigid insulation board with weatherproof finish, (such as fiber glass–reinforced mortar, moisture-treated plywood or cement-asbestos board) and backfill the trench again. Or, in new construction, place insulation as shown in Figure 1–11.

**Figure 1-11. Two alternatives in slab-edge insulation.**

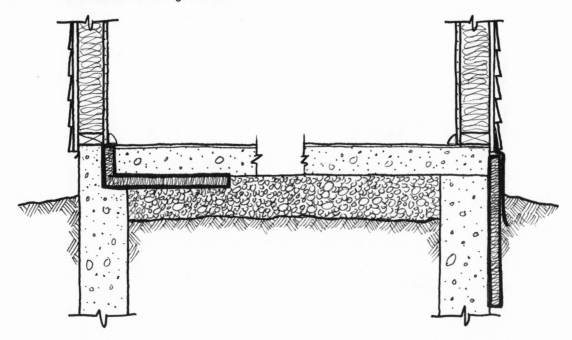

# Windows

Windows are second only to infiltration as major heat-loss culprits in a typical house. A single-glazed window loses up to twenty times as much heat as an equivalent area of wall. Proper treatment of window openings is therefore essential to the energy-conservative dwelling.

Table 1–23 at the end of this section illustrates the yearly fuel costs due to a typical 3-× 5-foot window in a house in Connecticut. It is apparent that heat loss can be dramatically reduced. But high installation costs can offset the economy of some energy-saving window strategies. It pays to examine the numbers carefully.

METHODS OF WINDOW INSULATION

**Double or triple-glazing.** Single glass has a U-value of 1.12 Btu/hr/sq.ft./°F. Double glazing reduces this to 0.56. Triple glazing further improves it to 0.41. Storm windows (a form of double glazing) can save $10 per window per year; they cost $20 to $40 each, installed. (Polyethylene film, tacked up by hand, is not quite so effective and will have to be replaced yearly; but it costs only 50¢ per window.) The glass itself may be double or triple thickness. *Thermopane* is a well-known brand name. Or use a plastic product like *Acrylite SDP*, a double-wall semitransparent cellular plastic sheet. Double or triple glazing may be more cost-effective than other more costly insulating approaches. And it requires no daily adjustment or attention. See Figure 1–12 for illustrations of these and other window treatments.

**Insulating shutters, doors or panels.** These appear in a variety of forms: folding, sliding, or hinging panels; Velcro or magnetic or friction sealed, manual or motor driven or Freon-activated. Materials range from highly insulative rigid foam boards (skinned with a nonflammable sheathing) to inexpensive materials like plywood and homosote. They can be easily homemade. One problem, though, is where to store the panels when they are removed. Table 1–13 compares the effectiveness of various insulating devices.

**Drapes.** Drapes are most effective if they are mounted on a track to seal the edges, particularly at the top and bottom, so that cold air cannot circulate into the room.

**Roll-down insulating shades or blankets.** Many types are available. Some are quilted fabric curtains filled with down, cotton or fibrous acrylics. Others are made of multiple layers of aluminized *Mylar*, capable of delivering R-10. The layers are separated either by self-inflating or by spring action. One type has three rollers that can be left up or down in different combinations according to thermal requirements.

Also available are external roll-down shutters such as the *Rolladen*, which are commonly used throughout Europe. Any shade or shutter must be sealed around the edges to prevent air infiltration and heat transfer.

**Blow-in window insulation:** In the ingenious *Beadwall* system, patented by Zomeworks,

Figure 1–12. Methods of window insulation.

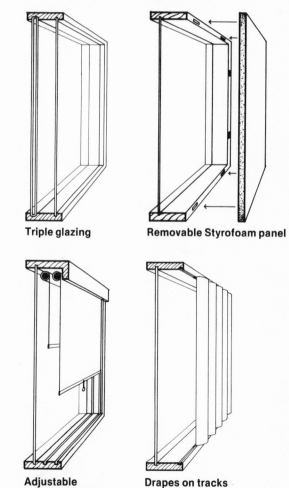

Triple glazing

Removable Styrofoam panel

Adjustable multi-roller shade

Drapes on tracks

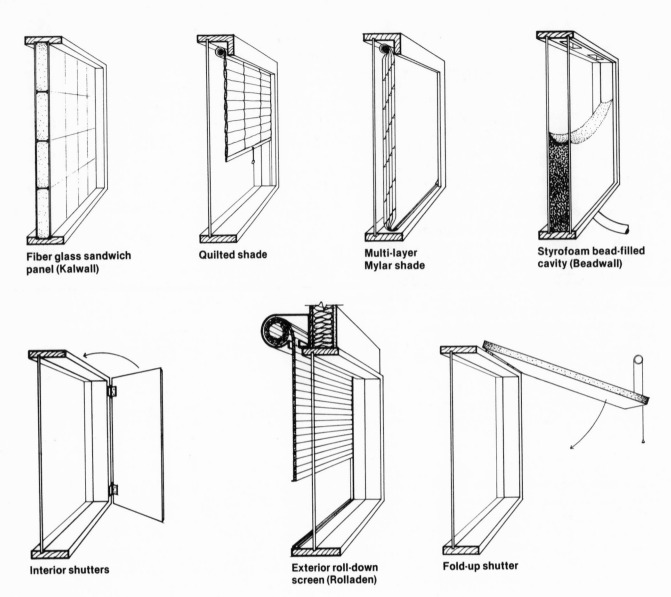

**Fiber glass sandwich panel (Kalwall)**

**Quilted shade**

**Multi-layer Mylar shade**

**Styrofoam bead-filled cavity (Beadwall)**

**Interior shutters**

**Exterior roll-down screen (Rolladen)**

**Fold-up shutter**

**Figure 1-12 (Continued). Methods of window insulation.**

styrofoam beads are blown into a 3 inch space between layers of glass, achieving an R-value of 10. The system can operate automatically if equipped with a photoelectric switch. Unfortunately, the beads deteriorate in high temperatures, so *Beadwall* cannot adequately serve as a translucent shade in hot sun. The system is very expensive ($12 to $24 per square foot, installed). Beads are stored in a large drum when not in use.

**Fiber glass sandwich panels** (*Kalwall*): These double-layer panels can be bought with translucent fiber glass insulation inside, increasing their R-value but decreasing their light and solar energy transmission. At R-2.5 (U-0.40), the panels will transmit 84 percent of the light strik-

**Table 1-13. Effectiveness of Various Window Insulation Devices.**

| Material | Heat Loss Reduced (relative to single glass) |
|---|---|
| Conventional roll shade | 28–36% |
| Clear plastic film with all perimeters sealed | 36–43% |
| Wood frame exterior storm windows | 50–57% |
| Low heat-emitting film shade sealed at bottom & sides | 57–64% |
| Double glazing | 45–55% |
| Triple glazing | 64–68% |
| Beadwall | 80–90% |
| Aluminized *Mylar* multilayer roll shade | 80–90% |

ing them. They are primarily an industrial product, available in 4- and 5-foot widths, up to 20 feet long.

METHODS OF WINDOW SHADING

**Trees and vines.** Deciduous trees and vines are natural sun-screens. They lose their leaves during the heating season and shade the house during the cooling season. Actually, they are slightly out of phase in some parts of the country, but no more beautiful window shades can be bought. Place trees to the east and west of the house as well as to the south, since most solar overheating comes from the morning and afternoon summer sun. Vines can climb on a lattice or trellis or hang from planter boxes. See Figure 1–14 for these and other shading methods.

**Overhangs.** The sun is lower in the winter, higher in the summer. You can make use of this difference to design overhangs for south-facing windows that keep out the summer sun. Figure 1–15 gives approximate design angles for overhangs in different latitudes.

**Awnings.** You can make awnings of canvas, aluminum, bamboo, or wood slats. One design uses snow fence that rolls down when needed, creating a pleasing latticed shadow. Awnings are quite economical. Design them as you would an overhang.

**External louvers.** Sun-shading louvers should be placed horizontally on south windows, vertically on east or west windows. They can be operable or removable, allowing hourly, daily or seasonal adjustment to maximize solar heat gain in winter and minimize overheating in summer. For example, Construction Specialties, Inc. makes an operable, insulated aluminum louver system for industrial applications. It is expensive ($10 per square foot) but combines insulation and adjustable sun control.

**Indoor devices.** These include roll-down shades, venetian blinds and louvers. They are not nearly as effective as external sun controllers, since they do not prevent heat from entering the room. So they must be vented to allow heat to escape. They are more easily adjusted, however, and are protected from the weather. One company, Rolscreen, makes an in-the-window louver, placed be-

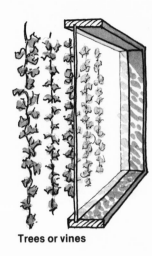
**Louvered blinds (they can also serve as a solar collector)**

**Trees or vines**

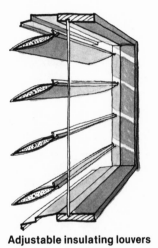
**Adjustable insulating louvers**

**Roll-down sun screen**

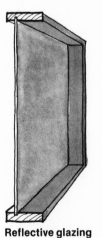
**Reflective glazing**

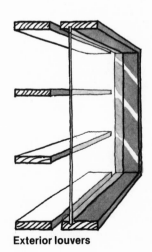
**Exterior louvers**

Figure 1–14. Methods of shading windows.

**11**

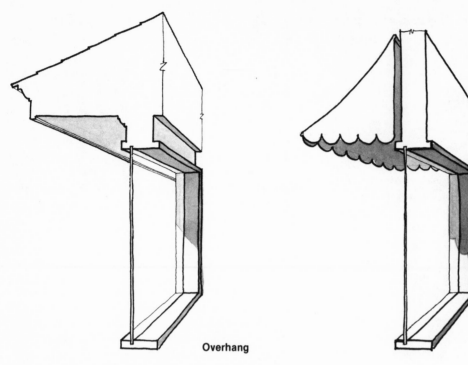

Overhang

Awning

**Figure 1-14 (Continued). Methods of shading windows.**

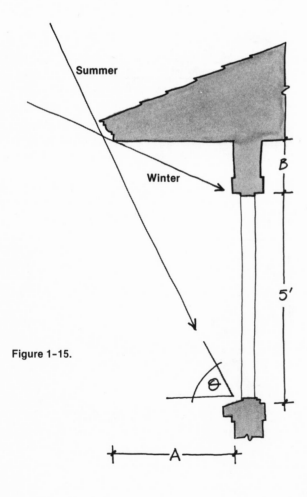

Summer

Winter

**Figure 1-15.**

tween two layers of glass. It can be adjusted like a venetian blind.

**Reflective glazing.** Low-transmittance glass can be used in warm climates to reduce heat gain. The glass is treated with a reflective coating that blocks the sun. This is not very suitable in cold climates, where heat gain is sometimes desired. Adhesive-backed film, costing $1.25 per square foot, may be applied to existing windows. It is reflective but transparent.

*Cloud-Gel* is a selective glazing, invented by Day Charhoudi, that automatically excludes the sun when the room reaches a certain temperature. The gel is transparent when cold but turns cloudywhite and reflective when the design temperature is reached. The phase-change temperature can be selected and the house

**Table 1-15. Determining the Correct Overhang.**

| Latitude | A | B | Angle θ |
|---|---|---|---|
| 30° | 2.50 ft. | 2.00 ft. | 70° |
| 40° | 2.75 | 1.75 | 68° |
| 45° | 3.00 | 1.50 | 65° |
| 50° | 3.25 | 1.25 | 63° |

"tuned" for maximum solar gain with minimum overheating. *Cloud-Gel* is under development and is not currently available at affordable prices. For more information write to: Day Charhoudi, Suntek Research Associates, 500 Tamal Vista Road, Corte Madera, California 94925.

# Infiltration of Outside Air

In most homes, infiltration is the biggest cause of heat loss. Cold outside air, driven by icy winter winds, enters the house through doors and windows, cracks and holes, and pushes out the warmer air inside. Under a 15-mph wind, a typical house will undergo one to four complete air changes per hour through air infiltration. This loss could represent as much as $300 worth of heat lost during a season of heating. By contrast, a well-sealed house may undergo only one air change every two hours. The practical lower limit of infiltration for an occupied house is about 0.4 air change per hour, dependent on the occupants, lifestyle and habits. Only about 0.2 air change per hour is necessary for good ventilation and preventing stuffiness.

REDUCING INFILTRATION LOSSES

**Landscaping** to form windbreaks could reduce heating bills by 20 percent or more. One government-sponsored study of two identical houses in South Dakota reported a savings of 34 percent simply by creating a windbreak. In many areas, winter winds come from the *north*west, summer winds from the *south*west, so the northwest windbreak won't block cooling summer breezes. The most effective windbreaks, interestingly, are those that allow some of the wind through (such as trees) rather than those that completely block the wind, creating eddy currents. A study at Princeton found that a five-foot wood fence could reduce air infiltration 26 to 30 percent. A tall row of evergreens would reduce infiltration 40 percent. The combination would reduce infiltration by 60 percent. Figure 1-16 shows proper placement for a windbreak.

**Caulking and weatherstripping** are very sound investments. If you spend $80 to $120, you can achieve a saving of $50 to $150 per year in heating bills (plus an additional $35 to $90 saving if your house is air conditioned). When caulking and filling, examine door and window frames on the outside of the house, filling all visible cracks where air might penetrate. Check the corners of the building. Check where walls meet the roof and chimney. Be sure to caulk along the lowest line of shingles or clapboard where the walls meet the foundation—this is a frequent spot for infiltration. Seal any through-the-wall water faucet outlets as well as holes for electric and telephone lines, TV antenna lines, and electrical outlets. Silicone or acrylic latex caulk are the most expensive, ($2 to $4 per tube, good for 25 feet of bead) and the best (they will last ten years). Avoid vinyl or butyl caulk, which will last only two to five years, or oil-based caulk, with an even shorter life. Some caulks are paintable; others that are not paintable are available in clear, white, gray or black. If the gap is wide, fill it first with oakum, felt or foam tubing before caulking.

**Figure 1-16. Place a windbreak at the correct distance. (Maximum distance: 5h)**

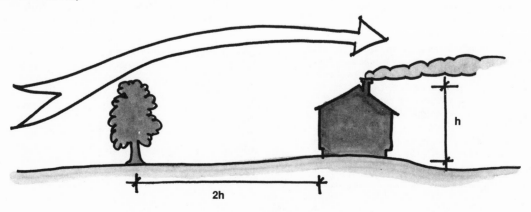

Inexpensive weatherstrip is available in felt fiber or adhesive-backed foam. More elaborate versions are extrusions of interlocking metal, or rolled vinyl with an aluminum channel backing. Consult your local hardware store. Don't forget to weatherstrip sliding glass doors and windows. Strips of closed-cell foam around the edges can reduce infiltration 50 percent and pay for themselves in less than two years.

**Storm doors and windows** can further reduce infiltration, even after caulking and weatherstripping. They impose an extra barrier to the wind.

**Vestibules** are more effective than storm doors at reducing heat loss when the door is opened. A vestibule should be large enough to allow a person to close one door before opening the other.

**Exhaust vents and fans** often are neglected as infiltration spots. Kitchen, bathroom and clothes dryer vents should be fitted with dampers so that they may be closed unless needed. And don't omit a damper for the chimney flue. Without it, heated inside air will simply escape up the chimney, drawing in cold outside air as it does.

# Ventilation

In warm climates, carefully planned natural ventilation can provide cool comfort through the summer, reducing or eliminating the need for costly air conditioning. Even when the air is hot, a breeze gives a cooling effect, so the key is to control air movement through the house. If you are building a new house, make sure that every living area has cross-ventilation. Determine the direction of prevailing winds in your area, and arrange the windows to take advantage of them.

In an existing house, consider installing new windows or vents to improve the air movement. A small intake vent and a larger exhaust opening will optimize air flow in the room. Since warm air rises, place exhaust openings high and intake openings low (Figure 1-17). All vents or openings will require insect screens, weather protection and tight-fitting insulated closures for cold weather.

Figure 1-17. For optimum air flow in summer, place small intake vents on the windward wall, larger exhaust openings on leeward side.

In a tall space with vents at top and bottom, warm air will rise and escape out the upper vent, creating a flow that draws in cooler air below (Figure 1-18). This is the *chimney effect*—it can be useful. Provide an attic fan or vent to exhaust the hottest air, and cooler air can be drawn in through vents or windows on the first floor. Operable skylights or a roof monitor will accomplish the same effect. If the chimney effect does not provide enough air movement, add a fan. Draw in cool air from the shaded north side of the house, or place intake vents beneath overhanging shade trees. Underground air ducts are a costly solution but a good one—the cool earth absorbs heat from the intake air, providing natural air-conditioning.

Zoning—dividing the house into separately heated or cooled sections—can increase comfort and decrease energy use. Porches and patios are delightful in hot weather, offering shade and full exposure to cool breezes. In winter, the house can close up again, as the family retreats into a buffered inner sanctum. If air-conditioning is essential, a good strategy is to provide a smaller inner

---

**DRYER VENT DAMPER**

In the laundry room, there is a potential source of heat and humidity that you probably never thought about—your clothes dryer.

A new item on the market is a two-position damper system which attaches easily to your plastic or metal vent pipe and allows you to recycle heat and humidity into your home instead of losing it all outside. A special filter bag traps dust and lint.

By venting the dryer heat and humidity into your home, you reduce the required operating time of your furnace and/or humidifer, thus reducing fuel consumption and saving you money during the heating season. How much money? The estimate is from $20 to $30 per heating season.

Figure 1-18. The *chimney effect* uses the sun and the prevailing wind to create a natural cooling draft.

zone, such as the bedrooms, that can be mechanically cooled. The surrounding rooms can then be left open to natural ventilation.

# Equipment and Appliances

Machines consume, convert and distribute the energy used in your home. If you control the machines, you control the energy.

CHOOSING A FUEL

**Coal.** The United States has plenty of coal—enough to last us hundreds of years at projected rates of consumption. Unfortunately, there are serious environmental problems involved: Strip-mining is unsightly; deep mining is dangerous; and coal contains sulphur and other pollutants emitted when burning. Nonetheless, the Federal Energy Administration is directing major fuel-

burning installations to shift from oil to coal. The coal industry is not yet tooled up to provide this increased supply, though, especially to small customers. Transportation and distribution systems may not be adequate, so you should inquire in your local area. (Coal may be either *anthracite* or *bituminous*. Anthracite coal, found principally in Pennsylvania, is older and harder than bituminous. It burns hotter and cleaner, emitting less pollutants—and is more expensive than bituminous coal.) Table 1-19 allows you to compare the costs of six common heating fuels.

**Oil.** Over half the oil used in this country is imported. Domestic supplies may last 40 to 100 years. Prices have risen sharply and steadily since 1973 and they will probably continue to do so. But oil is readily available everywhere, easily transportable, and easy to store and burn.

**Gas.** Natural gas is rapidly becoming unavailable for new construction in the East. Domestic supplies are dwindling, though they may last ten to thirty-five years. But gas is still very cheap in the producer states. In addition, liquefied gas from the Middle East, synthetic gas, and coal gasification are increasingly available—but at much higher cost.

**Wood.** Available in most of the United States. Whether wood is economical varies with the species and density of wood available. See the Wood Heat section.

**Electricity.** Electricity is generated from coal (46 percent), oil (16 percent), gas (15 percent), hydroelectric (14 percent), and nuclear plants (9 percent). These proportions vary greatly across the United States: Connecticut, for example, generates up to 70 percent of its electricity from nuclear power plants, while in the Pacific Northwest generation is largely hydroelectric. Electric power is universally available except in remote areas.

Costs have risen sharply as the price of generating fuel has risen, and electricity remains the most expensive energy source. Low initial equipment costs still lure many builders into installing electric heaters, but high operating costs quickly wipe out the homeowner's apparent saving.

You should realize, too, that increasing demand for electricity creates pressure to build additional nuclear power plants, with their attendant prob-

**Table 1-19. Comparative Fuel Costs.**

| Fuel | Quantity Needed to Provide 1 million Btu (1 MBtu) | × | Local Fuel Cost | = | Comparative Cost per MBtu |
|------|---------------------------------------------------|---|-----------------|---|---------------------------|
| Coal | 118 lb. (or 0.06 ton) | | _____ per lb. (per ton) | | ____ |
| #2 Fuel Oil | 9.6 gallons | | _____ per gallon | | ____ |
| Natural Gas | 1270 cu. ft. | | _____ per cu. ft. | | ____ |
| LP gas (propane) | 14.5 gallons | | _____ per gallon | | ____ |
| Wood | 0.1 cord* | | _____ per cord (4 × 4 × 8) | | ____ |
| Electricity | 293 kwh | | _____ per kwh | | ____ |

* Wood varies widely with species and density.

lems of high cost (Connecticut's rates are among the nation's highest), reactor safety (an accident could kill 3000 people and injure 50,000), long-term health hazards (cancer rates in a town near Connecticut's Millstone plant went up 58 percent between 1970 and 1975) and waste storage (by 2000, the United States will have generated 160 million pounds of plutonium; *one* pound could induce cancer in up to 380 million people).

CONSERVATION
AT THE HEATING PLANT

Proper adjustment and maintenance of the house heating system will help keep fuel costs down. Yearly servicing of your oil or coal furnace will cost about $25 and save you $40 to $120 per year by burning more efficiently. Gas furnaces should be serviced once every three years. In a hot-water system, drain a bucket of water from the boiler every three weeks to remove sediment from the tank. Ask your servicer to show you how to do it. If there are radiators in the system, bleed them of air once in a while. If you have an air system, clean or replace the air filters every one to two months. Once a year, clean the fan blades of built-up grease and dirt. Keep all registers clean and unobstructed by rugs or furniture. Shade air conditioning units from the hot sun (but do not obstruct free air movement around the unit). Keep the condenser coils clean of dust or grass clippings.

If some rooms are too cold while others over-heat, your system needs balancing. In a hot-water system, turn down the valves in the warmer rooms. This actually will give more heat in the colder rooms. For a steam system, you can purchase adjustable radiator valves to accomplish the same thing. If you have a forced-air heating system, install adjustable registers to allow balancing.

Water heaters require yearly servicing for peak efficiency. Drain a bucket of water from the bottom of the tank to remove sediment. Have your servicer adjust the flame or check the electrodes, and de-lime the tank. Reduce the thermostat setting to the temperature you need—no more than 120° F. (or 140° if you have a dishwasher). This will save $8 to $60 per year. Settings over 140° F. can reduce the life of a water heater, especially one that is glass lined.

If you have central air conditioning, consider adding a heat exchanger to extract waste heat from the condenser coils to provide hot water. Energy Conservation Unlimited, Inc., of Longwood, Florida sells an Energy Conservation Unit (ECU) that can reduce hot water costs 80 percent during the cooling season. At the same time, the air conditioner runs more efficiently and economically.

THERMOSTATS

As everyone must know by now, turning down the thermostat in winter (and up in summer) is the best energy investment you can make. A 6° setback costs nothing, and saves $35 to $120 per year. If you have air conditioning, a 6° increase in setting will save $10 to $30 per cooling season.

Additional savings are possible if you install an *automatic set back thermostat* that turns the heat down at night and back up in the morning (Table 1-20). Or it can be set to turn the heat down during the day when the house is vacant, and back up in time for your return in the evening. Several types are available. If you follow a fairly regular daily schedule, the best is a *twenty-four hour clock-type*, which can be programmed according to your patterns. Look for one which allows more than one setback period during a twenty-four-hour period.

If your daily schedule is too variable to be programmed, select an *interval timer*-type thermostat. This operates like a kitchen timer. It must be manually set each time. Avoid the *switch* type, which offers no real advantage over a regular thermostat.

Another variety is the *photocell* thermostat, which responds to light as a detector of occupancy. Unfortunately this type does not allow for a setback during the day when the house may be unoccupied. It may require that the thermostat location be moved nearer to a window, so that the heat goes on in the morning.

**Table 1-20. Fuel Bill Savings With Automatic Set-Back Thermostat.**

| Degree Days | 68–60° Setback | 68-55° Setback Between 10 PM & 6 AM |
|---|---|---|
| 2000 | 23% | 30% of present bill |
| 3000 | 20% | 25% |
| 4000 | 17% | 22% |
| 5000 | 14% | 20% |
| 6000 | 12% | 18% |
| 7000 | 10% | 16% |
| 8000 | 9% | 14% |

"Decoy" thermostat heater devices are also available as a cheaper alternative to the more expensive units just described. A decoy device consists of a timer and a small heating coil placed just below the existing thermostat, which "fools" the thermostat into thinking that the room air is a few degrees warmer than it is. These units require no special wiring; setting is by trial-and-error. They are available as clock or interval timers.

If your house has several heating zones, different areas may be on different time/temperature schedules. The bedrooms need less heat during the day; guest rooms may be kept cool unless in use. As with cooling, the use of several zones of activity according to thermal requirements can make a house flexible and energy efficient.

## APPLIANCES

Table 1-21 lists typical energy consumption of various home appliances. As you can see, the big-

gest consumers are the water heater, refrigerator, air conditioner, range and clothes dryer. But these are only typical figures. Different models vary considerably. Use this table to look for ways to cut your electric bill. Use a clothesline instead of a dryer. Install a fan instead of an air conditioner. Put on an extra blanket instead of using an electric one. Avoid frostless refrigerators and instant-on televisions. When possible, run appliances and tools in the evening or on weekends, to reduce the electric company's peak power demand. In some areas, off-peak use will save you money.

**Table 1-21. Annual Energy Requirements of Electric Household Appliances\***

The estimated annual kilowatt-hour consumption of the electric appliances listed in this reference is based on average-size appliances and normal use.

| Appliance | Average Wattage | Est. kwh Consumed Annually | Est. Annual Operating Cost @ 8¢ per kwh |
|---|---|---|---|
| **HEALTH & BEAUTY** | | | |
| Germicidal Lamp | 20 | 141 | $11.28 |
| Hair Dryer | 381 | 14 | 1.12 |
| Heat Lamp (infrared) | 250 | 13 | 1.04 |
| Shaver | 15 | 0.5 | .04 |
| Sun Lamp | 279 | 16 | 1.28 |
| Tooth Brush | 1.1 | 1.0 | .08 |
| Vibrator | 40 | 2 | .16 |
| **HOME ENTERTAINMENT** | | | |
| Radio | 71 | 86 | 6.88 |
| Radio/Record Player | 109 | 109 | 8.72 |
| Television | | | |
| black & white | | | |
| tube type | 100 | 220 | 17.60 |
| solid state | 45 | 100 | 8.00 |
| color | | | |
| tube type | 240 | 528 | 42.24 |
| solid state | 145 | 320 | 25.60 |
| **HOUSEWARES** | | | |
| Clock | 2 | 17 | 1.36 |
| Floor Polisher | 305 | 15 | 1.20 |
| Sewing Machine | 75 | 11 | .88 |
| Vacuum Cleaner | 630 | 46 | 3.68 |

\* Figures developed by Edison Electric Institute, 90 Park Ave., New York, NY 10016.

*(Continued on p. 18)*

**Table 1–21 (Continued). Annual Energy Requirements of Electric Household Appliances.**

| Appliance | Average Wattage | Est. kwh Consumed Annually | Est. Annual Operating Cost @ 8¢ per kwh | Appliance | Average Wattage | Est. kwh Consumed Annually | Est. Annual Operating Cost @ 8¢ per kwh |
|---|---|---|---|---|---|---|---|
| **FOOD PREPARATION** | | | | **FOOD PRESERVATION** | | | |
| Blender | 300 | 1 | $ .08 | automatic defrost, | | | |
| Broiler | 1,140 | 85 | 6.80 | 16–18 cu. ft. | — | 1,795 | $143.60 |
| Carving Knife | 92 | 8 | .64 | automatic defrost, | | | |
| Coffee Maker | 894 | 106 | 8.48 | 20 cu. ft. & up | — | 1,895 | 151.60 |
| Deep Fryer | 1,448 | 83 | 6.64 | | | | |
| Dishwasher | 1,201 | 363 | 29.04 | **LAUNDRY** | | | |
| Egg Cooker | 516 | 14 | 1.12 | | | | |
| Frying Pan | 1,196 | 100 | 8.00 | Clothes Dryer | 4,856 | 993 | 79.44 |
| Hot Plate | 1,200 | 90 | 7.20 | Iron (hand) | 1,100 | 60 | 4.80 |
| Mixer | 127 | 2 | .16 | Washing Machine | | | |
| Oven, microwave (only) | 1,450 | 190 | 15.20 | (automatic) | 512 | 103 | 8.24 |
| Range | | | | Washing Machine | | | |
| with oven | 12,200 | 1,175 | 94.00 | (nonautomatic) | 266 | 76 | 6.08 |
| with self-cleaning oven | 12,200 | 1,205 | 96.40 | Water Heater | 2,475 | 4,219 | 337.52 |
| Roaster | 1,333 | 60 | 4.80 | (quick-recovery) | 4,474 | 4,811 | 384.88 |
| Sandwich Grill | 1,161 | 33 | 2.64 | | | | |
| Toaster | 1,146 | 39 | 3.12 | **COMFORT CONDITIONING** | | | |
| Trash Compactor | 400 | 50 | 4.00 | | | | |
| Waffle Iron | 1,200 | 20 | 1.60 | Air Cleaner | 50 | 216 | 17.28 |
| Waste Dispenser | 445 | 7 | .56 | Air Conditioner (room) | 860 | 860† | 68.80 |
| | | | | Bed Covering | 177 | 147 | 11.76 |
| **FOOD PRESERVATION** | | | | Dehumidifier | 257 | 377 | 30.16 |
| | | | | Fan (attic) | 370 | 291 | 23.28 |
| Freezer (15–21 cu. ft.) | | | | Fan (circulating) | 88 | 43 | 3.44 |
| chest type, | | | | Fan (roll-away) | 171 | 138 | 11.04 |
| manual defrost | — | 1,320 | 105.60 | Fan (window) | 200 | 170 | 13.60 |
| upright type | | | | Heater (portable) | 1,322 | 176 | 14.08 |
| manual defrost | — | 1,320 | 105.60 | Heating Pad | 65 | 10 | .80 |
| automatic defrost | — | 1,985 | 158.80 | Humidifier | 177 | 163 | 13.04 |
| Refrigerators/Freezers | | | | Oil burner or Stoker | 260 | 372 | 29.76 |
| manual defrost, | | | | Water Pump | 335 | 204 | 16.32 |
| 10–15 cu. ft. | — | 700 | 56.00 | | | | |

† Based on 1,000 hours of operation per year. This figure will vary widely depending on area and specific size of unit.

# Economics

Any of the energy-conserving measures suggested in this chapter will save money. But most of them cost money, too. It is difficult to predict precisely how much fuel will be saved, so the cost-effectiveness of a given investment can only be approximated. So much depends on your specific site, fuel costs in your area, the condition and configuration of your house, and your lifestyle. An exact determination of costs versus benefits requires an engineer or architect, and their answers may be no closer than the rule-of-thumb figures given in Table 1–22.

But such precision is unnecessary, anyway. What is important is to attune yourself to the patterns of energy use in your own home. Understand where the problem areas are and tackle those first. Acquire an energy sense before considering more elaborate and expensive items like solar collectors or windmills. Study your real energy needs and eliminate waste. You will then be better equipped to explore the alternative sources of energy described in the sections that follow.

**Table 1-22. Economics of Various Conservation Strategies.**

| Item | Added Cost | Yearly Saving on Heat Bills | Additional Saving on Cooling Bills |
|---|---|---|---|
| Insulate the attic | $300–500. | $75–125. | $50–100. |
| Insulate the walls | 400–1600. | 90–350. | 25–120. |
| Insulate the floor | 40–200. | 50–350. | |
| Insulate the heated basement | 250–500. | 75–350. | |
| Insulate the hot water tank | 10–20. | 15–60. | |
| Insulate all hot water pipes | 50. | 80–120. | 5–15. |
| Insulate air ducts | 60. | 75–150. | 15–30. |
| Insulate slab perimeter below grade | 70–150. | 65–150. | |
| Caulk & weatherstrip | 80–120. | 50–150. | 35–90. |
| Adjust thermostat 6° F. | — | 25–90. | 10–30. |
| Storm window (each) | 20–40. per window | 8–15. | 5–8. |
| Plastic storm window | .50 per window | 5–10. | 2–5. |
| Insulating shutters, shades, etc. | 10–60. per window | 10–15. | 5–8. |
| Double-glazing | 35–40. additional | 6–12. | 4–7. |
| Triple-glazing | 80–100. additional | 8–20. | 5–10. |
| Windbreaks against winter wind | 20–200. | 30–300. | |
| Dampers for kitchen, bathroom, dryer exhausts, chimney flue | 60–150. | 40–90. | 15–40. |
| Showerhead flow restrictor | 10–17. | 35. | |
| Solar dryer (clothesline) | 5. | 20–40. | 5–10. |
| Replace pilot lights with ignition | 50. each | 30. | 5–10. |
| Automatic setback thermostat | 50–100. | 30–100. | 20–50. |
| Install flue damper on gas furnace | 100. | 100–200. | |
| Improve fireplace | (see section on Wood Heat) | | |
| Install attic fan & vent | 100. | | 100–400. |
| Install timer on outside light | 12. | 3–100. | |

**Table 1-23. Calculating the Saving from Various Insulators.**

$$\text{Yearly Cost (\$ year)} = \text{U factor} \times \text{Area (Sq. ft.)} \times \text{Degree-days} \times \text{Cost per MBtu} \times \frac{1 \text{ MBtu}}{1{,}000{,}000 \text{ Btu}}$$

*Example:* North-facing picture window, 30 square feet, in a house in Connecticut, with 6000 degree-days. Oil heat, at $10 per MBtu.

What is the energy cost if the window is

(a) single-glazed?
(b) double-glazed?
(c) triple-glazed?
(d) fitted with an insulating shade, R-10, in place 12 hours per day?

| Type | R | U × | A × | 24 Hr./Day × | Degree Days × | $/MBtu × | $\frac{1}{1{,}000{,}000}$ = | Yearly cost |
|---|---|---|---|---|---|---|---|---|
| Single glazing | 0.8 | 1.13 | 30 ft² | 24 | 6000. | $10. | | $48.80 |
| Double glazing | 1.8 | 0.56 | 30 | 24 | 6000. | 10. | | 28.08 |
| Triple glazing | 2.4 | 0.41 | 30 | 24 | 6000. | 10. | | 20.30 |
| High "R" shade (night) | 10 | 0.10 | 30 | 12 (night) | 6000. | 10. | | 2.16 |
| Single glass (day) | 0.8 | 1.13 | 30 | 12 (day) | 6000. | 10. | | + 24.40 |
| | | | | | | | | 26.56 |

| Type | Yearly Saving | Extra Cost | Years to Pay Back |
|---|---|---|---|
| Single glass | — | — | — |
| Double | $20.72 | $85.00 | 4.1 years |
| Triple | 28.50 | 200.00 | 7.0 years |
| High-R Shade | 21.84 | 100.00 | 4.6 years |

**Figure 1-24. A degree-day map of the United States.**

**Table 1-25. Design Temperatures (Heating Season).**

| State | City | Design Temperature (°F) | State | City | Design Temperature (°F) |
|---|---|---|---|---|---|
| Alabama | Birmingham | 19 | Nevada | Reno | 2 |
| Alaska | Anchorage | −25 | New Hampshire | Concord | −11 |
| Arizona | Phoenix | 31 | New Mexico | Albuquerque | 14 |
| Arkansas | Little Rock | 19 | New York | Buffalo | 3 |
| Calfornia | Los Angeles | 41 | New York | New York | 12 |
| California | San Francisco | 35 | North Carolina | Raleigh | 16 |
| Colorado | Denver | −2 | North Dakota | Bismarck | −24 |
| Connecticut | Hartford | 1 | Ohio | Columbus | 2 |
| Florida | Tampa | 36 | Oklahoma | Tulsa | 12 |
| Georgia | Atlanta | 18 | Oregon | Portland | 21 |
| Idaho | Boise | 4 | Pennsylvania | Philadelphia | 11 |
| Illinois | Chicago | −3 | Pennsylvania | Pittsburgh | 5 |
| Indiana | Indianapolis | 0 | Rhode Island | Providence | 6 |
| Iowa | Des Moines | −7 | South Carolina | Charleston | 23 |
| Kansas | Wichita | 5 | South Dakota | Sioux Falls | −14 |
| Kentucky | Louisville | 8 | Tennessee | Chattanooga | 15 |
| Louisiana | New Orleans | 32 | Texas | Dallas | 19 |
| Maryland | Baltimore | 12 | Texas | San Antonio | 25 |
| Massachusetts | Boston | 6 | Utah | Salt Lake City | 5 |
| Michigan | Detroit | 4 | Vermont | Burlington | −12 |
| Minnesota | Minneapolis | −14 | Virginia | Richmond | 14 |
| Mississippi | Jackson | 21 | Washington | Seattle | 28 |
| Missouri | St. Louis | 4 | West Virginia | Charleston | 9 |
| Montana | Helena | −17 | Wisconsin | Madison | −9 |
| Nebraska | Lincoln | −4 | Wyoming | Cheyenne | −6 |

# References

Adams, Anthony. *Your Energy-Efficient House.* Charlotte, VT: Garden Way Publishing, 1976. $4.95. Building and remodeling ideas that can drastically reduce fuel bills. Emphasizes natural heating and cooling techniques that use ventilating and insulation to best advantage.

ASHRAE. *ASHRAE Handbook of Fundamentals.* New York: 1977. Available in libraries. An authoritative, highly technical reference book that treats the subject of heat loss in buildings, ventilation, refrigeration, solar energy and air conditioning. Not light reading, but if you are a serious student of energy, this is a primary source book.

*Climates of the United States.* U. S. Department of Commerce, 1973. Sixty-three pages of maps and charts showing maximum and minimum temperatures, rainfall, degree days, windspeed and direction, humidity, tornados, hail, and so on. Send $1.85 to Superintendent of Documents, U.S. Government Printing Office, Washington, D.C. 20402. Ask for UDC 551.582(73).

"Home Heating: Systems-Fuels-Controls." U. S. Department of Agriculture, 1975. Send 50¢ to Superintendent of Documents, U.S. Government Printing Office, Washington, D.C. 20402. Ask for Farmers Bulletin #2235.

"In the Bank—or UP the Chimney?" HUD, 1977. Provides a detailed worksheet enabling the homeowner to evaluate his or her house for energy efficiency and to determine the relative economy of various energy-conserving measures (storm windows, added insulation, adjusting the thermostat). It also gives tips on making those changes oneself. Send $1.85 to Superintendent of Documents, U. S. Government Printing Office, Washington, D. C. 20402. Ask for Booklet #023-000-00297-3.

Olgyay, Victor. *Design With Climate.* Princeton, NJ: Princeton University Press, 1963. Subtitled "Bioclimatic approach to Architectural Regionalism," this classic in the field performs highly detailed climatic analyses on four different zones in the United States and shows their impact on house design for energy efficiency.

Rothchild and Tenney. *The Home Energy Guide.* New York: Ballantine Books, 1978. $1.95. Comprehensive, up to date, and very practical, this book explores all aspects of energy saving in dollars-and-cents terms. The authors point out energy savers that are bargains and those that are not.

*Window Design Strategies to Conserve Energy.* National Bureau of Standards, 1977. Very specific and technical, but easy to understand. Analyzes thirty-three strategies that can improve the energy functioning of windows. Economic comparisons, extensive research references. Send $3.75 to Superintendent of Documents, U.S. Government Printing Office, Washington, D.C. 20402. Ask for SD Catalog Number C13.29/2:104.

"Energy-Saving Thermostats." *Consumer Reports,* October 1977.

"Exterior Caulking Compounds." *Consumer Reports,* May 1976.

"Fuel-Saving Devices for the Home." *Consumer Reports,* January 1977.

"The Overselling of Insulation." *Consumer Reports,* February 1978.

"Water Heaters: Gas and Electric." *Consumer Reports,* March 1976.

"Weather Stripping." *Consumer Reports,* February 1977.

# Energy Conservation Catalog

The following pages show products and companies that are currently working in the many fields that touch on energy conservation. Naturally, this is not a complete catalog—there are many excellent products not represented here, and more are coming on the market all the time.

All information contained in the catalog sections was supplied by the various manufacturers or organizations listed; we have given a summary of what is available from each. Our goal is to help you, the reader, locate materials or products that will aid you in using energy more efficiently.

Within the catalog section are product comparison charts that we have created to help you make specific comparisons among similar products. Keep in mind in reading these charts that prices are constantly changing. If you want more information about any products or ideas shown in the catalog section, we request that you write directly to the company, *not* to Garden Way Publishing.

# Thermostats

## Champion Home Builders Co.
### Dryden, Michigan 48071

Champion's *Energy-Dial*™ is an automatic set-back accessory that attaches to most round-type room thermostats. The mechanism is controlled by a 24-hour clock; extra setback periods are available.

## Dynelco
### Dynamic Electronic Controls, Inc.
### P.O. Box 193
### 47 Mill Plain Road
### Danbury, Connecticut 06810
### (203) 792-8877

Dynelco makes automatic thermostats with setbacks sensitive to light conditions. *Therm-O-Guard* models SST–2 and SST–3AC sense when a building is unoccupied and set back the temperature automatically. Model SST–3AC can also operate on a programmable switchbase. Light sensitivity and temperature controls are adjustable.

The *Multistat* thermostat works on the same principle and allows total energy setback, ie. no heating or cooling. The Multistat can also control fans and furnace dampers. All Dynelco thermostats are 100 percent solid state, do not require extra wiring or batteries, are self-recovering in case of power failure, and feature a two-year warranty. They can be easily retrofitted by the homeowner.

## Honeywell, Inc.
### Honeywell Plaza
### Minneapolis, Minnesota 55408
### (612) 870-5200

Honeywell's nonelectric, heavy-duty thermostatic radiator valve is fitted to pipe radiators. It can also be used with convectors and baseboard units to control heating costs or problems in larger buildings. It measures the room temperature and regulates the steam or hot water supply as needed, solving problems of overheating and wide temperature swing. Honeywell claims the valve can save the consumer 35 percent of his fuel costs. It can be fitted by the homeowner on new or older buildings.

*Honeywell radiator valve.*

The *Chronotherm* clock-type setback thermostat allows just one setback period per day. The unit is powered by battery or optional power supply. The same product is sold under a different brand name at Wards (#69107) and at Sears (#9108). The Sears model can also be used for air conditioning setback.

| NIGHT SETBACK — WINTER | | | | | |
|---|---|---|---|---|---|
| Setback: | 5° | 10° | Setback: | 5° | 10° |
| **City** | | | **City** | | |
| Atlanta | 11% | 15% | Milwaukee | 6% | 10% |
| Boston | 7% | 11% | Minneapolis | 5% | 9% |
| Buffalo | 6% | 10% | New York City | 8% | 12% |
| Chicago | 7% | 11% | Omaha | 7% | 11% |
| Cincinnati | 8% | 12% | Philadelphia | 8% | 12% |
| Cleveland | 8% | 12% | Pittsburgh | 7% | 11% |
| Dallas | 11% | 15% | Portland | 9% | 13% |
| Denver | 7% | 11% | Salt Lake City | 7% | 11% |
| Des Moines | 7% | 11% | San Francisco | 10% | 14% |
| Detroit | 7% | 11% | St. Louis | 8% | 12% |
| Kansas City | 8% | 12% | Seattle | 8% | 12% |
| Los Angeles | 12% | 16% | Washington, | | |
| Louisville | 9% | 13% | D.C. | 9% | 13% |

"Reprinted from the August 1973 issue of ASHRAE JOURNAL by permission of the American Society of Heating, Refrigerating and Air-Conditioning Engineers, Inc."

*Typical savings for setback thermostats as projected by a computer study.*

## Robertshaw/Consumer Products Division
### P.O. Box 2222
### Corona, California 91720

Four thermostats are available that offer 24-hour clock-type setback of heating and/or cooling, with single or double setback periods. List prices range from $50 to $60; do-it-yourself installation instructions are included.

*Robertshaw thermostat.*

## Thermostats Compared

| Manufacturer | Make & Model | Price | Features |
|---|---|---|---|
| Champion Home Builders | Energy-Dial™ | | One set-back period.<br>Adapts to round-type thermostats.<br>Four cycle Time Dial and thermostats available.<br>Can be retrofitted.<br>Can be installed by homeowner. |
| Dynamic Electronic Controls, Inc. | Therm-O-Guard thermostats:<br><br>Model SST-2<br>Model SST-3<br>Model SST-3AC | <br><br><br>$79.95<br>89.95<br>99.95 | Set-backs sensitive to light conditions.<br>Automatically controlled.<br>Adjustable.<br>100 percent solid state.<br>No extra wiring or batteries.<br>Self-recovering in event of power failure.<br>Can be retrofitted.<br>Can be installed by the homeowner. |
| | Multistat | | Allows for periods of no heating or cooling.<br>Additional output modules allow for damper and fan control.<br>Adjustable but tamperproof.<br>No extra wiring or batteries.<br>Self-recovering in event of power failure.<br>Can be retrofitted.<br>Can be installed by the homeowner. |
| Honeywell, Inc. | Chronotherm thermostat | $58.00 | One set-back period per day.<br>Powered by battery or optional power supply.<br>Can be retrofitted.<br>Can be installed by homeowner.<br>Also available from Montgomery Ward as Cat. No. 69107 ($58), and from Sears Roebuck as Cat. No. 9108 ($68). |
| | Thermostatic radiator valve | | Can be controlled directly or by remote sensor.<br>Can be used with baseboard units and convectors.<br>Heavy-duty construction.<br>Nonelectric.<br>Can be retrofitted.<br>Can be installed by the homeowner. |
| Robertshaw | Automatic heating set-back thermostats:<br><br>Model T30-1141<br>Model T30-1241<br>Model T30-1143<br>Model T30-1243 | <br><br><br>$49.95<br>51.95<br>59.95<br>61.95 | Powered by self-charging battery.<br>Can be retrofitted.<br>Can be installed by the homeowner.<br><br>Heating only—Automatic single set-back.<br>Heating only—Automatic dual set-back.<br>Heating/Cooling—Automatic single set-back.<br>Heating/Cooling—Automatic dual set-back. |

# Insulation

**Advance Cooler Manufacturing Corp.**
**Clifton Park, New York 12069**
**(518) 371-2140**

Advance manufactures *Zerotherm®* R–40 insulating panels using urethane foam in a sandwich construction. Originally designed for commercial walk-in freezers, the system has been adapted to residential use. Joints between panels are hermetically sealed. Windows are triple- or quadruple-glazed. Ventilation is reduced and carefully controlled. Doors are thick, tight, and gasketed. When walls, roof, and floor are completely fitted and sealed, the building retains heat like a thermos bottle.

Zerotherm *panels in new construction.*

Advance also makes *Zerotherm®* rigid urethane foam for foamed-in-place applications in building cavities. As it is flammable, it must be encased in 24-gauge galvanized steel and/or 5/8 inch fire-rated sheet rock. Like *Zero-therm®* panel insulation, it has an R-value of 40 for 4 inches, 50 for 5 inches, and 60 for 6 inches.

**Borden Chemical**
**Division of Borden, Inc.**
**180 East Broad St.**
**Columbus, Ohio 43215**

Borden's *Insulspray®* foamed-in-place urea-formaldehyde insulation is suitable for new construction or old. It must be installed by trained personnel. Sensitive to water vapor, it cannot be used in completely sealed cavities and cannot be considered a water vapor barrier. It is slightly corrosive to steel.

**C.P. Chemical Co., Inc.**
**39 Westmoreland Ave.**
**White Plains, New York 10606**
**(914) 428-2517**

*Tripolymer®* foam insulation, made by C.P. Chemical Co., is a cold-setting urea foam that will not expand or decompose after its initial setting period of 10 to 30 seconds. It must be injected by trained applicators; it can go into selected building cavities in new or existing structures. Besides being an effective thermal and acoustical insulation, it is highly fire resistant and prevents smoke development. If fire occurs, *Tripolymer®* foam insulation self-insulates by forming a charred crust that prevents the fire from moving farther. It does not retain or collect moisture, is nontoxic, noncorrosive, and rodent resistant.

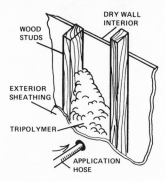

**Dow Chemical**
**Construction Materials**
**Midland, Michigan 48640**

*Styrofoam*™ Brand Insulation Sheathing is a rigid sheathing board made from extruded polystyrene foam. It is installed from roofline to frostline on residential exterior walls and on ceilings. It should completely cover the walls except for openings for doors and windows, thus eliminating thermal weak spots and reducing drafts and convection currents. It is moisture resistant and durable. *Styrofoam*™ insulation should be used with normal vapor barriers, fibrous batting, and an interior dry wall. It is combustible, and vulnerable to attack by vermin and termites.

**L.M. Dearing Associates**
**12324 Ventura Blvd.**
**P.O. Box 1744**
**Studio City, California 91604**
**(213) 769-2521**

Dearing makes *Solarcap®*, an insulating blanket for swimming pools. The blanket is a large roll of cellular plastic bubble-sheet (such as is used for protective packaging) that can be stored on a reel at poolside during the day, when the pool is in use. Nightly heat loss is reduced up to 75 percent. The blanket itself costs $0.54/square foot; complete systems with all the hardware may cost $0.90 to $1.50/square foot.

*L.M. Dearing* Solarcap *pool blanket.*

**Owens/Corning Fiberglas Corp.**
**Fiberglas Tower**
**Toledo, Ohio 43659**
**(419) 248-8000**

Owens/Corning manufactures *Fiberglas®* Blanket Type Insulation, one of the most common types available to the homeowner. Six-inch *Fiberglas®* has a rating of R-19. The blankets or batts are available with or without Kraft or foil vapor barriers. This type of insulation can be easily installed by the homeowner in new construction, but must be used with vapor barriers and proper venting to prevent condensation.

Owens/Corning provides a computer service to help the homeowner determine the best and most economical insulation system.

**Rapperswill Corp.**
**305 East 40th Street**
**New York, New York 10016**

Rapperswill manufactures *Rapco-Foam®* urea-formaldehyde thermal and acoustical insulation. It is foamed in place by professionals in new buildings or can be used for remedial work in occupied buildings. It will not settle or expand after its initial setting period of 10 to 60 seconds. Its de-oiling effect repels rodents and insects. In addition, it resists moisture and mold and is mildly bactericidal.

**Teledyne Monothane**
**3850 Granger Road**
**Akron, Ohio 44313**

Teledyne's *Foamedge* pipecover is an inexpensive and easy way to insulate water pipes to reduce heat loss and to eliminate sweating from cold water pipes in the summer. The vinyl-covered, polyurethane foam tubing is simply slipped over pipes by spreading a side-slit.

It is carried by plumbing and hardware wholesalers nationwide, including Sears, Roebuck; True Value; and Murphy's Marts.

**Urethane Molding, Inc.**
**RFD 3**
**Route 11**
**Laconia, New Hampshire 03246**

*Insuljac®* insulated pipe jackets are used to protect water lines from freezing. The urethane insulation is protected by a casing of PVC plastic, and can be slipped over any kind of metal or plastic piping. The stuff is expensive ($4/foot), but very useful for insulating outdoor pipe connections to solar collectors, or places where water lines cannot be buried.

**United States Mineral Products Co.**
**Stanhope, New Jersey 07874**
**(201) 347-1200**

USM's *Suprathane®* Sheathing Insulation Boards are used as a substitute for plywood in light-frame construction. They consist of closed-cell urethane foam sandwiched between aluminum foil fiber glass-reinforced skins. *Suprathane®* is lightweight and easy to handle, yet strong.

"Superwall"—*Suprathane®* combined with R–11 mineral fiber batting—is rated at R–22. *Suprathane®* is flammable and should not be exposed to flame during installation. It must be covered.

**Zomeworks Corporation**
**P.O. Box 712**
**Albuquerque, New Mexico 87103**
**(505) 242-5354**

Well-known in the field of solar energy, Zomeworks has developed several energy conservation devices.

*Beadwall®* is an insulating window. Styrofoam beads are blown between two panes of glass to prevent heat loss at night in the winter or heat gain in the summer. The beads are sucked out to allow heat and light in.

*Skylid®* is used with skylights or large windows. Insulated louvers open when the sun shines and close during nighttime and periods of heavy overcast. Freon moving from a warm canister to a cooler canister tips the balance of the louvers either open or closed. A manual override allows the *Skylid®* to be kept closed during the summer.

In *Drumwall®* south-facing walls are made of 55-gallon drums filled with water in racks behind glass. The outside facing ends are painted black. The winter sun warms the water in the barrels through the glass and the heat radiates into the room. Large insulating doors are lowered in the mornings in the winter—they allow the sun to shine in and warm the barrels and act as reflectors to intensify heat from the sun. The doors are raised when the sun goes down to prevent heat loss. During the summer, the doors are kept closed and the cool water in the drums acts as a heat sink.

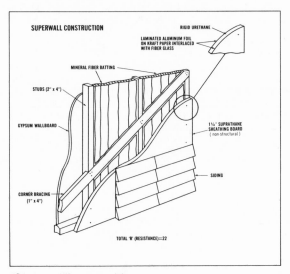

*"Superwall" construction.*

## Insulation Compared

| Manufacturer | Make & Model | Description | R-Value | Price | Features & Limitations |
|---|---|---|---|---|---|
| Advance Cooler Manufacturing Corporation | Zerotherm® R-40 insulation panels | Urethane foam in a sandwich construction | R-40/4″ R-50/5″ R-60/6″ | $1.50/sq. ft. $3.50/sq. ft. with galvanized steel finish | "Foam locked" together for side walls and roof inside and out. Can be retrofitted. Professional installation necessary. |

## Insulation Compared (Continued)

| Manufacturer | Make & Model | Description | R-Value | Price | Features & Limitations |
|---|---|---|---|---|---|
| Advance Cooler Manufacturing Corporation | Zerotherm® foamed-in-place insulation | Rigid urethane foam | R-40/4″ R-50/5″ R-60/6″ | | Toxic when burned. Highly flammable—must be encased in 24 gauge or thicker steel and/or 5/8″ fire rated sheet rock. Professional installation necessary. |
| Borden Chemical | Insulspray® foamed-in-place insulation | Urea formalde-hyde foam | R-4.3/1″ R-25.8/6″ | $0.80/sq. ft. 2 × 4 walls | Shrinkage: 1.6–3.8 percent. Initial Setting: 10–60 seconds. Curing: 1–3 days. Noncombustible; provides soundproofing. Can be retrofitted. Professional installation necessary. Not to be used in completely sealed cavities. Slightly corrosive to steel. |
| C.P. Chemical Co., Inc. | Tripolymer® foam insulation | Organic urea foam | R-26.88/ 6 inches | $0.80/sq. ft. 2 × 4 walls | Shrinkage: 0.5–3 percent. Initial setting: 10–30 seconds. Curing: 2–3 days. Superior fire resistance. Provides soundproofing. Moisture resistant; noncor-rosive; rodent resistant; nontoxic. Can be retrofitted. Professional installation necessary. |
| Dow Chemical | Styrofoam™ Brand insula-tion sheating board | Extruded poly-styrene foam | R-5.41/1 inch at 40° F. R-5/1″ at 75° F. | $0.30/sq. ft. | Installed from roofline to frostline on exterior walls. Can also be used on ceilings. Strong, rigid, stable. Lightweight, easy to handle. To be used in new construc-tion and re-siding. Can be installed by homeowner. Combustible. |
| L.M. Dearing Associates | Solarcap™ modular pool blanket | Cellular bubble sheet in roll; with or with-out portable reel | | $0.54/sq. ft. With reel: $0.90–$1.50/ sq. ft. | Transparent. Allows sun to heat pool and stores heat overnight. Stored in reel at poolside. Can be retrofitted. Can be installed by home-owner. |
| Owens/Corning Fiberglas® Corp. | Fiberglas® insulation blankets, batts, and rolls. | Fiberglas® in rolls of various thicknesses. Unfaced or faced with foil or Kraft. | R-11/3½″ R-13/3⅝″ R-19/6″ R-22/6″* | 6″—$0.28/sq. ft. | Can be retrofitted in attic. Can be installed by homeowner. Cannot be easily retrofitted in walls. |

* (Combinations of these thicknesses can yield an R-value up to R-38.)

## Insulation Compared *(Continued)*

| Manufacturer | Make & Model | Description | R-Value | Price | Features & Limitations |
|---|---|---|---|---|---|
| Rapperswill Corp. | Rapco-Foam® foamed-in-place insulation | Urea formaldehyde foam | R-26.88/6″ | $0.80/sq. ft. 2 X 4 walls | Shrinkage: 1.8–3 percent (exceeds 3 percent in case of rapid or forced drying). Initial setting: 10–60 seconds. Curing: 1–2 days. Noncombustible; provides soundproofing. Moisture resistant; noncorrosive; rodent-resistant; mold-resistant; mildly bactericidal. Can be retrofitted. Professional installation necessary. To be used in closed cavities only. |
| Teledyne Monothane | Foamedge insulated pipe covers | Vinyl covered polyurethane foam tubing | R-4.35 | $0.51/ft. ¾″ I.D. | Can be used over metal or plastic pipe above or below ground. Can be retrofitted. |
| United States Mineral Products Corp. | Suprathane® sheathing insulation boards | Closed-cell urethane foam sandwiched between aluminum foil skins reinforced with fiber glass | R-7.7/1″ R-9.6/1¼″ | $10.28/ 4′ × 8′ × 1″  $12.40/ 4′ × 8′ × 1¼″ | Replaces plywood in light-frame consruction. Can be used in re-siding. High dimensional stability. R-value permanent. Lightweight, easy to handle. Strong. Combustible. |
| Urethane Molding, Inc. | Insuljac® insulated pipe covers | Urethane tubing in PVC plastic casing | R-7.14 | $3.50/foot | For use on indoor pipes. Inexpensive. Can be retrofitted. Can be installed by the homeowner. |

# Window Coverings

**Appropriate Technology Corp.**
**P.O. Box 975**
**Brattleboro, Vermont 05301**

Appropriate Technology manufactures the *Window Quilt Insulating Shade* from a polyester fabric quilted together by an ultrasonic welding machine. The shade is fitted to windows as easily as conventional shades, yet reduces heat loss by 80 percent, according to ATC. A track system at the edges ensures a complete seal and further reduces heat loss or gain. A special fire-retarded version for commercial buildings is also available.

**Construction Specialties, Inc.**
**55 Winans Ave.**
**Cranford, New Jersey 07016**
**(201) 272-5200**

Primarily a manufacturer of industrial equipment, CS makes an operable louver that could be adapted for residential use, combining insulation, ventilation, and adjustable sun-shading in one system. It is made of one-piece extruded aluminum sections filled with polyurethane foam insulation. It is gasketed to provide airtight integrity.

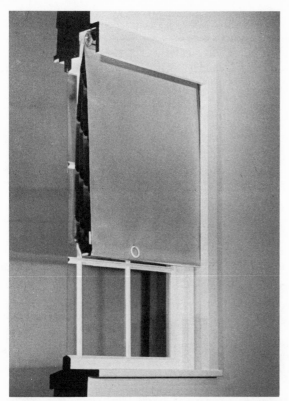

*The IS* High "R" Shade *expands into five air-trapping pockets that join with an edge seal to insulate the window.*

**Insulating Shade Co.**
**17 Water St.**
**Guilford, Connecticut 06437**
**(203) 435-9334**

The IS *High "R" Shade* is an insulating shade made up of five layers of plastic film that expand to form air spaces when rolled down. Adhesive-backed jamb seals reduce circulation. The shade is operated manually and can be easily retrofitted by the homeowner. The manufacturer claims a reduction of 15 to 30 percent in heating and cooling costs.

**J.G. Wilson Corp.**
**P.O. Box 599**
**Norfolk, Virginia 23501**
**(804) 545-7341**

Wilson's *Klassic* Rolling Wood Closures are built of 1 3/4 inch by 7/16 inch fir slats strung on steel bands with special springs that ensure easy operation. They roll down from a coil box to form partitions and counter or cabinet closures, and may be adapted for use as an attractive insulating shutter of natural wood.

**Pease Company/Ever-Strait Division**
**7100 Dixie Highway**
**Fairfield, Ohio 45023**

Pease Rolling Shutters are mounted externally to provide shade, insulation and privacy. Slats of hollow extruded PVC provide an additional insulating air space.

**Rolscreen Co.**
**Pella, Iowa 50219**

The manufacturer of Pella windows offers a narrow-slat blind called *Slimshade* that fits between the panes of Pella double-glazed windows. The system is available as an optional accessory for all models of Pella double-glass windows, which are framed with wood for energy efficiency.

**Solar Energy Construction Co.**
**Box 718**
**Valley Forge, Pennsylvania 19481**
**(215) 783-7735**
**(215) 935-2707**

Seco's *Thermo-Shade*™ roll-down plastic shade is mounted on the inside of the window with an adhesive foam strip and rolls into a valance. *Thermo-Shade*™ provides insulation through reflective surfaces and sealed space. It can be controlled manually or automatically with timers, thermostats, or light switches. The manufacturer claims that heat loss is reduced more than 75 percent.

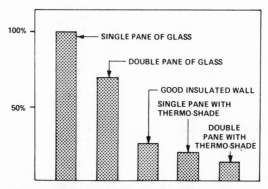

*Heat loss differences (Btu/hr/ft²) among single-pane, double-pane, and insulated walls & windows.*

**Solex/Division ELR, Inc.**
**244 San Lorenzo Ave.**
**Coral Gables, Florida 33134**
**(305) 443-1053**

Solex wood roll-down shutters provide ventilation, protection from the elements, and an insulation value of R–.52. They come in a variety of fine woods and finishes and can be manually or automatically operated. In addition, they are specially treated for mildew, rot, and termites. Solex shutters are also available in a PVC plastic version in an assortment of colors.

# Window Coverings Compared

| Manufacturer | Make & Model | Description | R-value | Control | Price | Features |
|---|---|---|---|---|---|---|
| Appropriate Technology Corp. | Window-Quilt | Polyester fabric quilted together. Track system at edges. | R-4.5 with single-glazed window R-5.5 with double-glazed window | Manual | $2.89/sq. ft. $3.66/sq. ft. for commercial version | Mounted on interior window frame. Can be retrofitted. Can be installed by home-owner. |
| Construction Specialties, Inc. | Operating insulated airfoil louvers | One-piece extruded aluminum filled with foam insulation. Head, sill, and mullion of aluminum filled with polyurethane beadboard. | | Manual and automatic | $28–$31/sq. ft. depending on surface finish | Five-position electric operation can be set to automatic temperature control system. Available in acrylic and anodized finishes. Professional installation necessary. |
| Insulating Shade Co. | High "R"™ Shade | Multiple layers of plastic film spacers sandwiched between vinyl. Adhesive backed jamb seals. | R-15 | Manual | $2.75/sq. ft. | Mounted on interior window frame. Can be retrofitted with modification to window trim. Can be installed by home-owner. |
| J.G. Wilson Corp. | "Klassic" Rolling Wood Closures | Fir slats 1¾" × 7/16" strung on steel bands with special springs, rolling into coil. Fir guides. | R-0.6 | Manual and automatic | | Includes bronze hardware. Furnished unfinished. Can be retrofitted. Can be installed by home-owner. |
| Pease Co. | Pease Rolling Shutters | Hollow PVC plastic slats. Prefinished aluminum tracks. | | Manual | | Externally mounted. Can be retrofitted. Can be installed by home-owner. |
| Rolscreen Co. | Pella Slimshade® blinds | Narrow aluminum slats on polyester cord ladders. | | Manual | | Fits between panes of Pella Double-glazed Windows (optional). Requires little maintenance, but can be removed for cleaning. Cannot be retrofitted in any other than Pella Double-glazed Windows. Cannot be installed by homeowner. |
| Solar Energy Construction Co. | Thermo-Shade™ thermal barriers | Double plastic slats with rounded backs. Self-adhering track. | | Manual and automatic | Under $3/sq. ft. plus $15–25 for valance | Mounted on interior window frame. Can be retrofitted. Can be installed by home-owner. |
| Solex/Division ELR, Inc. | Solex wood roll-down shutters | Individual slats of wood held together at 16" intervals by a metallic strap or chain. Anodized aluminum guides. | R-.52 | Manual and automatic | $10/sq. ft. $250/100 sq. ft. with electric operation. Installation extra. | A variety of woods and finishes available. Specially treated to resist mold, mildew, termites. PVC plastic version available in assorted colors. |

# Glazing Materials

**ASG Industries, Inc.**
**P.O. Box 929**
**Kingsport, Tennessee 37662**
**(615) 245-0211**
**Toll Free: (800) 251-0441**

CREATIVE IDEAS IN GLASS

ASG manufactures a line of glass for glazing in solar energy applications. The most effective one in this line is *Sunadex®*. It is a virtually iron free, water white rolled glass with one side nearly smooth and the other lightly textured. When facing out, the textured side reduces glare by diffusing reflected light. It also obscures a solar collector interior for a more pleasing appearance.

*Solatex™* is a rolled glass with reduced iron content that is also lightly textured. *Lo-Iron®* is a clear sheet glass with a low iron content. *Starlux®*, a float glass with the highest iron content of them all, is the least expensive of ASG's solar glasses.

**Bio-Energy Systems, Inc.**
**Mountaindale Road**
**Spring Glen, New York 12483**
**(914) 434-7858**

*SolaRoll™* architectural extrusions are continuous runs of synthetic elastomer (an elastic rubberlike substance) specially formulated to withstand extremes of temperature, ozone, UV light, chemicals and abrasives. It will not crack, dent, or rust.

A number of forms are available to perform a variety of functions: to hold down and seal glazing on storm windows, skylights, and greenhouses; to enclose and protect framing members of such structures; and to flash skylights and solar collectors to the roof or wall.

Not rigid itself, any *SolaRoll™* extrusion must be bonded to plastic glazing, wood, or metal with BESI's adhesive and lock-strip system.

*SolaRoll™* extrusions are inexpensive, easy to install, long-lasting, and can be retrofitted and moved. Instruction manuals are supplied free of charge for each kind of *SolaRoll™* application. Prices for *SolaRoll™* extrusions run from $1.60 to $2.50 per linear foot.

**Chave and Early, Inc.**
**American Bleached Goods Division**
**1460 Broadway**
**New York, New York 10036**
**(212) 391-1010**

Chave and Early manufactures *Loretex* glazing film made of woven high-density polyethylene coated with polyethylene. It is strong, flexible, waterproof, and ultraviolet resistant. Light transmission is 98 percent.

Uses include greenhouse covers, swimming pool covers, solar pond liners and covers, outdoor protective covers, and temporary shelters. It is available in natural, orange, yellow, blue, light green, dark green, white, and black in 72-inch widths in 500 yard rolls.

**Cy/Ro Industries**
**Wayne, New Jersey 07407**
**(201) 839-4800**

*Acrylite®* SDP™ double-skinned acrylic sheet is a primary glazing material for skylights, curtain walls, covered walkways, greenhouses, and similar structures. Made entirely of extruded acrylic, each sheet consists of integral ribs sandwiched between two exterior skins. It is lightweight and easily workable, yet offers good impact resistance and rigidity. (A polycarbonate version is available for even greater strength). It also provides, at a lower cost, thermal insulation equal to that of insulated glass. The sheets are available in clear, white, and solar bronze tints. A weep system should be used to drain the air cells of accumulated water. Cy/Ro Industries also makes gadgets for joining the sheets together.

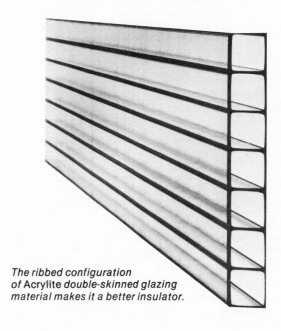

*The ribbed configuration of* Acrylite *double-skinned glazing material makes it a better insulator.*

**General Electric Company**
**Plastics Division**
**One Plastics Avenue**
**Pittsfield, Massachusetts 01201**

G.E. makes *Lexan® 9030* polycarbonate glazing sheet. It is a Class 1 building material combining outstanding flammability performance with impact resistance, weatherability, high heat resistance, UV stability, and superior light transmission. These characteristics make it an excellent choice for solar collector covers.

It is also valuable for energy conservation. When used as window glazing, it prevents excessive heat gain in summer and heat loss in winter, creating considerable energy savings.

**Kalwall Corporation**
**Solar Components Division**
**88 Pine St.**
**P.O. Box 237**
**Manchester, New Hampshire 03103**
**(603) 688-8186**

Kalwall manufactures glazing materials. Their *Sunlite*®
(fiber glass-reinforced plastic glazing material) is designed for use as low-temperature collector covers, as insulating windows, and as greenhouse glazing. It is inexpensive, lightweight, easily handled and installed, and impact resistant. It has an ability to transmit solar energy
equal to glass. *Sunlite*® also comes in a double-faced insulating glazing panel for use in collectors where maximum solar energy transmission is required and with a
bonded *Teflon*® interior for use in high-temperature collectors.
   *Sunwall*® is the Kalwall panel system made of double
sheets of *Sunlite*® Premium II permanently bonded to an
aluminum grid. It is highly insulating and heat transmit-
ting. It is available in a multilayered version with increasing insulating values, decreasing solar transmissions. It
can be used as collector covers, walls, skylights, and insulated solar windows in passive systems.
   Kalwall sells its products directly or by mail from its
store and warehouse at the above address. The largest in
the country, it carries not only Kalwall but other brands
of glazing as well. They will send a catalog upon request.

**Libbey-Owens-Ford Company**
**811 Madison Ave.**
**Toledo, Ohio 43695**
**(419) 247-3731**

Libbey-Owens-Ford manufactures glass products for glazing, some of which can be useful for conserving energy.
Heat-absorbing *float glass* is strong, yet offers high
visibility. It reduces solar transmission, reducing glare
and air conditioning costs.
   *Vari-tran*® coated products (annealed or tempered)
reduce solar heat gain even further. *Vari-tran*® coating, a
durable, transparent, metallic film, is available in insulating glass, single-pane glass, or laminated glass. It is
offered in six colors—silver, golden, bronze, blue, gray,
and light gold. It is suitable for reglazing and recladding
existing structures.
   LOF also offers *Thermopane*® insulating glass, com-
posed of two or more lights of glass separated by a
sealed air space containing dry air. *Thermopane*® helps
reduce heat loss and minimizes condensation.

**Martin Processing, Inc.**
**Film Division**
**P.O. Box 5068**
**Martinsville, Virginia 24112**
**(703) 629-1711**

Martin manufactures *Llumar*™ weatherable polyester
film, a glazing film specially treated with protective
agents that screen out ultraviolet rays. *Llumar*™ is
available in four forms: clear, dyed a variety of colors in
transparent and opaque densities, partially reflective, and
fully reflective. Its protective agents are incorporated into
the film itself and cannot be scratched or worn off. It is
available in several thicknesses in rolls up to 60 inches
wide.

**Minnesota Mining & Manufacturing**
**(3M Company)**
**General Offices**
**Saint Paul, Minnesota 55105**
**(612) 733-1110**

*Flexigard* Brand Protective Film #7410 from 3M Company
is an inexpensive composite film to be used as a replacement for glass on solar collectors, storm windows, and
greenhouses. It is a durable, flexible, weather-resistant
film with the light-transmission and insulating properties
of glass.

**PPG Industries, Inc.**
**One Gateway Center**
**Pittsburgh, Pennsylvania 15222**

PPG manufactures *Solarcool* reflective glass, a bronze-
tinted glass with a transparent reflective coating durably
bonded to the outdoor surface. *Solarcool* glass cuts the
sun's brightness and heat by 50 per cent, resulting in
substantial savings in air conditioning costs.
   PPG also produces tinted glasses in bronze, gray, and
green that also reduce entry of the sun's heat. PPG
glasses can be factory-installed in windows for new construction and used in add-on panels and storm windows
for existing homes. PPG glass is also available in double-
glazed units.

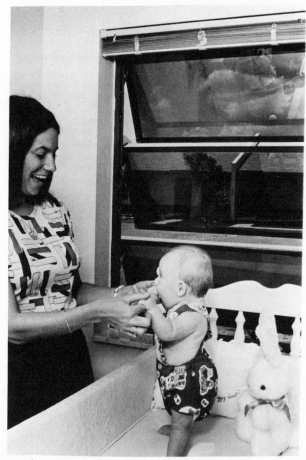

*PPG's* Solarcool *bronze reflective glass saves on air conditioning costs.*

## Glazing Materials Compared

| Manufacturer | Make & Model | Description | Shading Coefficient | Features |
|---|---|---|---|---|
| ASG Industries, Inc. | Sunadex® | Water white rolled glass with one side slightly textured | 1.08 | 0.01 percent iron-oxide content.<br>Installed with textured side out.<br>Reduces glare.<br>Obscures collector interior.<br>Can be retrofitted.<br>Can be installed by homeowner. |
| | Solatex™ | Slightly textured rolled glass | 1.05 | 0.04 percent iron-oxide content.<br>Installed with textured side out.<br>Reduces glare.<br>Obscures collector interior.<br>Can be retrofitted.<br>Can be installed by homeowner. |
| | Lo-Iron® | Clear sheet glass | 1.05 | 0.06 percent iron-oxide content.<br>Can be retrofitted.<br>Can be installed by homeowner. |
| | Starlux® | Float glass | 0.97 | 0.12 percent iron-oxide content.<br>Inexpensive.<br>Can be retrofitted.<br>Can be installed by homeowner. |
| Bio-Energy Systems, Inc. | SolaRoll™ elastomeric extrusions | Extruded continuous runs of synthetic elastomer in various forms. | | For glazing and bonding solar structures.<br>Resists extremes of temperature, ozone, UV light, chemicals, abrasives.<br>Will not crack, dent, rust.<br>Can be retrofitted.<br>Can be installed by homeowner.<br>Must be bonded to rigid substrate. |
| CY/RO Industries | Acrylite® SDP™ double-skinned acrylic sheets | Extruded plastic with hollow, ribbed space between 2 acrylic skins. | clear: 0.97<br>white: 0.31<br>white: 0.81<br>bronze: 0.72<br>bronze: 0.46 | Rigid, lightweight, impact resistant.<br>Provides thermal insulation.<br>Available in clear, white, bronze.<br>Joining systems available.<br>Can be installed by homeowner.<br>User should employ weep system. |
| Libbey-Owens-Ford Co. | Vari-tran® coated glass | Glass coated with metallic film | | Reduces heat transmission.<br>Available in insulating, single-pane, and laminated glass.<br>Available in silver, golden, bronze, blue, grey, light gold.<br>Can be retrofitted.<br>Can be installed by homeowner. |
| | Thermo-pane® insulating glass | Two or more lights of glass separated by a sealed air space containing air | | Reduces heat loss.<br>Minimizes condensation.<br>Available in tints and with Vari-Tran® coating.<br>Triple-glazing available.<br>Can be retrofitted.<br>Can be installed by homeowner. |
| Martin Processing, Inc. | Llumar™ | Polyester film made with protective agents incorporated into the film itself | | Weather-resistant.<br>Screens out UV light.<br>Available in clear, tinted, or reflective.<br>Can be retrofitted.<br>Can be installed by homeowner. |

## Glazing Materials Compared *(Continued)*

| Manufacturer | Make & Model | Description | Shading Coefficient | Features |
|---|---|---|---|---|
| Minnesota Mining and Manufacturing Co. | Flexigard Brand Protective Film #7410 | Transparent composite film | | Durable, flexible, weather-resistant. Light transmission and insulating properties of glass. Can be retrofitted. Can be installed by homeowner. |
| PPG Industries, Inc. | Solarcool reflective glass | Bronze-tinted glass with a transparent reflective coating bonded to outdoor surface. | 0.45 | Cuts heat gain. Factory-installed in new windows or used in add-on panels and storm windows for retrofit. Available in double-glazed units. |
| Chave and Early, Inc. | Loretex glazing film | Woven high-density polyethylene coated with polyethylene | 0.98 | Strong, flexible, waterproof, ultraviolet resistant. Available in a variety of colors. |
| General Electric Company | Lexan® glazing sheet | Polycarbonate | | Outstanding flammability performance. Impact resistant, UV resistant, high-heat resistant. Weatherable. Superior light transmission. Retards heat loss in winter, gain in summer. |
| Kalwall Corporation | Sunlite® | Fiberglass reinforced plastic | | Lightweight, easy to handle. Impact resistant. Solar transmission equal to glass. |
| | Sunwall® | Double Sunlite® Premium II bonded to aluminum grid | 0.84 (R-2.5) 0.30 (R-4.2) 0.09 (R-10) | High insulation and solar transmission values. |

# Water-Saving Devices

**American Standard**
**U.S. Plumbing Products**
**P.O. Box 2003**
**New Brunswick, New Jersey 08903**
**(201) 885-1900**

AMERICAN STANDARD

American Standard manufactures Water-saver toilets and fittings. The *Water-saver Cadet* toilet features siphon jet action and close-coupled tank with water-saving trim. It uses 3.5 gallons per flush and is available in round or elongated bowl design.

The *Aquamizer™* flow regulator for the shower creates a water flow of 2.5 gallons per minute regardless of water pressure. Simply unscrew the shower head, screw on the *Aquamizer™*, and screw the shower head back on, using pipe joint compound for a good seal.

American Standard also makes restricted-flow *Heritage* and *Aquarian II* single-lever control faucets for kitchen and bathroom. Both produce a constant flow rate of 3.5 gallons per minute, compared to 6 gpm for ordinary faucets.

**Briggs**
**P.O. Box 22622**
**Tampa, Florida 33622**

Briggs makes water-saving *Conserver™* toilets in one-piece or standard two-piece designs.

The two-piece toilets are available in round or elongated bowl designs with siphon jet action, or in round bowl design with reverse trap action. They use 3.5

gallons of water per flush as compared to the usual 4.

The Brigg's one-piece *Silhouette II Conserver*™ toilet combines an elegant low profile with water saving-ability—it flushes with no more than 3.5 gallons. It works with siphon jet action.

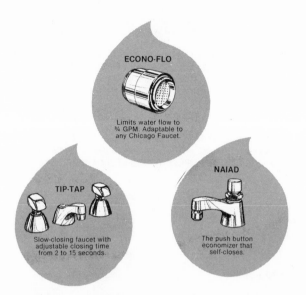

**ECONO-FLO**
Limits water flow to ¾ GPM. Adaptable to any Chicago Faucet.

**TIP-TAP**
Slow-closing faucet with adjustable closing time from 2 to 15 seconds.

**NAIAD**
The push button economizer that self-closes.

## The Chicago Faucet Co.
2100 So. Nuclear Drive
Des Plaines, Illinois 60018
(312) 694-4400

Chicago Faucet manufactures water-saving fixtures. The *Econo-Flo* device adapts to any Chicago faucet by simply screwing onto the faucet outlet. It is also available with adapters to fit most major brand faucets. It limits water flow from a faucet to a constant ¾ gallon per minute regardless of pressure. The *Stedi-Flo* limits water to a constant 2 gpm on all faucets and 3 gpm on all shower heads.

Chicago Faucet also makes the *Klo-Self* self-closing, drip-tight faucet; the *Naiad* self-closing, push-button faucet; and the *Tip-Tap* self-closing faucet with adjustable closing time from 2 to 15 seconds.

## Eaton Corporation
**Controls Division**
**Plumbing and Heating Products**
191 East North Ave.
Carol Stream, Illinois 60187

Eaton makes Dole® Flow Controls for plumbing, heating, cooling, and water distribution systems. Dole® automatic shower volume flow controls maintain a near-constant flow of water regardless of pressure. They screw in between the shower head and the shower water supply pipe.

There are four styles: chrome-plated brass in standard length, chrome-plated brass in short length, chrome-plated ABS plastic, and black finish ABS plastic. Each style is available with 2, 2.5, 3, or 4 gallons-per-minute flow rates to accommodate the size of the shower head.

The Dole® *Conservationist Mark III* shower head incorporates the Dole® automatic shower volume flow control in a chrome-plated ABS plastic head. It maintains a near-constant flow of 3 gpm regardless of water pressure.

## Ecology Products Plus, Inc.
1200 Welsh Road
P.O. Box 1517
North Wales, Pennsylvania 19454

Ecology Products Plus manufactures the *Nova* Controlled Flow Shower Head, which reduces water flow to 2.1 gallons per minute at a pressure of 60 psi. A special *Nova* model is also available with throttle control valve to enable the user to cut water flow to 0.1 gallon per minute and to restore flow to normal without readjusting temperature.

Aerators are also available for kitchen and bathroom sinks. They create a water flow of approximately 1.5 gpm.

Ecology Products Plus also distributes Watersavers' *Moby Dike*™ toilet tank water-saving device—plastic panels installed by the homeowner on the bottom of the tank. The panels create reservoirs on each side of the tank that trap from 1.5 to 3 gallons of water usually lost on each flush. This device can be used on most standard toilets, except 3.5 gallon water-saver toilets, one-piece toilets, and toilets with "silent flush."

| *Comparison of Water Consumption and Heating Costs For One 10 Minute Shower* | ORDINARY SHOWER HEAD | NOVA SHOWER HEAD | NOVA SAVINGS PER SHOWER |
|---|---|---|---|
| Gallons of water used | 80 | 21 | 59.0 gals. |
| Gallons of water heated (50% of total) | 40 | 10.5 | 29.5 gals. |
| Gallons of oil to heat water used for shower | .3333 | .0875 | ¼ gals. |
| Water heating cost for one shower (Oil @ $1 per gallon) | 26.6¢ | 7¢ | 19.6¢ |

## Total Savings with NOVA - 73%

## Eljer Plumbingware
**Wallace Murray Corporation**
Three Gateway Center
Pittsburgh, Pennsylvania 15222
(412) 471-2402

All products in the Eljer line of toilets and fixtures are designed to save water. Eljer toilets have siphon jet or whirlpool jet action. Models are floor-mounted or wall-hung with round or elongated bowls and are available in a variety of colors. They flush with approximately 3 gallons of water at a pressure of 60 psi.

Eljer's flow control brass fittings for sinks use about 2 gallons of water per minute at 60 psi. Their *Ultima* and *Regata* shower heads provide an adjustable spray pattern and supply about 3 gpm at 60 psi.

**Energy Recovery Systems, Inc.**
**P.O. Box 233**
**Lincroft, New Jersey 07738**

The *Aqua-Miser* is a water-saving device to be installed in the toilet tank by the homeowner. Its two thermoplastic rubber panels create reservoirs at the bottom of the tank, saving 2 gallons of water normally flushed.

**Kohler Co.**
**Kohler, Wisconsin 53044**

Kohler manufactures water-saving toilets and fixtures. Their *Wellworth Water-Guard* toilets are designed to flush with 3.5 gallons of water. They are available with round or elongated bowls and come in a variety of colors.

All Kohler shower heads feature automatic flow control, which limits water flow to 3 gallons per minute at 40 psi. These *Water-Guard* shower heads are available in two styles in gold electroplate or chromium, satin or polished.

*Water-Guard* faucets also feature automatic flow to 2 gpm per valve at 40 to 80 psi. Kohler *Centura* single-control faucets limit water flow to 3 to 4 gpm at 40 to 60 psi.

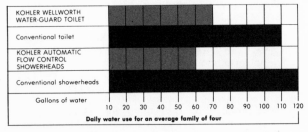

*Water-saving toilets and showerheads can cut a family's water consumption in half.*

**Microphor, Inc.**
**P.O. Box 490**
**Willits, California 95490**
**(707) 459-5563**

The Microphor Low Flush Toilet is a tankless toilet that completely replaces the conventional toilet. It reduces to two quarts the amount of water needed for flushing.

Water feeds to the toilet through a water line that hooks up directly. Upon flushing, waste and water are deposited in a secondary chamber, which is pressurized with compressed air. The waste and water are then deposited into the normal sewer line and fresh water is supplied to the bowl.

The Microphor toilet can be installed by the home-owner with help from the local plumber or contractor; no special plumbing is needed. Compressor and air tank are not supplied. (A ½-hp compressor and 12-gallon air tank will meet the requirements of most homes.)

**Moen®**
**A Division of Stanadyne**
**377 Woodland Ave.**
**Elyria, Ohio 44035**
**(216) 323-5481**

Moen® manufactures water-saving, single-handle faucets and shower heads. A frictionless cartridge is used in place of washers and seats. This cartridge eliminates leaking and adds the convenience of "remembering" a comfortable temperature that the owner presets. You waste no water trying to find the right temperature.

In addition, the Moen® *Flow-Rator*™ reduces water flow to 2.5 gallons per minute under normal line pressure, while maintaining a constant but sufficient flow of water.

**Ny-Del Corporation**
**P.O. Box 155**
**740 E. Alosta Ave.**
**Glendora, California 91740**
**(213) 335-2213**

Ny-Del makes water-saving devices and fixtures. Their water-saving shower heads reduce water flow to 2.5 to 3 gallons per minute. Both the *ND-540* and *ND-550* are available white or chrome-plated and have an adjustable spray pattern. Model *ND-540* features an internally fitted valve that allows for on/off volume control. A turn of the shower head cuts water flow to a minimum; another turn restores it to the preset flow.

Their *Conservarator* aerator reduces water flow in faucets to 2 gallons per minute in line pressures of 40 to 100 psi. Special vandal-proof *Conservarators* are also available.

Ny-Del makes two flow restrictors for use with the existing shower head. Model *ND-77* restricts flow to 3 gallons per minute and is to be used with shower heads with a ball joint on the supply pipe. Model *ND-76* is a pressure-compensating type that reduces flow to 2.5 gallons per minute with line pressures of 15 to 100 psi. Regardless of whether water is being used elsewhere in the house, the *ND-76* maintains a constant, even flow of water.

The *SA-720 Watersaver* is a plastic insert that fits around the flush valve in the toilet tank to enable the toilet to flush efficiently with only 3.5 gallons of water. It is easily installed by the homeowner in standard toilet tanks.

**Savway Co., Inc.**
**930 Clarkson Ave.**
**Brooklyn, New Jersey 11203**
**(212) 342-1267**

Savway manufactures *Dual Flush* water-saving devices for toilet tanks. The mechanism is a plastic tube that attaches to the inside of the toilet tank permitting control of the amount of water released by the length of time the handle is held down.

The *Dual Flush* is claimed to save up to 40 percent on water bills. It is easily installed with a screwdriver by the homeowner.

**Ultraflo Corporation**
**Perkins Industrial Park**
**4515 South Columbus**
**P.O. Box 2294**
**Sandusky, Ohio 44870**
**(419) 626-8182**

Ultraflo Corporation makes a centralized, push-button water distribution system. This one-line system is made possible by a console containing banks of solenoid valves located near the water heater.

The valves are operated by push-button control panels installed near the kitchen sink, bathtub/shower, and bathroom sink. Buttons represent various preset temperatures and flow rates: on, off, fast, slow, cold, warm, hot. The kitchen sink control includes buttons for simultaneous disposal/water flow and for drinking water, also charcoal filtered water, desalted water, or water softener bypass. For safety, the shower/bathtub control has no direct hot water button.

The system is claimed to be able to save the homeowner 30 percent of water and water-heating costs. There is no wasted water in the lines to be heated or to drip from faucets. The system is also less expensive to install than conventional two-line systems. Small-diameter, flexible copper or plastic tubing is all that is needed, since water is blended at the source.

The system can be installed by the homeowner, who sets temperature limits with a screwdriver at the time of installation. It can be retrofitted and requires little maintenance since there are no faucet valves with washers to wear out.

**Walker, Crosweller & Co., Ltd.**
**140 Greenwood Ave.**
**Midland Park, New Jersey 07432**
**(201) 447-1200**

Walker, Crosweller & Company's Unatap Spray Mixing Faucets have a single handle for temperature selection and a built-in adjustable flow restrictor, which can be preset by the homeowner to give an adequate flow (usually 5–6 pints per minute) under pressures from 5 to 125 psi. The spouts can be adjusted during installation to give maximum projection into any shape basin and then locked into position. The vandal-proof spray averts lime deposits and can be removed for cleaning.

Five models are available. *Unatap 11* with black control knob and *Unatap 11A* with clear control knob are for use in private residences. The following models are suited for use in hospitals and other institutions that require rugged construction and ease of use: *Unatap 24* with chrome-plated lever, *Unatap 24M* with chrome-plated stub lever, and *Unatap 24A* with clear control knob. They are also ideal for the handicapped and arthritic.

The *Rada* shower head has specially designed waterways that provide a dense and well distributed water flow at only 2.5 gallons per minute at 60 psi. Swivel action and fixed position heads are available.

*Rada* shower heads and *Unatap* faucets are available from: Lynnwood Distributors, 348 Railroad Avenue, Hackensack, New Jersey 07601.

*Walker, Crosweller's*
Rada *showerhead.*

**Walter Control Products/N.A., Inc.**
**1100 Owendale**
**Suite E**
**Troy, Michigan 48084**
**(313) 689-1700**

Walter Control Products manufactures *Flushmate*® toilet tank, which uses 2 to 2.5 gallons of water per flush. It completely replaces the tank on conventional toilets in existing two-piece toilets or new installations.

*Flushmate's*® flushing efficiency is produced by water supply line pressure. Water entering an empty *Flushmate* tank compresses the air in the tank until water and air pressures are equal, and the water flow stops. A push on the *Flushmate* button opens the main valve. The entrapped air, under compression, forces water through the bowl, flushing it immediately.

The *Flushmate*® is easily installed by the homeowner and uses existing water supply connections. It costs $69.95 with a white cover; a selection of designer colors is also offered at a slightly higher cost.

**Wrightway Manufacturing Co.**
**371 East 116th St.**
**Chicago, Illinois 60623**

Wrightway manufactures *Bubble-Stream*® ecology water saver kit, containing one push-button shower head and two water-saving aerators for the sink: basic and swivel. Both aerators use 2.5 gallons of water per minute at 60 psi.

The *on* and *off* control featured in the push-button shower head permits minimum water flow through the head while button is in the *off* position. In the *on* position, water flow rate is measured at 2.5 gpm at a pressure of 60 psi.

# Water-Saving Devices Compared

| Manufacturer | Make | Water Used | Price | Features |
|---|---|---|---|---|
| **TOILETS** | | | | |
| American Standard | Water-saver Cadet toilet | 3.5 gallons per flush | $71.55 w/o seat | Siphon jet action.<br>Close-coupled tank with water-saving trim.<br>Round and elongated bowl design. |
| Briggs | Conserver™ toilet | 3.5 gallons per flush | | One- or two-piece design.<br>Round or elongated bowl.<br>Siphon jet or reverse trap action. |
| Eljer Plumbingware (Wallace Murray Corporation) | Eljer toilet | 3 gallons per flush | | Siphon jet or whirlpool action.<br>Round or elongated bowl.<br>Floor- or wall-mounted. |
| Kohler Company | Wellworth Water-Guard | 3.5 gallons per flush | $82.85 w/o seat | Round or elongated bowl. |
| Microphor, Inc. | Microphor toilet | 2 quarts per flush | | Tankless.<br>Water line hooks directly to toilet.<br>Works by air compression.<br>Requires compressor and air tank. |
| **TOILET DEVICES** | | | | |
| Ecology Products Plus, Inc. | Watersaver's Moby Dike™ | About 3 to 3.5 gallons per flush | $4.95 | Two plastic panels inserted in toilet tank create reservoirs to trap 1.5 to 2 gallons of water per flush.<br>Cannot be used on 3.5 gallon toilets, one-piece toilets, and "silent flush" toilets. |
| Energy Recovery Systems, Inc. | Aqua-Miser | About 3 to 3.5 gallons per flush | $5.98 | Two thermoplastic rubber panels inserted in tank create reservoirs to trap 2 gallons of water per flush.<br>Can be installed by homeowner. |
| Ny-Del Corporation | SA-720 Watersaver | 3.5 gallons per flush | | Plastic insert that fits around the flush valve in the tank. |
| Savway Company, Inc. | Dual-Flush | 2.5 to 3.5 gallons per flush when in use | $4.95 | Plastic tube attaching to toilet handle from inside tank.<br>Controls amount of water used per flush by length of time handle is held down.<br>Permits full flush or half flush.<br>Can be installed by homeowner. |
| Walter Control Products | Flushmate® toilet tank | 2 to 2.5 gallons per flush | $69.95 | Replaces conventional toilet tank.<br>Works by air pressure from water supply pipe.<br>Can be installed by homeowner. |
| **FIXTURES** | | | | |
| American Standard | Aquamizer™ flow regulator | 2.5 gpm | $5.00 | For shower heads.<br>Can be installed by homeowner. |
| | Heritage faucets and shower heads | 3.5 gpm | | Built-in flow control. |

## Water-Saving Devices Compared *(Continued)*

| Manufacturer | Make | Water Used | Price | Features |
|---|---|---|---|---|
| | Aquarian II faucets and shower heads | 3.5 gpm | | Single lever control. |
| Chicago Faucet Company | Econo-flo flow regulator | ¾ gpm | $5.22 | For Chicago faucets. Adapters available for most faucet brands. Can be installed by homeowner. |
| | Stedi-flo flow regulator | 2 gpm on faucets; 3 gpm on shower heads | | For all faucets and shower heads. Can be installed by homeowner. |
| | Klo-Self faucet | | | Self-closing. Drip-tight. |
| | Naiad faucet | | | Self-closing. Push button. |
| | Tip-Tap faucet | | | Self-closing. Adjustable closing time from 2 to 15 seconds. |
| Eaton Corporation | Dole® Automatic Shower Volume Flow Control | 2, 2.5, 3 or 4 gpm (depending on size of shower head | | Comes in chrome-plated brass and ABS plastic and black finish ABS plastic. |
| | Dole® Conservationist Mark III shower head | 3 gpm | | Incorporates Dole® Automatic Shower Volume Flow Control. Chrome-plated ABS plastic. |
| Ecology Products Plus | Nova controlled flow shower head | 2.1 gpm at 60 psi | $12.95 | Built-in flow control. |
| | Nova B6402 | 2.1 gpm at 60 psi (full rate) | $16.95 | Built-in flow control. *On/Off* control for minimum flow. |
| | Aerators | 1.5 gpm | $1.95 to $2.95 | For kitchen and bathroom faucets. |
| Eljer Plumbingware | Eljer faucets | 2 gpm at 60 psi | | Built-in flow control. Brass construction. |
| | Ultima and Regata shower heads | 3 gpm at 60 psi | | Built-in flow control. Adjustable spray pattern. |
| Kohler Company | Water-Guard shower heads | 3 gpm at 40 psi | | Built-in flow control. Gold electroplate or chromium, satin or polish finish. |
| | Water-Guard faucets | 2 gpm at 40 to 80 psi | | Built-in flow control. |
| | Centura faucets | 3 to 4 gpm at 40 to 60 psi | | Single lever control. |
| Moen® | Faucets and shower heads | 2.5 gpm | | Incorporates Moen® Flowrator™ for built-in flow control. Single lever control. Cartridge construction for elimination of leaking. Owner-preset temperatures. |

# Water-Saving Devices Compared *(Continued)*

| Manufacturer | Make | Water Used | Price | Features |
|---|---|---|---|---|
| Ny-Del Corporation | ND-550 shower head | 2.5 to 3 gpm | | Built-in flow control. White or chrome-plated. Adjustable spray pattern. |
| | ND-540 shower head | 2.5 to 3 gpm (full rate) | | *On/Off* control for minimum flow. Built-in flow control. White or chrome-plated. Adjustable spray pattern. |
| | ND-77 flow regulator | 3 gpm | | For shower heads with ball joint on supply pipe. |
| | ND-76 flow regulator | 2.5 gpm | | For shower heads. Pressure-compensating. |
| | Conservarator aerator | 2 gpm | | For faucets. Vandal-proof model available. |
| Ultraflo Corporation | Ultraflo plumbing | | $231.75–$479.40 | One-line water distribution system. Push-button controls. Owner-preset temperatures. Drinking water and disposal in kitchen. No direct hot water in shower. Includes kitchen and bathroom sink spouts. Can be retrofitted. Can be installed by homeowner. Tub spouts, shower heads, tubing, fittings, and electrical wire not supplied. |
| Walker, Crosweller, and Co. | Unatap spray mixing faucets | 0.6–0.75 gpm | $62.20–$83.15 | Built-in flow control. Single-lever control. Vandal-proof. Adjustable position. Special models for handicapped and for institutional applications. |
| | Rada shower heads | 2.5 gpm at 60 psi | $4.09 | Swivel action and fixed-position. |
| Wrightway Manufacturing Company | Bubble-Stream® kit includes: shower head  aerators | 2.5 gpm at 60 psi (full rate)  2.25 at 60 psi | | Built-in flow control. *On/Off* control for minimum spray. Swivel and fixed-position. |

# 2
# Solar Energy

**Traditional Maine farmhouse blends well with new solar addition.**

Control of the sun to heat and cool dwellings is not new. Many of the most current designs and inventions are based upon ideas that are thousands of years old. Solar hot water heaters were common in Florida and California eighty years ago (Figure 2–1), and they are in widespread use throughout the Middle East and in Japan. Solar heating for houses was successfully demonstrated in this country in the 1930's. The recent burst of interest in the sun's energy is a simple result of the changing economics of fuel supply and demand. Solar power just didn't make economic sense in 1955. Now it does make sense. The resulting boom in research, technology, production and marketing of solar energy is a direct response to this new economic equation.

# Principles of Solar Heating

All solar heating systems share the same basic objectives:

- to collect the sun's heat
- to store that heat
- to distribute it when and where needed, to avoid underheating or overheating of the living space.

Behind all the jargon and complexity of current solar technology stand a few fundamental facts of physics and astronomy, the keys to effective control of the sun's energy. The first of these is the movement of the earth around the sun, illustrated in Figure 2–2. The changing seasons are a consequence of the 23½° tilt of the earth's axis. This tilt causes the sun's rays to favor the Northern Hemisphere in our summer months, the Southern Hemisphere during our winter. The sun is 47° higher in the sky in summer than in winter; the summer sun strikes the earth more directly, and warms it up. The heat is absorbed by the ground, the oceans, lakes, plants, buildings, and the air. Winds temper and distribute this summer heat and create weather. It takes a few months to heat up the tremendous mass of the ground, sea and sky, so that the period of greatest summer warmth is somewhat out of phase with the June

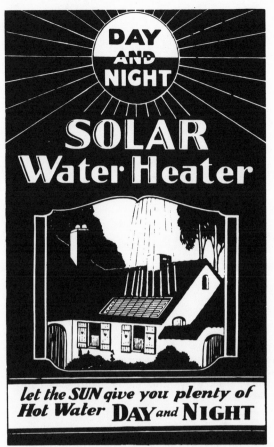

(Illustration from "The Golden Thread" by Ken Butti/John Perlin)

**Figure 2–1. Solar collector advertisement from the Day and Night brochure, California, 1923.**

21 summer solstice. Likewise, the coldest time of year is not December 21, but several weeks later in January or February.

Meanwhile, of course, the earth spins daily, causing the sun to appear to rise in the east and set in the west. In winter, the sun rises several degrees south of due east, and sets to the south of due west. In summer, it rises and sets somewhat north of due east and west (see Figure 2–3).

A house with good solar orientation will take advantage of both the daily and the yearly cycles of the sun. In winter, when heat is needed, the sun is low in the southern sky. In summer, the sun's rays come from high overhead, and from the east and west. Properly oriented, the house will maximize southern exposure and minimize the east-west exposure.

The basic idea, then, is to *face windows and collectors south* to obtain winter heat and to avoid summer overheating. (Precision is not crucial. The orientation is fine if within 25° of true south, best if within 15° of south.)

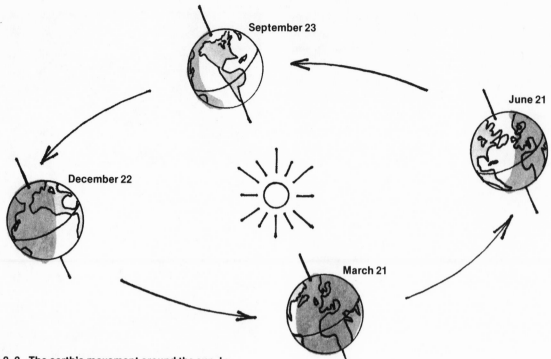

Figure 2–2. The earth's movement around the sun. In winter we are closer to the sun, but tipped away from it; in summer the sun's rays strike the northern hemisphere more directly.

Just as the heating and cooling requirements vary around the country, so does the amount of sunshine available in different regions. Figure 2–4 shows the *insolation* (solar energy) available on a clear day, and the annual percentage of possible sunshine, for different areas of the United States. Sunshine also varies seasonally, of course; in the Northeast, the sky is cloudiest in

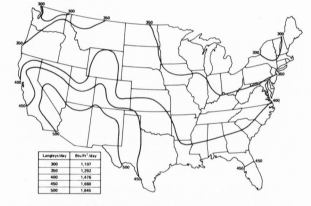

| Langleys/day | Btu/ft²/day |
| --- | --- |
| 300 | 1,107 |
| 350 | 1,292 |
| 400 | 1,476 |
| 450 | 1,660 |
| 500 | 1,845 |

Figure 2–4. *Above*: Mean daily solar radiation, measured in Langleys per day. One Langley equals 3.7 Btu/ft.² *Below:* Mean percentage of possible sunshine over the year for the United States.

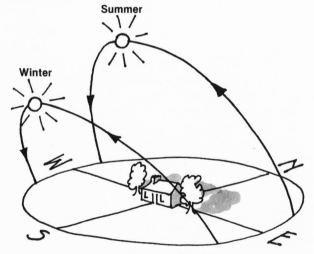

Figure 2–3. The sun's *altitude* above the horizon is greater in summer; in winter, it is low and to the south.

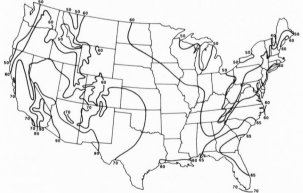

Source: *The Solar Home Book*, by Bruce Anderson with Michael Riordan (Harrisville, N.H.: Brick House Publishing, 1976).

winter. But even on cloudy days the diffuse radiation amounts to 30 percent of clear-day values, so some heat is still available. Figure 2-5 shows Philadelphia sunshine data as an example. Even though the sun shines only 49 percent of the time in January, a south-facing wall or window will still receive more than twice the sun that it receives in June. (The roof, by comparison, gets only one-quarter as much heat in January as in June).

**Table 2-5. Available Sunshine in Winter and Summer, Philadelphia.**

|  | Clear-Day Insolation | | Percent of Possible Sunshine | | Net Insolation | |
|---|---|---|---|---|---|---|
|  | January | June | January | June | January | June |
| South wall | 1726 Btu/ft² | 610 | 49% | 65% | 846 Btu/ft² | 396 |
| Roof | 948 | 2648 | 49% | 65% | 464 | 1721 |

Any surface exposed to the sun will rise in temperature as it absorbs radiant solar heat. When the surface becomes hotter than its surroundings, it will begin to lose heat in three ways: (1) by *conduction* through any object with which it is in contact; (2) by *convection* through contact with a fluid medium such as air or water; and (3) by *reradiation* to the sky or to other surrounding cooler objects. By manipulating these three routes of heat flow, we can create solar heating systems that collect, store and distribute the heat of the sun.

For example, a flat-plate collector panel made of a conductive metal such as copper or aluminum will absorb heat on its blackened surface, conduct it to a tube soldered to its surface, and heat the fluid within the tube by convection. The fluid may then be pumped to where the heat is needed, or to a heat storage tank for later use.

*Thermal stratification*, a natural convective effect, is another useful tool for collecting and distributing heat. As a fluid (such as air or water) is heated, it tends to rise. The hottest water in a tank (or the hottest air in a room) is near the top. If a solar collector has a storage tank above it, the heated water or air will rise into the tank, while the cooler fluid will naturally flow down into the collector. Thus a natural convective flow, or *thermosiphon*, is created. Similarly, the air warmed

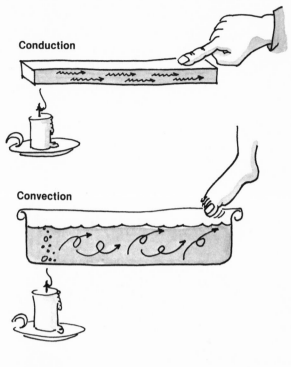

**Figure 2-6. Conduction, convection, and radiation.**

by the sun through a window will rise to the top of the house if permitted, drawing in cooler air to the sunlit room to take its place. The sun then acts as a driver for a natural heat distribution system.

Glass has certain characteristics that make it especially useful for capturing and controlling the sun's heat. It is transparent to visible light, but it will absorb and reflect thermal radiation. Sunlight entering a glass-enclosed space is trapped inside as heat (Figure 2–8). This is the *greenhouse effect*, familiar to anyone who has felt the trapped solar heat inside a parked car in winter. Some plastics have similar heat-catching properties, making them also suitable for window or collector glazing.

Control of *radiant heat flow* is also important. If the walls, floor and ceiling are warm we feel comfortable, even if the air in the room is cold. Conversely, a large exposed window area makes us chilly, even if the air is warm. This is why ra-

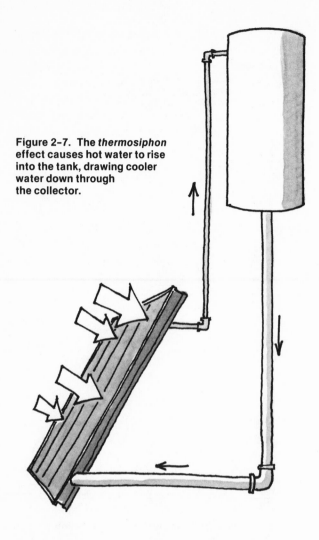

Figure 2-7. The *thermosiphon* effect causes hot water to rise into the tank, drawing cooler water down through the collector.

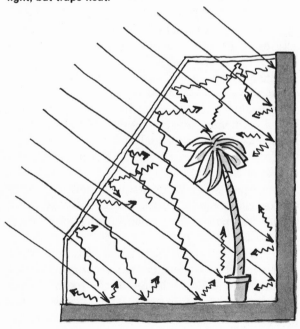

Figure 2-8. The *greenhouse effect:* Glass admits sunlight, but traps heat.

diant floor or ceiling heating systems work—and why drapes are so important for comfort in the winter. Of course, radiant cooling is welcome in summer, when radiant heat loss to the clear night sky can freeze water, even at air temperatures as high as 50° F. Harold Hay's Skytherm House makes use of such radiant cooling for a natural air conditioning effect, as we shall see later.

# Passive Solar Heating and Cooling

A solar heating or cooling system is *passive* if energy is collected, stored and distributed by natural forces, without mechanical aids or elaborate hardware. This is solar energy at its most elegant—silent, simple and automatic, with no need for expensive and complex equipment, and no wall of technology between you and the sun.

Sounds great, doesn't it? It is—but it isn't as easy as it sounds. Passive solar heating systems require very careful design to avoid overheating or underheating, and to distribute heat evenly throughout the house. Performance of passive systems can be greatly improved by including a few small fans or pumps to aid in storage and distribution of heat. Such systems may require more occupant participation (opening or closing vents, shutters, fans) than do automatic systems.

Passive heating and cooling arrangements are much less expensive than active solar equipment, and the money saved will pay for a little extra effort to make it work well. Passive solar design ideas are a good first step even if an active solar system is also planned.

COLLECTING THE SUN'S HEAT

**Windows** are the most common, direct and obvious solar collectors for passively heated houses. Sunlight warms the space directly, or shines onto surfaces that retain the heat until needed. Instead of living *behind* a collector, one lives *inside* a collector—one that allows sunlight, views and ventilation (Figure 2-9). Because windows would be included in any house construction budget anyway, these passive collectors add little or nothing to the cost of the building.

Careful placement and design is important,

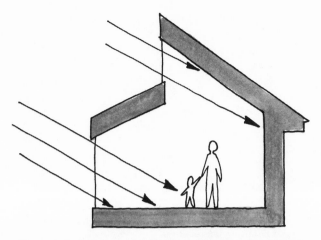

Figure 2-9. Passive solar heating: Windows allow *direct-gain* of heat that is absorbed by massive walls and floor.

however, if windows are to be useful as heat collectors. Remember that windows are also big *losers* of heat; the trick is to maximize heat gain while minimizing heat loss. South windows are most important. They should be placed to receive the low winter sun, but protected with overhangs to block the high summer sun. East- and west-facing windows also are useful as collectors during morning and afternoon, respectively. But they may need to be insulated when not receiving sunlight. In summer, east and west windows should be shaded against the hot morning and afternoon rays. Deciduous trees are good for this purpose; see Figure 1-14. North windows should be minimized or eliminated; they are useless as collectors.

Table 2–10 gives the net heat gain available from south-facing glass on a house in Boston. Note that south windows can contribute substantially to fuel savings, even in a cold and cloudy climate like New England. Notice, too, what an improvement is possible with insulating shutters.

**Table 2-10. How Much Heat is Available?**

|  | Heat Collected Annually | Fuel Savings @ $10/MBtu |
|---|---|---|
| Windows (insulating glass) | 56,669 Btu/ft² | $0.56/ft² |
| Windows (insulating glass) with insulating shutters | 109,695 Btu/ft² | $1.10/ft² |
| Solar collectors | 141,518 Btu/ft² | $1.42/ft² |

Figures are based on a typical heating season in Boston.
Source: Barber & Watson. *Design Criteria For Solar-Heated Buildings.*

The importance of good window insulation was discussed in Section 1. Installation of storm windows, shutters, shades or drapes is an excellent investment, especially in the coldest areas.

Direct solar gain from south-facing windows is difficult to control. Overheating is a potential problem on sunny days even in February. If you have to open the windows, you've lost valuable heat. What's needed is a well-planned storage strategy, which we'll discuss in detail later. Be aware, too, that sunlight may bleach or fade furniture and rugs in the sunlit space. Natural dyes and materials are most resistant to fading but still are somewhat vulnerable.

Plan the house so that the sun follows your family through the house during the day—warming the bedrooms and breakfast area in the morning, the living and play areas in the afternoon. Bedrooms might be allowed to overheat somewhat during the day when they are vacant, retaining warmth into the evening.

Figure 2-11. Passive solar heating: A south-facing *sunspace* collects solar heat, which rises into the room. As it cools, the air sinks to the floor and is convected back into the sunspace.

A **sunspace**, solarium or greenhouse can provide even more efficient collection of solar heat (Figure 2-11). It consists of a highly glazed, south-facing room that is allowed to overheat in the day, providing warm air that is ducted to adjacent rooms. At night, the sunspace acts as a buffer against the cold. Because the sunspace may undergo severe temperature swings (90° or more in the day, 40° or less at night) it may not be suitable as a greenhouse for some plants. Effective heat distribution and/or storage can temper the overheating, of course; and window insulation will

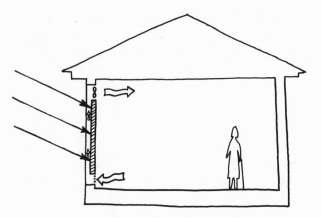

Figure 2-12. Passive solar heating: a wall collector.

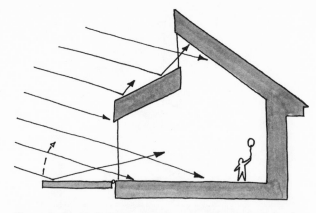

Figure 2-14. Reflectors can increase the amount of solar radiation your house receives.

keep the sunspace warmer at night. Many plants that are resistant to temperature fluctuation will thrive, producing fresh vegetables throughout the winter. Like an indoor porch, a sunspace can be a delightful addition to the family living space, usable much of the year for dining, gardening or relaxing.

**Wall collectors** are the next step upward in mechanical sophistication, being pieces of hardware specifically installed to collect heat. One type, shown in Figure 2-12, is a hotbox that col-

lects and distributes warm air in the space by the thermosiphon principle. These boxes may be homemade or commercially manufactured. They may be integral with the wall, or added on to an existing building. Some thermosiphon collectors are designed to sit in a window.

Examine the collector carefully for quality of construction, insulation and durability. Solar researcher Peter Calthorpe warns that a thermosiphoning collector should have at least six feet of vertical rise to operate properly. Keep furniture and drapery clear of the intake and exhaust

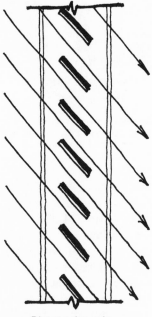

Direct solar gain

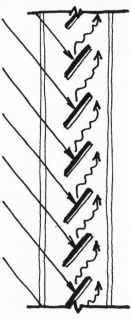

Collection of heat
(black side out)

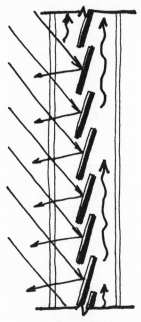

Reflecting excess heat
(shiny side out)

Figure 2-13. Passive solar heating: Using movable solar venetian blinds to allow direct gain, to *absorb* the sun's heat on black absorber side, or to *reflect* the sun from reverse side.

Figure 2-15a. The thermal mass of a house will hold and radiate heat long after the sun has set.

Paul Koch photo

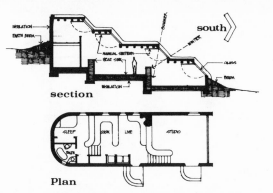

Figure 2-15b. Karen Terry house has terraced south-facing glass for passive solar heating, with adobe thermal mass for storage.

vents. And close the vents at night to prevent *reverse* thermosiphoning, which will cool the house. In summer, the thermosiphon draft may be directed outside, suctioning cool air into the house.

A related type of wall collector uses a venetian blind between double glazing. One side of the blind is reflective, the other side black. Several configurations allow for direct gain, indirect collection, insulation, or reflection, as shown in Figure 2-13.

**Reflectors** can economically increase solar gain to a collector or window, since they can double the collection area more cheaply than adding another collector (Figure 2-14). A fold-down reflector might also serve as a nighttime insulating panel. Snow or water in front of the collector, too, will reflect a surprising amount of heat. Better still are aluminized or polished steel mirrors. But they are expensive, and they must be protected against corrosion, wind damage and dirt.

STORING THE COLLECTED HEAT

The mass of a house and its contents provide a certain amount of thermal storage. Walls, floors, furniture, potted plants, fish tanks all act to hold heat, and to even out the temperature fluctuations through the day and night. All this mass acts as a sort of thermal flywheel, tending to keep the house at an even temperature. The more mass, the more even the temperature. Castles with thick stone walls remain the same temperature year-round. But modern light wood-frame houses do not offer enough mass to work

well as a thermal flywheel. To overcome this storage problem you have several choices:

1. **Build the house of massive materials.** Common are concrete, brick or stone (Figure 2-15). This is a very good idea in any building that is continuously occupied. *Apply insulation outside the mass*; if the insulation were on the inside, the mass would be useless for internal heat storage. One problem—the more mass in the house, the longer it takes to warm up. If the house is unoccupied, it may take many hours to bring the house back to warmth upon your return. Also, setting back the thermostat at night offers no advantage, since the response is delayed. But building a massive house will still give you a net saving, especially in moderate or in hot, dry climates.

Figure 2-16. Beds of earth placed in sunspace will act as thermal storage.

Figure 2-17. Water jugs, glass or plastic, used as thermal mass heat storage.

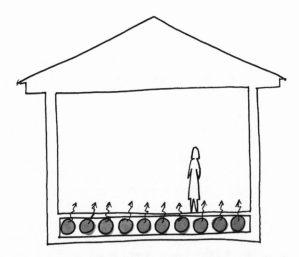

Figure 2-18. A concrete slab can be constructed to contain the heat storage medium—drums, jugs, or rocks.

2. **Fill the sunlit space with massive contents.** These may be drums of water, stacks of bricks, flatbeds full of earth (Figure 2-16), or fish tanks (with hardy fish inside). At least 3 gallons of water, or 100 pounds of rocks, should be provided per square foot of south-facing glass; much more is needed if it is not directly exposed to the sun. Some passively heated houses use plastic water-jugs by the hundreds (Figure 2-17), stacked in the attic, under the floor, or on shelves next to the windows. (Do not stack jugs directly or they will rupture. Place them on shelves or racks.)

3. **Let the sun warm a floor slab.** Again, this may be brick, concrete or stone, or a chimney mass rising within the room (Figure 2-18). Or duct the heated air under the floor past jugs or drums, or through concrete blocks on their sides. Or place a waterbag under the floor. At least one square foot of floor area or heat storage surface area should be provided per square foot of window area. Surfaces should be dark to absorb heat effectively.

4. **Build a Michel-Trombé wall.** This ingenious collector-storage-distribution idea has become a classic approach to passive solar heating (Figure 2-19). Sunlight warms a masonry wall a few inches behind a glass wall, creating a natural thermosiphon during the day. At night, the concrete wall reradiates the heat absorbed back into the space. Because the wall is thick (12 to 16 inches is optimum), the heat takes several hours to pass through the wall and reach the interior of the room. In summer, the wall is shaded by overhangs, and vented outside to prevent heat build-up.

The Trombé wall works best when insulated at night, to prevent reradiation of heat through the glass. *Beadwall*, rolldown shades, or tilt-up insulating reflector panels may be used. The Trombé wall is a good choice for a solar heating system that is expected to provide only a portion of the total heating requirement of the house, supplemented by auxiliary heat.

5. **Build a "waterwall."** This is a better system if you expect the sun to provide most or all of your heat. Similar to the Michel-Trombé system, a waterwall uses plastic columns filled with water, instead of concrete (Figure 2-20). Water has three times the heat capacity of rock by weight, so less mass is needed (six inches is the optimum waterwall thickness). In addition,

natural convection distributes the heat quickly throughout the water tank, while heat takes hours to pass slowly through a masonry wall. Air may be circulated around the vertical columns of water to extract heat when needed.

A complete waterwall system, with glazing of Kalwall plexiglass panels, may cost around $6 to $8 per square foot, installed. This is significantly less than the installed cost of high-performance collector panels, and can obtain comparable performance: A waterwall system in Wisconsin with reflectors and night insulation collects 150,000 Btu per square foot annually; 200,000 Btu/square foot is possible in less severe climates.

Steve and Holly Baer's house near Albuquerque is 75 percent solar-heated by his *Drumwall*, a system of racks carrying steel oil drums filled with water (Figure 2–21). The ends of the drums are blackened to absorb the sun's heat. Reflective insulating panels (costing $2 per square foot) are opened in the morning and shut at night. Daily temperature swings of more than 5° F. are rare; auxiliary heat is provided by two small wood stoves.

6. **Build a roof pond.** Similar to a waterwall, Harold Hay's *Skytherm* system places the water mass in plastic bags on the flat black metal roof. During the day, sun warms the plastic bags of water. At night, insulating panels mounted on a garage-door mechanism close above the bags, and the heat is radiated down into the living space through a metal ceiling (Figure 2–22). In summer, the sequence is reversed: The panels are closed by day to reflect excess heat, and the water mass above absorbs heat from the house below, keeping the rooms cool and comfortable. At night, this absorbed heat is reradiated to the clear night sky, cooling the waterbags for the next day's work. Occupants report that both heating and cooling are even and comfortable.

The Skytherm system works best in clear-weather regions like the Southwest. Cooling will not work effectively when the night sky is cloudy. Northern latitudes present further problems: the sun strikes the horizontal waterbags obliquely in winter, heating them inefficiently; reflector panels can improve Skytherm's performance, but they must be sturdy against wind damage. The system requires that large panels move twice daily; this may be a problem in areas of heavy snowfall. Also Skytherm will not heat the lower floors of multilevel houses. Finally, extra structural support will be needed to carry all that water.

Figure 2-19. Michel-Trombé wall combines solar collection and massive heat storage.

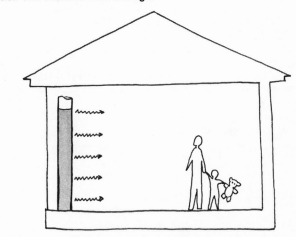

Figure 2-20. The *Waterwall*, like Trombé wall, absorbs heat during the day and releases it during the night.

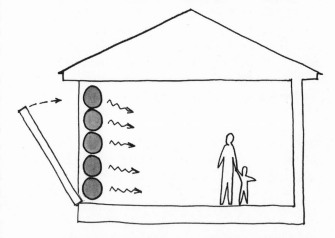

Figure 2-21. The *Drumwall*—55-gallon drums filled with water and placed in racks in south window—uses the same principle.

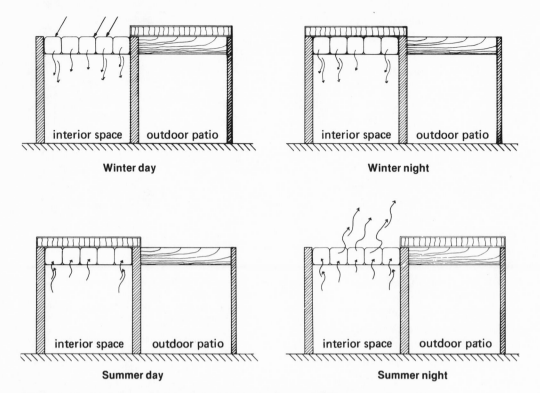

interior space | outdoor patio
**Winter day**

interior space | outdoor patio
**Winter night**

interior space | outdoor patio
**Summer day**

interior space | outdoor patio
**Summer night**

**Figure 2–22.** *Skytherm* principle places thermal mass—water bags—on the roof, where they are alternately exposed to sun or covered with movable insulated slab.

Nonetheless, the Skytherm system is highly appropriate for single-level dwellings in sunny, moderate climates where cooling is desired. The system may be built for about $5 per square foot, installed.

7. **Install thermic diode panels.** Developed by Shawn Buckley of MIT, these panels perform the tasks of collection, storage and distribution within a self-contained modular building unit (see Figure 2–23). Thermosiphon action is similar to that of the wall collectors described previously, but using a liquid medium instead of air. Water in the outside part of the sandwich panel is warmed by the sun and siphons into the retaining tank on the inside of the panel, facing into the room. Here the collected heat is reradiated into the space. An oil check-valve prevents reverse siphoning at night. The panels are passive heat pumps, requiring no separate storage or elaborate plumbing. They may be mounted on the roof or wall—though roof mounting may impose waterproofing problems at the panel edges.

8. **Install eutectic salt panels.** Eutectic salts are substances with great promise for heat storage. Several compounds are potentially useful. They all have melting points in the 70° F. to 140° F. range. As the salts melt, they absorb large quantities of heat without increasing in temperature. This absorbed heat is called the *latent heat of fusion*, and allows energy to be stored at the fairly low temperatures of passive solar heat collection.

One storage system uses eutectic salts in thin tiles mounted to the ceiling or walls (Figure 2–24). Aluminized window blinds reflect the sunlight up onto the ceiling, warming the panels while permitting visibility through the windows. At night, the tiles reradiate their heat as they cool.

DISTRIBUTING SOLAR HEAT

Several passive methods of heat distribution have already been discussed. *Reradiation* directly into the space is the principle of a radiant floor slab or a Skytherm roof pond. Thermic diode panels also heat by this method. For more even heating, many people prefer *convective* action, such as the thermosiphon effect (Figures 2–25 and 2–26). It is also possible to make use of *heat stratification* to keep lower living areas cool and

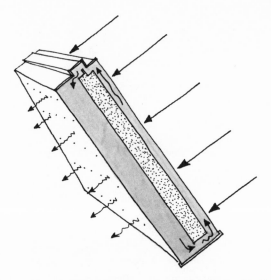

Figure 2-23. A thermic diode panel. A thermosiphon pattern within the panel itself allows heat to be absorbed and released into the living space.

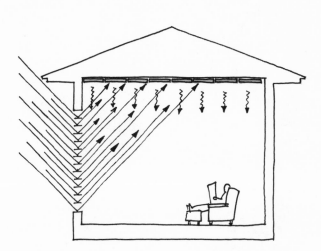

Figure 2-24. Aluminized blinds reflect sun's radiation onto ceiling tiles, which contain eutectic salts for thermal storage.

comfortable by day, and higher sleeping areas warm at night. The *chimney effect* can be used to cool the house passively in summer.

The problems of slow warmup time and overheating can be greatly relieved by appropriate use of small fans to aid the natural circulation, by insulation to reduce heat losses, and by careful design to size and balance heat collection, storage and distribution. Passive solar heating and cooling is simple; but a fully solar-heated house requires accurate analysis and design. If you are considering this approach, consult with an architect or engineer familiar with passive solar system design. Or consult the references listed at the end of this chapter if you want to try to work it out yourself. Partial solar heating by pas-

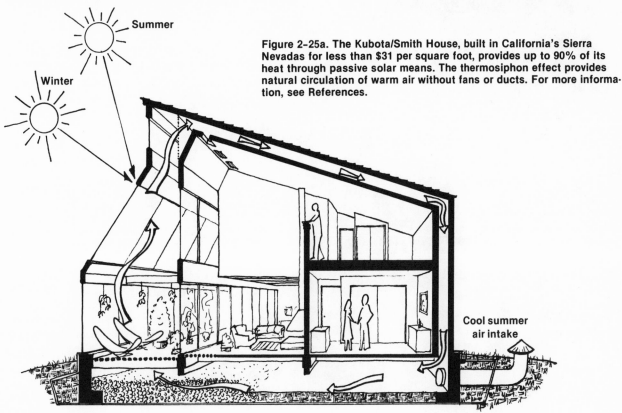

Figure 2-25a. The Kubota/Smith House, built in California's Sierra Nevadas for less than $31 per square foot, provides up to 90% of its heat through passive solar means. The thermosiphon effect provides natural circulation of warm air without fans or ducts. For more information, see References.

Reprinted from Michel Phillips, "Don't Build a House til You've Looked at This," *CoEvolution Quarterly*, summer 1978, by permission.

**Figure 2-25b. The Kubota/Smith house, exterior.**

Photo courtesy of Donald Watson, AIA

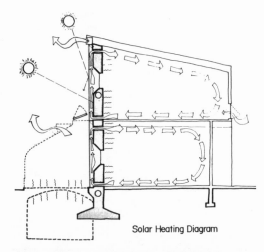

Solar Heating Diagram

**Figure 2-26. The Kelbaugh house, Princeton, New Jersey. Direct gain through south glass wall and greenhouse; thermal storage in modified Trombé wall (see solar heating diagram).**

sive methods can be accomplished without such elaborate analysis, using rule-of-thumb approaches described above. Because of its low cost, simple construction and directness, passive solar heating and cooling may be your best energy investment.

# Active Solar Heating and Cooling Systems

The solar energy industry is burgeoning. Over 200 manufacturers sold solar equipment to an estimated 24,000 homeowners during the first half of 1977. The market has doubled every year since the 1973 oil embargo, with most of the emphasis on hardware for *active solar systems*. An active system is one in which mechanical pumps or fans are used to transport heat from an absorber to a storage tank for later use. Equipment is more elaborate and costly than that for a passive system. (It is also more profitable to manufacture, which is why industry emphasizes

active systems rather than the more direct passive approaches.)

But active systems do offer several distinct advantages. They can achieve hotter, more useful temperatures than passive systems. Because the collectors are more efficient, less collector area is needed. They may be easier to retrofit onto existing buildings than bulkier passive equipment. And mechanically controlled active systems do not require the careful balancing necessary for natural passive heat distribution and storage.

Because of high equipment costs, proper sizing of an active solar system is critical to economy. The coldest day of the year only comes around once. If the solar system is sized for this extreme condition, it will be oversized 99 percent of the year. Extra collector area and storage, bought at a high cost, will stand idle most of the time. It will take much longer to pay back the investment on an oversized system than for a smaller system that works more constantly through the winter at peak capacity. Currently it is most economical to plan for a system that provides 80 percent of the house heating annually. As fuel costs rise and collector costs drop, the optimum solar heating fraction will rise. If the system can also provide air

Figure 2-27. Solar house, Westbrook, Connecticut, that combines passive direct gain with active collection system.

conditioning, it becomes much more economical—the same equipment is working all year rather than standing idle half the year. This is the principle of *maximum capital utilization*: If you can keep your equipment busy, it will pay for itself quicker.

## SOLAR COLLECTORS

For a well-insulated house, collector area equal to about 30 to 40 percent of the heated living area is needed to provide about 75 percent of the heat. A 1500-square-foot house, therefore, needs about 300 to 500 square feet of collection area—depending, of course, on the specific configuration of the house and the system, the efficiency of the collector panels, and the habits of the occupants (Figures 2–28 a and b).

**Table 2–28a. Collector and Storage Tank Sizes Required for 1,500-Square-Foot Home.**

| Climatic Zone | Collector Area (sq. ft.) | Storage Tank (gal.) |
|---|---|---|
| 1 | 800 | 1,500 |
| 2 | 500 | 750 |
| 3 | 800 | 1,500 |
| 4 | 300 | 500 |
| 5 | 200 | 280 |
| 6 | 750 | 1,500 |
| 7 | 500 | 750 |
| 8 | 200 | 280 |
| 9 | 600 | 1,000 |
| 10 | 500 | 750 |
| 11 | 200 | 280 |
| 12* | 45 | 80 |

\* Includes only hot water needs.
Source: Wells & Spetgang, *How to Buy Solar Heating . . . Without Getting Burnt* (Emmaus, Pa.: Rodale Press, 1978).

**Figure 2–28b. Climatic zones, United States.**

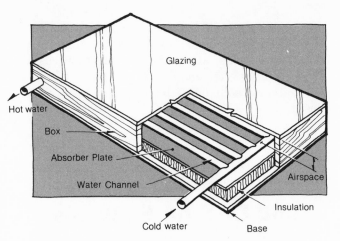

**Figure 2–29. Section through solar collector showing assembly of various components.**

A collector consists of an *absorber surface* made of metal, rubber or plastic, and *glazing* of glass or plastic to reduce heat loss (See Figure 2–29). Absorbers usually are painted black for high *absorptivity* (ability to absorb radiation); a theoretically perfect absorber would have an absorptivity ($\alpha$) equal to 1.0. Copper painted dull black has an $\alpha$ of 0.95; but it also has an *emissivity* ($\varepsilon$) of 0.95, meaning that it has a high tendency to reradiate the collected heat back out into the sky. Look for collectors with high absorptivity ratings, but low emissivity ratings. Some collectors, such as Sunworks' *Solector*, have *selective coatings* with high absorptivity and low emissivity. They appear blue-gray, like the color of a gun barrel. See Figure 2–30 for examples of absorptivity and emissivity for various surfaces.

Glazing reduces heat losses from the wind, rain and snow, besides trapping heat by the greenhouse effect. Glass is best for trapping heat. *Teflon* and *Lexan* are also good; some plastics, like polyethylene film, are not. But glazing also blocks and reflects some of the heat, particularly at oblique angles of incidence. So only one layer of glass is optimum for selective surface collectors. Two or three layers may be best for black-painted collectors.

Manufacturers most often quote impressive figures for "instantaneous efficiency," but actual day-long efficiency will be 10 to 20 percent less. Some collectors have raised edges that will shade the absorber at low sun angles, reducing efficiency still more. Make sure that collectors do not shade each other more than 10 percent at noon on December 21, and that they receive at least six hours of unobstructed sunlight on this date. (The

**Table 2-30a. Properties of Selective Surfaces for Solar Energy Application.**

| Surface | $\alpha$ | $\varepsilon$ |
|---|---|---|
| "Nickel Black" on polished nickel | 0.92 | 0.11 |
| "Nickel Black" on galvanized iron* | 0.89 | 0.12 |
| CuO on nickel | 0.81 | 0.17 |
| Co₃O₄ on silver | 0.90 | 0.27 |
| CuO on aluminum | 0.93 | 0.11 |
| Ebanol C on copper* | 0.90 | 0.16 |
| CuO on anodized aluminum | 0.85 | 0.11 |
| PbS crystals on aluminum | 0.89 | 0.20 |

* Commercial processes
$\alpha$ = Absorptance for solar energy
$\varepsilon$ = Emittance for long wave radiation

Source: Duffie and Beckman, *Solar Energy Thermal Processes*, 1974.

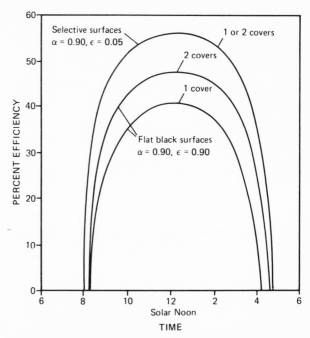

Source: *The Solar Home Book*, by Bruce Anderson with Michael Riordan (Brick House Publishing, 1976), p. 159.

**Figure 2-30b. Flat-plate collector performance of selective and flat black absorber coatings.**

noon sun on December 21 is at an angle equal to the local latitude minus 23½°.)

**Flat-plate collectors** are by far the most common type of collector currently in use; and at present they are the most economical, costing $5 to $15 per square foot plus installation. Different products vary widely in efficiency, of course, depending on glazing, surface coating, insulation and design features. Flat-plate collectors (Figure 2-31) may be incorporated into a roof or wall, if it is favorably oriented. Or they may be mounted on racks or brackets that place them at optimum tilt. Normally flat-plate collectors are fixed; tracking to follow the sun is possible but expensive. The optimum tilt for space-heating collectors is an angle equal to the latitude plus 15°. For best results, the actual tilt should be no more than 15° from this optimum. If reflection from snow or water is available, the tilt can be steeper. In fact, *wall-mounting* may be a good choice—above 40° latitude, a vertical collector will receive about 90 percent of the sunlight available to a collector mounted at the optimum tilt. Wall mounting affords protection from leaks and weather damage, and may be shaded by overhangs from the summer sun.

Optimum orientation is between due south and

**Figure 2-31a. Types of flat-plate air collectors.**

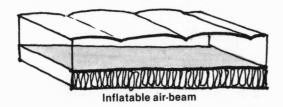

**Black-painted concrete**

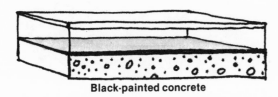

**Inflatable air-beam**

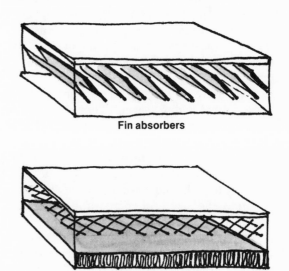

**Fin absorbers**

**Metal mesh absorbers**

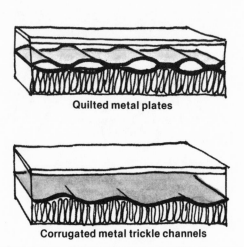

**Quilted metal plates**

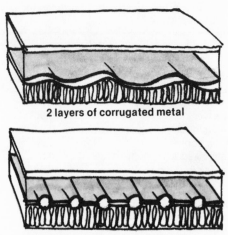

**2 layers of corrugated metal**

**Corrugated metal trickle channels**

**Metal sheet crimped over tubes**

**Figure 2-31b. Types of flat-plate liquid collectors.**

15° west of south. The slight westward shift is because the air is warmer in the afternoon, so that the collectors work more efficiently. Also, heat collected in the afternoon will charge the storage system with heat to last well into the next morning.

Flat-plate solar collectors use either *air* or *liquid* as a heat transport medium. Each has definite advantages, and the choice must be made according to the specific needs of the house.

*Air system* collectors (Figure 2–32) are somewhat less expensive than liquid collectors. They may be more easily fabricated by the do-it-yourselfer or local contractor. Leaks in the system, while not unimportant, pose no water-damage problem to the house. Freezing and corrosion are not serious threats. The heat from air collectors may be ducted directly into the space rather than first passing through heat exchangers or storage tanks. An air system thus has an appealing directness and simplicity (Figures 2–33, 2–34).

But air systems are not as efficient as liquid systems for hot water heating. They require large ducts, which may be very difficult to fit into an existing house. Large amounts of air must be moved; the fans may be noisy and consume more electricity than the pumps that drive a liquid system. The rock bed used for heat storage is three times the size of a comparable water-tank storage.

If room is available to accommodate the ducts and storage bed, or if a forced-air heating system is already in place, air collectors may be the best choice. Several absorber configurations have been

devised, all with the idea of obtaining maximum heat transfer between the blackened metal absorber and the air flowing through and around it.

A *liquid system* (Figure 2–35) has the advantage that it can supply domestic hot water all year round, increasing capital utilization of the equipment. Pipes are much smaller than air ducts, so installation is less cumbersome. Less power is needed to pump the heated fluid. Water storage is much smaller. And the collectors are generally more efficient.

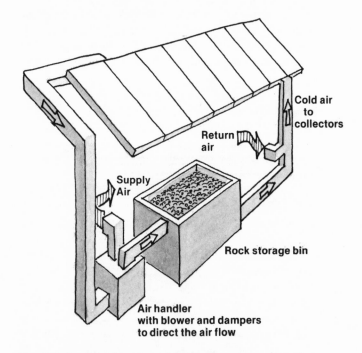

**Figure 2-32. Diagram of an air collection system. Heat is stored in a pebble bed.**

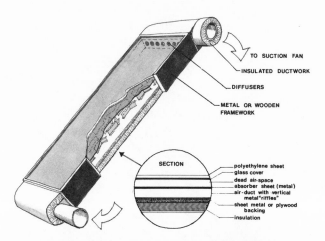

Figure 2-33. Cutaway of an air solar collector. Air to be heated passes *behind* the black absorber sheet.

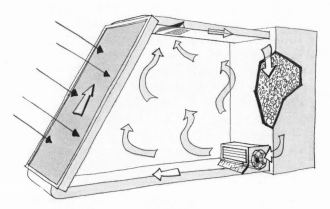

Figure 2-34. A simple solar air heater, or *solar furnace.* A heater like this may contain its own storage, or the air be ducted to storage under the house.

But leaks, when they occur, are very troublesome. For this reason, water collectors are difficult to make at home. They are generally more expensive than air collectors. And freezing or corrosion must be prevented.

To avoid damage from freezing, some systems are designed to drain down automatically when temperatures approach freezing, or if the power fails. A differential thermostat, such as Rho Sigma's *RS500 PH2L*, automatically opens one solenoid valve and closes another, draining the few quarts of water from the collectors.

An alternative is to use antifreeze instead of water in the system, and a heat exchanger to transfer collected heat into the storage tank. If domestic hot water is to be heated by the same system, be sure to use nontoxic propylene glycol to avoid contamination of the drinking water. Antifreeze is not cheap; a system may use up to 50 gallons of it; and it must be changed every two to four years. But an antifreeze system allows collection of solar heat even on very cold days, when a drain-down system stands idle.

Corrosion cannot be avoided but it can be retarded. *Copper* is the best metal for resisting corrosion, but it is also the most expensive. *Aluminum* is quickly corroded by water or antifreeze; special oil admixtures must be added to the transport fluid to inhibit corrosion. *Galvanized steel* is better, but it is a poor conductor of heat. So copper collectors are recommended. Whichever is chosen, however, make sure that only one metal is used for the entire plumbing loop, to avoid corrosive electrolytic action that occurs between dissimilar metals.

Many collector configurations are possible, some of which were shown in Figure 2-31. Most employ a flat metal absorber plate with either applied tubes or integrated fluid passages. An alternative is a *trickle-type* collector, as used in Harry Thomason's Solaris System, which has the advantage of being cheap and easy to build. Water drips out of perforations in a pipe at the top of the collector and flows down over a plate or corrugated sheet exposed to the sun. The warmed

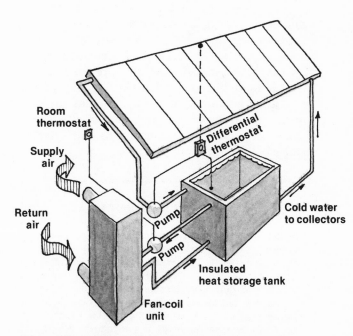

Figure 2-35. Diagram of a liquid collection system. In this case, storage is an insulated water tank; the heat is tranferred to the air heating system through a *heat exchanger*, lower left.

**61**

water is collected in a trough at the bottom. For efficient operation, the water should contact the whole absorber surface, not just the valleys. The collector is covered with glass or plastic. Condensation is a problem in a trickle design—water droplets on the cover glass reflect sunlight away, reducing collector efficiency. In cold weather, the condensation will freeze. A solution is to trickle the water between closely sandwiched corrugated sheets so that it makes full contact with the upper plate.

Researchers at Princeton University are developing a flat-plate collector made of plastic films in multiple layers. Pockets of trapped air insulate the absorber, and liquid flows through an interior channel. The collectors, made of *Tedlar, PVC* and *Teflon*, promise to be much cheaper than copper or aluminum panels but to have comparable efficiencies. Rigid plastic collectors are also being researched at Battelle Institute in Columbus, Ohio.

**Adjustable or tracking collector mounts** can be used to follow the sun for optimum heat collection. But they are not really practical if the system is used for heating only (see Figure 2–36). They may be worth the extra expense and maintenance, though, if the system also provides domestic hot water heating. If air conditioning is included, tracking or adjustable systems make even more sense. Adjustment may be as simple as manually changing the collector tilt twice a year, or it may involve motor driven equipment that continuously tracks the sun. Such tracking is very expensive, and the systems are susceptible to ice, snow and wind damage. But because reflection losses and oblique incident angles are reduced, a tracking system may *triple* the efficiency of collector performance. This means that a much smaller collector area is required.

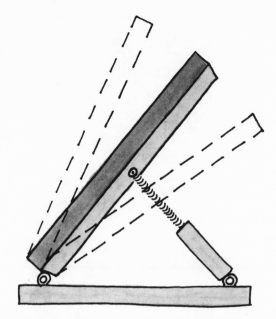

Figure 2-36. Flat-plate collector with adjustable mount.

**Efficient high-temperature collectors** may make sense with tracking systems. While they are more expensive than flat-plate units, high-temperature collectors (Figure 2–37) require less collector area, less storage capacity, and less space for ducts and pipes. Because they produce heat in the 180° to 260° range, a system using these collectors meshes nicely with conventional back-up heating systems. What is more, high-temperature collectors can be used to power solar air conditioning, allowing year-round capital utilization of the equipment.

Several methods are used to achieve higher collector temperatures. Convective heat losses within the panel can be reduced by a reflective grid of louvers between the absorber and cover plate that traps the heat within its cells (Figure 2–38). Or convection losses may be eliminated completely by evacuating the air from the collector. Or lenses and mirrors may concentrate the sun's rays on a small absorber area.

One design utilizes an array of *evacuated tube collectors*, as illustrated in Figure 2–37. Because of their cylindrical shape, they can receive insolation from all directions. Reflective losses from oblique sun angles are reduced, so day-long performance is much higher than that of flat-plate collectors. Currently they are quite expensive ($15 to $25 per square foot plus installation), but they could be readily mass-produced by a technology similar to fluorescent lightbulb manufacture. Material costs are about $5 per square foot, much less than copper panels. Some arrays use back-up reflectors to improve performance still further; others are half-mirrored individually. Because of the vacuum, the tubes lose no heat to wind or cold weather, performing at a steady efficiency of 40 to 50 percent. (Flat-plate collectors may operate at only 10 percent efficiency in very cold weather.)

**Concentrating collectors** can reach temperatures of 200 to 1000 degrees Fahrenheit. Mirrors and lenses are less expensive than collectors, so a concentrating collector system is theoretically economical. Although they are still being developed, concentrating collectors may eventually be available for $5 to $10 per square foot, making high-temperature collection very attractive. Concentrating collectors cannot make use of diffuse radiation, and they must be secured against wind damage. But the biggest design issue is sun tracking. Because the focal point moves during the day, three choices are available —move the concentrating lens; move the absorber; or optically widen the focal point so that the collector remains in approximate focus all day. Several such systems are illustrated in Figure 2–39.

HEAT STORAGE

Heat collected from active solar systems generally is stored in a large insulated tank until it is needed. Depending on the size, several hours' or several days' worth of energy may be stored;

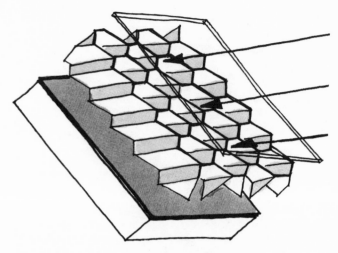

Figure 2–38. Reflective honeycomb material cut at an angle and mounted in a vertical flat-plate collector.

some tanks may be capable of carrying heat for a month or more if very well insulated. Large storage tanks for multidwelling use may be designed to store heat collected during the summer for use several months later, or to store winter coldness for next summer's use. But such long-term storage is not yet practical for single houses.

The hotter the storage, the easier it is to extract heat. If 60- to 70-degree indoor temperatures are desired, the storage must be at least 80 degrees or more. If the storage temperature drops below this useful range, the back-up heating system takes over. When the temperature of the air or water from the collector is lower than the storage temperature, circulation in the loop should automatically cut off by means of a differential thermostat operating a solenoid valve.

Figure 2–37. A *Sunpak* high-temperature collector. This type, made by Owens-Illinois, uses a vacuum tube, a return flow tube, and a reflector surface to increase radiation.

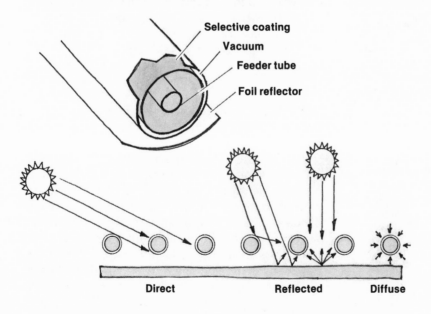

Selective coating
Vacuum
Feeder tube
Foil reflector

Direct          Reflected          Diffuse

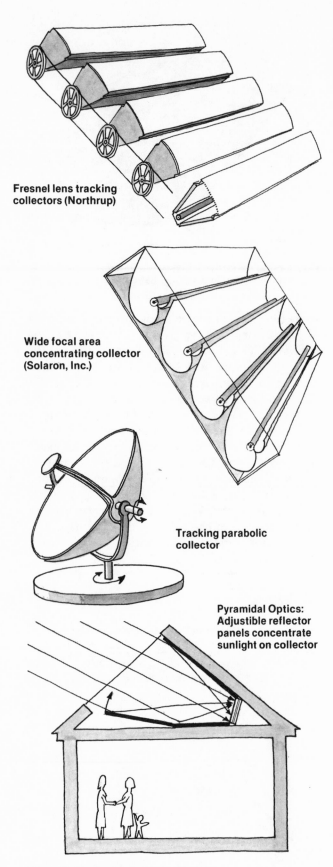

**Fresnel lens tracking collectors (Northrup)**

**Wide focal area concentrating collector (Solaron, Inc.)**

**Tracking parabolic collector**

**Pyramidal Optics: Adjustable reflector panels concentrate sunlight on collector**

Figure 2-39. Concentrating collectors.

If the configuration of the house permits, place the collectors below the storage tank, so that natural thermosiphon action (Figure 2-40) carries the warm fluid into storage without pumps or fans. Again, make sure to close the system at night to prevent reverse thermosiphoning.

The heat storage medium may be water, rocks, or phase-change materials (see Table 2-41).

**Water storage.** Water is cheap or free, and available everywhere. Its high heat capacity means that the storage tank can be small and compact. In moderate climates or with a drain-down system, the water can be circulated directly as the heat transport medium. And convection within the storage tank helps distribute the heat evenly.

But leaks, freezing and corrosion must be considered. Plan the tank for easy access for maintenance or replacement. Steel tanks will last ten to fifteen years. Corrosion inhibitors will extend this life, but they are toxic. So do not use them if the system also heats domestic hot water. Plastic tanks have longer lives, but they are two to three times as expensive as steel. Concrete tanks are durable but very hard to repair if leaks occur. The best choice may be a built-in container in the basement, integral with the foundation walls, lined with a thick plastic bladder that can be replaced if necessary. As a rough estimate, allow for one gallon of water storage per square foot of heated floor space in the house. For an 1800-square foot house, 1800 gallons or 250 cubic feet of storage may be needed for two to three days of heat. Such a tank might be 6 feet diameter, 12 feet long, and it will weigh nine tons. Make sure that the house can bear this heavy load. Insulate the tank well. Foam insulation is not recommended, as it is difficult to locate a leak under the foam. Rigid board insulation is a good method.

**Rock bed storage.** In a rock bed, leaks are no problem. The storage compartment is easily buildable. Rocks have the additional advantage that they can store heat above 212° F. But rock storage requires three times the volume that a comparable water tank would need. So if space is a problem, rocks may not be feasible. Rock beds, of course, are most appropriate with air collection —the warm air is blown through the rocks, transferring its heat. When heat is required, the air flow is reversed and the rocks give up their heat to the air. Round river rocks one to five inches in

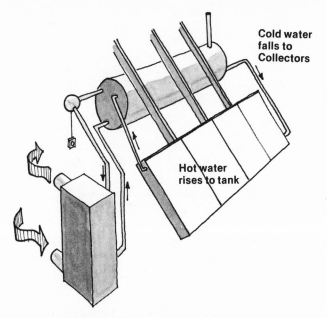

Figure 2-40. Thermosiphoning heat storage.

diameter are best. Smaller rocks transfer heat more efficiently, but they also create more resistance to air flow, necessitating more fan power to charge and discharge the storage bed. Rock storage is not suitable for domestic hot water heating, although various schemes have been proposed.

The thermal storage capacity of a rock bed depends on the temperature of heat available to the system. A rock bed at 140° F. has about 14 Btu per pound of rock; if the bed is at 85° F., only 3 Btu per pound of rock is available as useful heat. So the collection temperature determines the size of storage needed. A bed capable of storing 1 millon Btu (two or three days of heat) at 85°

Table 2-41. Properties of Heat Storage Materials.

| Material | Specific Heat (Btu/lb/°F) | Density (lb/ft³) | Heat Capacity (Btu/ft³/°F) No voids | 30% voids |
|---|---|---|---|---|
| Water | 1.00 | 62 | 62 | 43 |
| Scrap Iron | 0.12 | 490 | 59 | 41 |
| Scrap Aluminum | 0.23 | 170 | 39 | 27 |
| Concrete | 0.23 | 140 | 32 | 22 |
| Stone | 0.21 | 170 | 36 | 25 |
| Brick | 0.20 | 140 | 28 | 20 |

Reprinted from *New Energy Technology: Some Facts and Figures*, edited by Hottel and Howard by permission of The MIT Press, Cambridge, Massachusetts. Copyright © 1971 by The Massachusetts Institute of Technology.

F. would need 166 tons or 3320 cubic feet of rock, a volume about 20 feet square and 8 feet high. If 140° F. air is available, the bed needs only 36 tons or 720 cubic feet of rock, a volume about 10 feet square and 8 feet high. Of course, in clear-weather areas much less storage may be needed.

**Phase-change materials storage.** When eutectic salts (see page 54) are developed as a heat-storage medium, they will require even less space than a water tank to store an equivalent amount of heat. Moreover, they can store heat efficiently without requiring high temperatures.

Several problems remain to be worked out, however: Unless churned while solidifying, the salt hydrates tend to encapsulate, preventing efficient release of stored heat. The compounds expand when they solidify, creating problems of containment. And they seem to "fatigue" after several thousand freeze/thaw cycles, and need to be replaced. For these reasons, phase-change materials are not yet in use for residential heat storage.

General Electric currently is developing a revolving drum filled with Glauber's Salts, over which air is blown to distribute the heat. As the drum revolves, blades churn the salts like ice cream. The churning action prevents encapsulation, and the result is a very compact and efficient thermal storage unit.

## HEAT DISTRIBUTION

**Air systems.** The most economical approach to distribute heat in an active solar system is to use the existing pipes or ductwork of the backup heating system. Because solar systems typically operate at lower temperatures than conventional systems, however, modifications may be necessary. Conventional furnaces deliver 140° F. air for heating. In the north, solar storage is usually 85 to 120 degrees, so the system must move a lot more air to maintain the same comfort level. (If your existing system is sized for the larger air-handling requirements of central air conditioning, it may be suitable.) Placement of air registers may also be affected: Registers placed below windows require 95° air to counter the downdraft created by the cold glass (Figure 2-42).

If your storage temperature is only 85°, this location will not work well. A better configuration is to locate the supply high on an interior

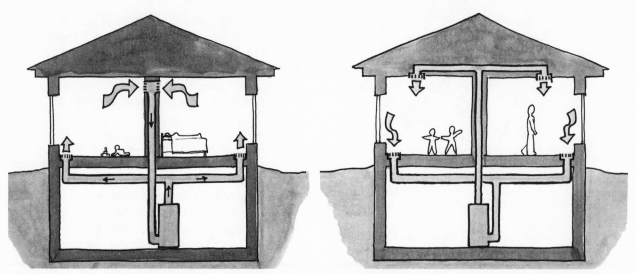

Figure 2-42. Placement of heating ducts: *supply low, return high* if supply air is 95° F. or hotter.

Figure 2-43. Placement of heating ducts: *supply high, return low* if supply air is sometimes less than 95° F.

Figure 2-44. Rock bed radiant heating: *lateral charging* of the storage bed produces hot and cold spots as heat migrates through the rocks.

Figure 2-45. Rock bed radiant heating: *vertical charging* produces even temperatures in the room.

wall, with the return register below the window. This approach (Figure 2-43) takes advantage of the natural downdraft at the glass rather than trying to fight it. Such an arrangement can utilize 85° air effectively.

If the rock bed is directly under the floor slab, a natural radiant heating effect (Figure 2-44) is possible with storage temperatures as low as 80° F. Walls, too, can provide radiant heating. Keep

in mind that the rock bed is not uniform in temperature: It is hottest at the point where warm air is introduced and coolest at the outlet. This gradient of temperature will affect the ability of the slab to provide heating comfort. If the air intake and outlet vents were arranged so that the rock bed charged *vertically* from top to bottom (Figure 2-45), then the warmest part of the bed would always be nearest the floor slab, and radiant heating would be most effective. Remember, too, that radiant heating is hard to control. Overheating may be a problem.

Air distribution can be combined with water collectors and storage, using fan-coil units to exchange the heat. Or a heat pump can be used to extract heat from water storage for forced-air space conditioning. More will be said about heat pumps later.

**Water systems.** Because baseboard hydronic heating units cannot operate effectively at temperatures below 130° F., such a system is not suitable for distribution of solar heat unless high-temperature collectors are used. Larger fin-tube units could be added, but this usually presents an architectural problem. Hot water could be used to heat a radiant floor or ceiling, which requires temperatures of 100 to 120 degrees. A heat pump to boost temperatures is also a possibility.

# Domestic Hot Water Heating

Solar heating of domestic hot water already is economically attractive. An investment of $800 to $1500 can reduce your house's total energy consumption by 20 percent or more. The equipment involved is less elaborate than that required for solar space heating. Little or no long-term storage is necessary, since hot water needs are more or less continuous. Only 40 to 80 square feet of collector area is sufficient for most families' hot water needs. And since hot water is used all year around, the solar equipment is more fully utilized; thus it pays for itself much faster than solar space-heating systems that operate only during the heating season.

The average adult uses 15 to 40 gallons of hot water per day. Biggest users are washing machines (40 gallons), dishwashers (15 gallons), and bathtubs (10 to 20 gallons). Conservation in these three areas will save considerably. Use warm or cold water cycles in the washing machine. Run the dishwasher only when it is full. Take showers instead of baths, and install a waterconserving showerhead.

Water need be no hotter than 120° for most uses (140° if you have a dishwasher). A good collector yields about one-half to one gallon of 140°

| | | | Net heat gain, Btu/hr/ft² through: | |
|---|---|---|---|---|
| City | Percent possible sunshine | Average temperature during heating season (°F) | Single glass | Double glass |
| Albany, N.Y. | 46 | 35.2 | − 12.8 | 5.6 |
| Albuquerque, N.M. | 77 | 47.0 | 18.0 | 30.2 |
| Atlanta, Ga. | 52 | 51.5 | 9.0 | 18.8 |
| Baltimore, Md. | 55 | 43.8 | 2.0 | 15.9 |
| Birmingham, Ala. | 51 | 53.8 | 10.9 | 19.5 |
| Bismarck, N.D. | 55 | 24.6 | − 20.1 | 4.0 |
| Boise, Id. | 54 | 45.2 | 22.9 | 16.0 |
| Boston, Mass. | 54 | 38.1 | 5.2 | 11.7 |
| Burlington, Vt. | 42 | 31.5 | − 19.5 | .9 |
| Chattanooga, Tenn. | 50 | 49.8 | 5.9 | 16.7 |
| Cheyenne, Wyo. | 67 | 41.3 | 5.7 | 20.9 |
| Cleveland, Ohio | 41 | 37.2 | − 13.7 | 3.7 |
| Columbia, S.C. | 51 | 54.0 | 11.2 | 19.6 |
| Concord, N.H. | 52 | 33.3 | − 12.0 | 7.4 |
| Dallas, Texas | 47 | 52.5 | 7.1 | 16.4 |
| Davenport, Iowa | 54 | 40.0 | − 3.1 | 12.8 |
| Denver, Colo. | 70 | 38.9 | 5.2 | 21.7 |
| Detroit, Mich. | 43 | 35.8 | 14.1 | 44.0 |
| Eugene, Ore. | 44 | 50.2 | 2.7 | 13.2 |
| Harrisburg, Pa. | 50 | 43.6 | − 1.5 | 14.1 |
| Hartford, Conn. | 53 | 42.8 | − .3 | 14.1 |
| Helena, Mont. | 52 | 40.7 | − 3.3 | 12.2 |
| Huron, S.D. | 58 | 28.2 | − 14.1 | 8.0 |
| Indianapolis, Ind. | 51 | 40.3 | − 4.6 | 11.2 |
| Jacksonville, Fla. | 40 | 62.0 | 13.9 | 18.1 |
| Joliet, Ill. | 53 | 40.8 | 2.9 | 12.8 |
| Lincoln, Neb. | 61 | 37.0 | − 2.2 | 15.3 |
| Little Rock, Ark. | 51 | 51.6 | 8.5 | 18.3 |
| Louisville, Ky. | 51 | 45.3 | 1.5 | 14.6 |
| Madison, Wis. | 50 | 37.8 | − 7.6 | 9.5 |
| Minneapolis, Minn. | 53 | 29.4 | − 15.7 | 5.8 |
| Newark, N.J. | 55 | 43.4 | 1.4 | 15.5 |
| New Orleans, La. | 37 | 61.6 | 11.7 | 16.1 |
| Phoenix, Ariz. | 59 | 59.5 | 21.9 | 27.5 |
| Portland, Me. | 52 | 33.8 | − 7.2 | 12.0 |
| Providence, R.I. | 54 | 37.2 | − 6.1 | 11.3 |
| Raleigh, N.C. | 57 | 50.0 | − 10.0 | 20.6 |
| Reno, Nev. | 64 | 45.4 | 8.6 | 21.7 |
| Richmond, Va. | 59 | 47.0 | 8.0 | 20.2 |
| St. Louis, Mo. | 57 | 43.6 | 2.6 | 16.6 |
| Salt Lake City, Utah | 59 | 40.0 | 0.0 | 15.9 |
| San Francisco, Cal. | 62 | 54.2 | 17.3 | 25.7 |
| Seattle, Wash. | 34 | 46.3 | − 7.3 | 5.2 |
| Topeka, Kan. | 61 | 42.3 | 3.8 | 18.4 |
| Tulsa, Okla. | 56 | 48.2 | 7.4 | 19.0 |
| Vicksburg, Miss. | 45 | 56.8 | − 10.7 | 17.7 |
| Wheeling, W. Va. | 41 | 46.1 | 3.7 | 9.0 |
| Wilmington, Del. | 56 | 45.0 | 3.7 | 16.9 |

**SOLAR BENEFIT VALUES**

Source: *The Solar Home Book*, by Bruce Anderson with Michael Riordan (Harrisville, N.H.: Brick House Publishing, 1976). Reprinted with permission.

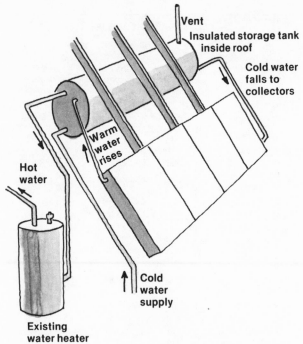

Figure 2-46. Solar hot water heating, using natural thermosiphoning.

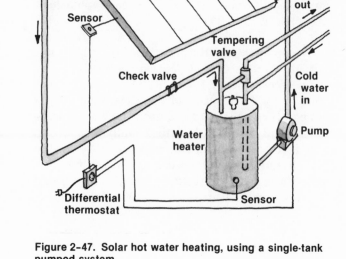

Figure 2-47. Solar hot water heating, using a single-tank pumped system.

water per square foot per day, depending on the amount of sunlight available. If the hot water system incorporates a conventional backup hot water heater, sunlight collected even on cloudy days can be used to preheat the hot water, cutting energy consumption considerably. On sunny days, the water may actually get too hot (165° to 185° or more), so be sure to install a tempering valve to avoid scalding yourself.

Because they operate all year, hot water collectors are best installed at a lower angle (equal to the local latitude), to receive the high rays of the summer sun. In areas where freezing is likely, collectors must either drain down automatically, or use a closed-loop system with a heat exchanger. This latter system allows collectors to be filled with antifreeze. Use nontoxic propylene glycol to avoid contamination of drinking water.

If you can place the hot water tank *above* the collectors, you can use a thermosiphoning system (Figure 2-46). Otherwise, pumps must circulate the water from collector to tank (Figures 2-47 and 2-48). Make sure that pumps meet all code requirements for potable water. Install a differential thermostat to control the pump. It should switch on when the collectors are 20° hotter than

storage and switch off when they are no more than 3° warmer than the water in the storage tank. Install air vents at all high points. Include also a pressure/temperature relief valve, and use check valves to prevent reverse thermosiphoning.

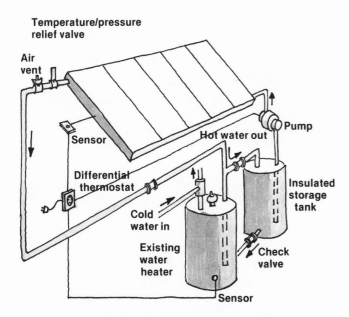

Figure 2-48. Solar hot water heating, with a retrofit to the existing water heater.

# Swimming Pool Heating

Many states now prohibit the use of fossil fuels for heating swimming pools—and with good reason. In the face of our current shortage, such a use is a wasteful extravagance. Fortunately, swimming pools can easily be heated by solar collectors (Figure 2-49).

The collector area should be equal to approximately 50 to 75 percent of the surface area of the pool. For an indoor pool, only about 30 percent is needed. Since the collectors will operate when the weather is mild or warm, they can be much simpler than those required for winter heating. Inexpensive, unglazed black plastic mat-type collectors are a good choice. Pool water is circulated at six gallons per minute through each collector, using the pumping system already in place for pool filtration. For best results, you can combine solar pool heating with an insulating swimming pool cover to retain the water's warmth at night. Another possiblity is to heat the pool with the same collectors that provide winter heat for your house, thus using your equipment most fully.

# Other Solar Options

COOLING WITH SOLAR ENERGY

Several heating systems already discussed can also provide summer cooling. Passive solar-heated houses can be designed to make use of the chimney effect to draw warm air out the roof, sucking in cool air from below. Houses built of masonry or concrete will stay cooler in the summer because of their high thermal mass, especially in places where the sky is clear and nights are cool in summer. Harold Hay's Skytherm House, for example, provides excellent cooling by radiating the day's heat into the night sky—up to 30 Btu of cooling per hour per square foot is possible in dry climates.

Active systems can also make use of this radiant cooling effect by circulating fluid through the collectors at night, when they can radiate heat to the night sky. For *this* purpose, collectors should have *high* emissivity, and they will operate best if the glass covers are removed.

Solar-powered mechanical air conditioning is just getting started and is not yet widely available. Several manufacturers, though, now sell small (three- to five-ton) liquid-type *absorption chillers* for residential use. These units require temperatures of 190 to 260 degrees, higher than conventional flat-plate collectors can supply. Tube-type concentrating collectors do

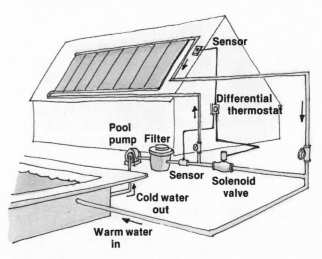

Figure 2-49. Solar swimming pool heating.

provide heat in this range, however. The use of high-temperature collectors will allow the sun to provide full air conditioning in the summer and full heating in winter—all with the same distribution system.

## HEAT PUMP SYSTEMS

Heat pumps have become much more efficient in the last few years. While not yet economical for conventional space heating in cold climates, heat pumps have many applications in solar systems for heating and cooling. Carrier Corporation now manufactures a water-source heat pump with a two- to four-ton capacity, which allows low-temperature heat from solar collectors to be upgraded for easier use. The heat pump extracts energy from the storage tank, which may be at 85°, and converts it to 140° heat, so that it may be used in conventional baseboard fin-tube convectors. This conversion is much more efficient than extracting heat from the cold outside air because a heat pump is most efficient when the temperature difference is small.

Heat pumps used for cooling can be operated at night if there is thermal storage available. Because the night air is cooler, the temperature difference is smaller and the heat pump is more efficient. In addition, many areas now offer lower off-peak electric rates, permitting further savings. "Coolness" is stored during the night for use the next day. A water source heat pump may also be used to extract coolness from well-water, river water or a large pond. Since ground water temperatures remain around 50 to 60 degrees all year, this is a very economical and attractive source of air-conditioning energy. It may even be useful for heating in winter: 50° water is much better than 0° air for efficient heat pumping. But bear in mind that you are changing the ground water temperature. If cooling your house, you are adding waste heat to the ground water. If heating

---

**WHERE TO START**

In seeking your own answers to questions about solar energy, a good place to start is the National Solar Heating and Cooling Information Center. The toll-free number is (800) 523-2929. This information center can provide you with bibliographies on solar technology, names of energy-related organizations, and lists of manufacturers of solar equipment around the country.

---

**HOW MUCH TO SPEND**

No one can say exactly how much a space heating or water heating system will cost—it all depends on where you live, how your house is oriented, and what your needs are. A general figure given in 1978 by the U.S. Department of Housing and Urban Development, however, was $5,000–$19,000 for a complete solar heating and hot water system. For hot water heating alone, they estimated a cost of $1000–$1500. These figures can vary tremendously, so your best bet is to investigate thoroughly before you buy.

---

the house, you are chilling the pond. This may raise legal and/or ecological questions.

## PHOTOELECTRIC CELLS

A photoelectric cell is a thin wafer of silicon that generates an electric current when exposed to sunlight. Truly a space-age technology (e.g., Skylab), photocells require no moving parts, and pose few maintenance or pollution problems. The electric power produced can be used for heating, air conditioning, lighting or mechanical needs.

Photoelectric cells, and the batteries to store the electricity, however, are still so costly that they are not economically feasible except in very remote areas. Egypt's government, for example, has just announced construction of a new town in the desert powered entirely by photoelectric cells. This presents the irony of a highly advanced technology that is useful only to some of the least developed areas of the globe.

Sharp reductions in cost are anticipated. Photocells are very similar in manufacture to transistors, which dropped in price by a factor of 1000 in ten years under mass production. A recent United Nations report estimated that 1 billion dollars (less than the cost of a nuclear power plant) invested in solar cells would reduce the cost of photoelectric power below that of nuclear power. Solar cells cost one-tenth of what they did five years ago; in that same time the cost of nuclear-generated electricity has doubled. Closer to home, a 1977 Federal Energy Office report stated that if the Defense Department spent $450 million for 150 megawatts of photoelectric equipment including batteries and power conditioning equipment, it would achieve a net saving of $150 *billion* over the next twenty-five years in fuel and maintenance costs for gasoline generators.

Photoelectric solar systems, then, will soon be

available and economical. Already under construction is a community college in Arkansas equipped with a tracking, concentrating photoelectric system capable of generating 362 kilowatts, at an installed cost of $6000 per peak kilowatt. Up to 2200 kilowatt-hours can be stored in newly developed "iron redox" batteries, which will be available at one-fifth the cost of standard lead-acid batteries when mass-produced. (Battery storage of electricity will be more fully discussed in Section 3.)

Photoelectric collectors may be available in panels similar to flat-plate collectors and should be mounted at the same tilt-angles previously prescribed. Because the photocells are expensive, a photocell system would also use concentrating or tracking collectors. Photocells need not be insulated, but all wiring should be protected from the elements.

# Solar Economics

In addition to the expensive equipment required for collection, distribution and storage of solar heat, most *active* solar systems include a conventional back-up heating system. Thus the total installed cost may be 2½ to 3 times that of a conventional oil-fired forced-air heating system—up to $10,000 for an average-sized house. Once the system is installed, of course, energy costs drop—but do not altogether disappear. Pumps and fans require some electric power; the auxiliary heating system consumes fuel on the coldest winter days, and occasional maintenance may be necessary. The time required to recoup the initial expense depends on the cost of fuel you would otherwise be burning, and on the rate at which those costs increase. As a rough estimate, figure that an active solar heating system will pay for itself in eight to ten years if it replaces an oil-fired system, or in four to six years if it replaces an electric heating system. Or, as Barber and Watson[1] observe, "For an additional $800 to $1200 down payment on a $40,000 house the owner can have a heating system that will save $20 to $60 per month or more of total owning and operating expenses."

*Passive* solar heating systems are usually integral with the house design, and hard to compare on the same basis. Some passive collectors, such as windows, represent no additional expense at all.

When shopping for active solar hardware, be careful to compare the total Btu output per gross area to choose the system with the best performance. And determine the *total installed cost*—most manufacturers quote prices for the collectors alone, and installation costs may be substantial. Don't buy a bigger system than you need; it pays to consult an architect or engineer experienced with solar design.

Most manufacturers offer guarantees that cover defective materials or labor and one year of free servicing. Best, of course, would be a guarantee promising a given flow of Btu at a given outdoor temperature and amount of insolation. Service contracts similar to those offered by furnace suppliers soon may become available.

Lending institutions have been wary of way-out ideas like solar energy, but they are learning fast. When you apply for a construction loan or mortgage, three factors will concern the bank: (1) the economic "life-cycle" savings expected from low operating costs; (2) the marketability of the house if the bank should ever repossess and sell it; and (3) insurability of the solar system. Insurance should be no problem; apart from the minor risks of possible glass breakage or tank leaks, a solar heating system is pretty tame—much safer than an oil or gas furnace. And thousands of installed systems will attest to the ever-increasing marketability of solar energy.

---

1. Everett M. Barber and Donald Watson, *Design Criteria For Solar-Heated Buildings* (Guilford, Ct.: Sunworks, Inc., 1975).

---

**THE SOLAR LOBBY**

While only an infant compared to those of established utilities and oil companies, the Solar Lobby has joined the Washington lobbyists. Its goal is the promotion of solar energy through low-interest solar loans, consumer protection, an industrial switch to solar for low-temperature needs, and increased competition in this growing field.

The Solar Lobby publishes the *Sun Times*, a monthly newsletter that reports on governmental action for or against solar energy around the country. A one-year subscription is $15. Write to Solar Lobby, 1001 Connecticut Avenue, N.W., Washington, D.C. 20036. Phone (202)466-6350. In ordering, make checks payable to *Sundries*.

The Solar Lobby also sells *Blueprint for a Solar America* ($2.30), an alternative to the current administration policy that contains specific recommendations, and an up-to-date listing of solar groups that are active around the country.

# References

Anderson, Bruce. *The Solar Home Book*. Harrisville, N.H.: Cheshire Books, 1976. $8.50. Another excellent solar text, covering fundamentals, calculations, equipment, and costing. Much hard-nosed technical information, but highly readable with plenty of illustrations and diagrams.

ASHRAE. *ASHRAE Handbook of Fundmentals*. New York: ASHRAE, 1977. Available in libraries. The new edition of this fundamental technical reference includes a large section on solar energy, as well as exhaustive data on heat loss calculation, available solar heat, infiltration, air conditioning, insulation, and refrigeration.

Baer, Steve. *Sunspots*. Albuquerque, N. Mex.: Zomeworks, 1975. $4.00. A readable, funky exposition of the principles of thermodynamics, designed to stir your creative juices and escape conventional thinking. Ideas for inventions and do-it-yourself systems fairly leap off the page.

Barber, Everett and Watson, Donald. *Design Criteria for Solar-Heated Buildings*. Guilford, Conn.: Sunworks, 1975. $10.00. This technical booklet presents a simplified method for calculating heat loss, collector requirements, payback period, and available energy, prefaced by a brief and cogent discussion of solar collectors. Includes ASHRAE's solar insolation and solar heat gain factor tables, monthly sunshine percentages by locale, and instructions on how to use them. Available from Sunworks, Inc., Guilford, Conn. 06437.

Daniels, Farrington. *Direct Use of the Sun's Energy*. New York: Ballantine, 1964. $1.95. A classic early examination of the many uses of solar energy: heating, cooking, agricultural and industrial drying, water distillation, cooling and refrigeration, photochemical and photoelectric conversion. The big picture; buy it and read it.

Davis, Norah Deakin and Lindsey, Linda. *At Home in the Sun: An Open House Tour of Solar Homes in the United States*. Charlotte, Vt.: Garden Way Publishing, 1979. $9.95. A thorough look at thirty-one solar homes and the reactions of their owners. What it's really like to *live* in a solar house.

National Solar Heating and Cooling Information Center. *Passive Design Ideas for the Energy Conscious Architect*. Many good ideas. You needn't be an architect. Available from the National Solar Heating and Cooling Information Center, P.O. Box 1607, Rockville, Maryland 20850.

*Solar Dwelling Design Concepts*. U.S. Dept. of Housing and Urban Development. Another introductory survey of solar energy. Lots of pictures, not much hard-nosed data. Send $2.30 to the Superintendent of Documents, U.S. Government Printing Office, Washington, D.C. 20402.

Watson, Donald. *Designing and Building a Solar House*. Charlotte, Vt.: Garden Way Publishing, 1977. $8.95. The most complete and comprehensive guide to understanding, designing, and constructing a solar heating system. Heat loss calculations, climatic data, photos, and descriptions of the construction process, life-cycle costing.

Wells, Malcolm and Spetgang, Irwin. *How to Buy Solar Heating . . . Without Getting Burnt!* Emmaus, Pa.: Rodale Press, 1978. $6.95. A consumer's guide to choosing, financing, and installing solar house heating equipment. Good information on contracts and contractors, and feedback (pro and con) from homeowners who have taken the plunge.

"Concentrating Collectors for Solar Heating and Cooling." *Popular Science*, October 1976.

"Don't Build a House Till You've Looked At This." *CoEvolution Quarterly*, summer 1978. A passively heated solar house built by contractors, using standard construction technology, for $31/square foot.

"Heat Pumps: More Sense Now For More Homes?" *Popular Science*, July 1978.

"Solar Heating—How to Pick the Right System for Your Home." *Popular Science*, July 1978.

"World's Most Advanced Solar Home." *Popular Science*, July 1977.

# Solar Energy Catalog

The following pages list solar products and companies that are currently working in this fast-changing field. Naturally this is not a complete catalog—there are many excellent products not represented here, and more are coming on the market all the time.

All information contained in the catalog sections was supplied by the manufacturers or organizations listed; we have summarized what is available from each. Our goal is to help you, the reader, locate equipment and information that will help you buy solar heating wisely.

Within the catalog section are product comparison charts. In reading these charts, keep in mind that prices are constantly changing; no book can be up to date. If you need more information about a specific product or company, we ask that you write directly to the company, *not* to Garden Way Publishing.

# Absorber Plates

## American Solarize Company
## 139 South St.
## Murray Hill, New Jersey 07974
## (201) 464-9555

American Solarize manufactures solar air collectors and components featuring honeycomb made of aluminum and carbon steel. Used as part of the cover plate, reflective honeycomb increases the amount of radiation concentrated onto the absorber. Used as the absorber itself, blackened honeycomb not only reflects rays onto the flat part of the absorber plate but catches and traps them as they bounce back. Honeycomb is sold separately or in cover plate assemblies.

American Solarize also makes air collectors using honeycomb as the absorber. They are single or double glazed with optional flat absorber plate and insulation.

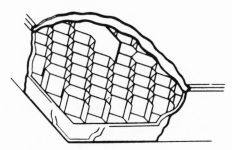

*American Solarize solar air collector.*

## Bio-Energy Systems, Inc.
## Mountaindale Road
## Spring Glen, New York 12483
## (914) 434-7858

BESI's elastomeric extrusion (described in the Energy Conservation catalog) is available in a special form to be used as a solar absorber plate. The T-2 Tube Plate is cut to the desired length and fitted to a home-built collector frame by the homeowner or contractor. It can be used with closed or open systems and can tie into hot-air heat distribution systems by means of a heat exchanger.

The T-2 Tube Plate extrusion is lightweight and easy to install. It costs 85¢ to 95¢ per linear foot or $5 to $7 per square foot of collector. Header sets are available in copper or plastic for $60 to $70 extra. All accessories and auxiliary components are supplied by the homeowner.

BESI will also provide Domestic Hot Water Kits, including the T-2 Tube Plate, header set, *SolaRoll*™ extrusions for bonding, lock-strip system, thermosetting mastic, *Tedlar* and fiber glass glazing, drain-back storage tank, air-purger relief valve, circulation pump, and differential controller. Two kits are available: the *KD-40* provides for 40 square feet of collector space and the *KD-80* provides for 80 square feet of collector space. Stonelined storage tanks with copper heat exchangers are sold at an additional cost in 40-, 65-, 80-, and 120-gallon capacities for $212, $303, $383, and $494 respectively.

## Olin Brass Roll-Bond® Products
## East Alton, Illinois 62024
## (618) 258-2000

Olin Brass manufactures *Solar-Bond®* products using its patented *Roll-Bond®* process. *Solar-Bond®* panels consist of an aluminum or copper sheet with integral tubes and headers. These panels are used as absorbers by collector manufacturers or do-it-yourselfers. The advantages of a *Solar-Bond®* absorber are its close tube spacing, uniform flow, and the high conductivity of its metals. Guidelines provided by Olin Brass should be followed to minimize corrosion in panels intended for liquid-type collectors.

## Terra-Light, Inc.
## P.O. Box 493
## 30 Manning Road
## Billerica, Massachusetts 01821
## (617) 663-2075

Terra-Light is a wholly owned subsidiary of Butler Manufacturing Company, which purchased Kennecott Copper Corporation's solar absorber plate activity in 1977.

The *Terra-Light®* absorber plate is made entirely of copper for superior thermal conductivity and corrosion resistance. It is lightweight to reduce roof loads and aid installation.

The fluid-carrying tubes are connected to the plate with a metallurgical bond and spaced to provide optimum heat transfer. The plates also feature internal manifolding and inlet/outlet connections.

Two types are available. One is suitable for high-pressure applications (150 psig); the other is a low-pressure (25 psig) plate intended for use as a pool heater. Both models are coated with Rust-Oleum # 5779 Midnight Black paint or may be left uncoated for selective coating by the customer.

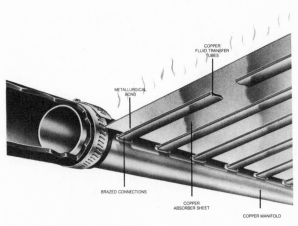

*Terra-Light absorber plate.*

**Tranter, Inc.**
735 East Hazel St.
Lansing, Michigan 48909
(517) 372-8410

The Tranter absorber plate is a quilted metal panel available in carbon steel or stainless steel. It offers a 90 percent internally wetted surface. These plates can also be used for storage tank heat transfer coils.

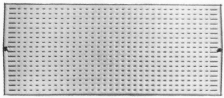

*Tranter absorber plate.*

## Absorber Plates Compared

| Manu-facturer | Make | Materials | Coating | Dimen-sions | Price | Features |
|---|---|---|---|---|---|---|
| American Solarize Company | Honeycomb plates | Aluminum and carbon steel in honeycomb configuration | Black paint on mill or brushed finish | | | Many reflective surfaces aid in heat collection of air-type collectors. |
| Bio-Energy Systems, Inc. | SolaRoll® T-2 Tube Plate | Elastomeric tube-in-sheet extrusion | | | 85¢ to 95¢ per linear ft.; $5 to $7 per ft.² collector area | Special synthetic rubber is nondegradable and is weather impact, UV resistant. Will not crack, dent, or rust. Header sets available in plastic or copper for $60 to $70 extra. Lock-strip system and thermo-setting mastic necessary for construction. Sold in BESI kit for water heating or separately. |
| Olin Brass Roll-Bond® Products | Solar-Bond® absorber plate | Aluminum or copper sheet with integral tubes and headers | | Copper: 22″ × 96″ 34″ × 96″ 34″ × 76″ <br><br> Aluminum: 24″ × 96″ 34″ × 76″ | Copper: $55.50 $83.00 $77.50 <br><br> Aluminum: $35.00 $32.50 | Close tube spacing. Uniform flow. High conductivity of metals. Integral headers. |
| Terra-Light, Inc. | Terr-Light® absorber plate | Copper plate; copper tubes | Rust-Oleum #5779 Midnight black paint optional | | $2.85 to $3 per ft.² | High and low pressure types available. Light weight. Corrosion resistant. High thermal conductivity. Tube spacing for optimum heat transfer. Internal manifolding and inlet/outlet connections. |
| Tranter, Inc. | Solar absorber plates | Quilted carbon steel or stainless steel | | 34¼″ × 82¼″ | | 90 percent internally-wetted surface. Can also be used for storage tank heat transfer coils. |

# Collectors—Flat-Plate

**Advance Technology, Inc.\***
See Domestic Hot Water Systems.


**Alpha Solarco.**
See Collectors—High Temperature.


**American Solarize Company.**
See Absorber Plates.


**Baker Bros.**
**1824 East Whitmore Ave.**
**Ceres, California 95307**
**(209) 632-5385**

**2417 Front St.**
**West Sacramento, California**
**(916) 372-2993**

Baker Bros. offers an all-copper, flat-plate, liquid-type solar collector that features recessed solder-bond copper tubing. These copper collectors have high thermal conductivity and corrosion resistance. The absorber panels are coated with Chem-Glaze Urethane finish and can be used glazed or unglazed. Insulation is urethane foam.

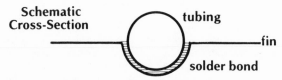

**Schematic Cross-Section** — tubing — fin — solder bond

*Baker Bros. recessed copper tubing.*

**Beasley Industries Pty. Ltd.**
**Bolton Ave.**
**Devon Park, South Australia 5008**

Beasley is quite successful in Australia, where it manufactures solar components and systems. Its *Solarpak* solar absorber is made of selectively coated copper with built-in waterways. This absorber is used in the Beasley collector, which can be covered with one or two layers of glass. The Beasley *Solatank* storage tank consists of an inner, all copper cylinder insulated with polystyrene beads and an outer casing of rustproof galvabond. A booster element and thermostat are built-in. In addition, Beasley manufactures a complete domestic hot water system and a small preheater unit that can be linked to an existing hot water heating system.

---

*\* To the reader: Advance Technology, like many companies, makes collectors as part of complete hot water systems or heating systems. Thus their collectors are described on page 94 under Domestic Hot Water Systems. Use the cross-references throughout the catalog sections to find special components that are described in other areas.*

**Chamberlain Manufacturing Corporation**
**Corporate Headquarters**
**845 Larch Ave.**
**Elmhurst, Illinois 60126**
**(312) 279-3600**

Chamberlain manufactures a factory-assembled, liquid-type solar collector with a steel tube-in-sheet absorber plate. The absorber is coated in black paint or selective black chrome. It is single or double glazed with low-iron glass and fiberglass insulation. It can be retrofitted and installed by the homeowner.

**Solar Division**
**Columbia Chase Corp.**
**55 High St.**
**Holbrook,**
**Massachusetts 02343**
**(617) 767-0513**

Columbia Chase manufactures *Redi-Mount®* flat-plate, liquid-type collectors with 100 percent copper tube-in-sheet absorber plates coated with flat black paint and single or double glazed with fiber-glass-reinforced polyester. They feature 2½ inch fiber glass insulation under the collector plate and foam insulation in the rails of the enclosure, which is of one-piece molded fiber glass. A variety of options is available by special order, such as glass glazing, solid fiber-glass insulation, and selective coating. The unit comes completely assembled and can be retrofitted and installed by the homeowner.

**Daystar Corporation**
**90 Cambridge St.**
**Burlington,**
**Massachusetts 01803**
**(617) 272-8460**

Daystar manufactures solar collectors and systems. The Daystar *21-B* flat-plate, liquid-type solar collector is used for high temperature application, such as space heating and cooling. Its absorber plate of copper-tubing-on-copper-plate is coated with high-temperature flat black paint and double-glazed with tempered, low-iron glass and a folded polymer heat trap, which inhibits convection and radiation losses. It is foam-insulated in an aluminum casing and insulated on the sides and bottom with foam. As a special feature, it offers a temperature limiter designed to maintain controlled internal temperatures below 270°F. It works automatically even in stagnation conditions.

The Daystar *21-C* flat-plate, liquid-type collector is used for moderate temperature applications, such as pool heating, hot water heating, and as a water source for water-to-air heat pumps. It is identical to the *21-B* collector except that it does not include the temperature limiter and the second glazing of folded polymer. Both collectors use Daystar Solargard-G nontoxic, nonflammable antifreeze solution as heat transfer fluid.

Daystar supplies numerous systems for space heating and cooling and hot water heating.

## Energy Converters, Inc.
## 2501 North Orchard Knob Ave.
## Chattanooga, Tennessee 37406
## (615) 624-2608

Energy Converters offers solar space- and water-heating equipment.

Their flat-plate, liquid-type collector is made of an aluminum or copper tube-in-sheet absorber coated in either slightly selective, high-temperature black paint or in moderately selective carbon particles. Single or double glazing is either low iron glass, fiber glass, or regular window glass.

The *Solarsaver* domestic water heater combines the collectors with a glass-lined, 80-gallon steel storage tank with external heat exchanger, pumps, surge tank, electronic controls, and auxiliary heating element. It includes a drain-down system for freeze protection.

The *460 Gallon Residential Solar Energy System* supplies all domestic water and space heating requirements. It includes collectors, galvanized steel storage tank with optional heating element, pumps, and differential thermostat. It can be used with antifreeze solution or drain-down freeze control.

All equipment by Energy Converters is furnished assembled and can be retrofitted and installed by the homeowner.

## Energy Design, Inc.
## 1925 Curry Road
## Schenectady, New York 12303
## (518) 355-3322

Energy Design's liquid-type, flat-plate collector, *Maxim I*, is double glazed with reinforced fiber glass. Its absorber plate is one-piece aluminum or copper sheet with integral tubing. It operates with nontoxic, noncorrosive heat transfer fluid that will not freeze or boil. It is insulated with molded polyurethane. The collector is housed in a galvanized steel box framed with brushed aluminum.

The *Model-01 Water Heater*, providing domestic hot water, includes two EDI collectors; a 40-gallon, stone-lined, steel storage tank with built-in heat exchanger; thermostat control; and hot water circulation pump. It is fully automatic and should be used with an existing electric water heater as an auxiliary. It can be retrofitted.

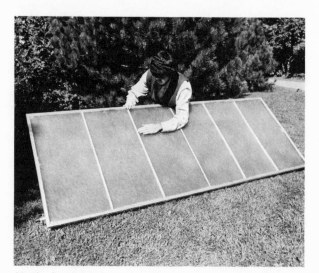

Maxim I *collector.*

## Fafco Incorporated
## 235 Constitution Drive
## Menlo Park, California 94205

Fafco makes an inexpensive collector for low-temperature applications, such as pool heating, heat pumps, acquaculture, and hydroponics. It is a plastic tube-in sheet module with ultraviolet inhibitors that lengthen its life considerably—the manufacturer offers a ten-year warranty. It is easy to install and operate because it is uncoated, unglazed, and uninsulated.

---

*Southern Exposure and Required Panel Area*

The table below recommends the amount of solar panel area required for various orientation. These figures assume an installation on a normally sloped roof.

(1) All South facing:    A minimum of 50% of the pool's area.

(2) All West facing:    A minimum of 75% of the pool's area.

(3) East and West:    Maximum on West and balance on East with a minimum of 75% of the pool's area.

---

## Falbel Energy Systems Corp.
See Collectors—High Temperature.

## Future Systems, Inc.
See Solar Furnaces.

## Halstead and Mitchell
## A Division of Halstead Industries
## Highway 72 West
## Scottsboro, Alabama 35768
## (205) 259-1212

The *Sunceiver*® liquid-type flat-plate collector can be used for space and hot water heating. It has a dual cover plate of tempered water-white glass. The absorber is a self-draining copper tube with aluminum fins coated in black paint. It is insulated with PC Foamglas. It can be installed and retrofitted by the homeowner.

The *Sunceiver*® Solar Hot Water System consists of collectors, 80-gallon hot water tank with heat exchanger, controls, valves, pumps, and expansion tank.

## Heilemann Electric
## 127 Mountainview Road
## Warren, New Jersey 07060
## (201) 752-6060

Heilemann makes patented liquid-type *Solar Tube* collectors that consist of a Lexan tube with a flat copper absorber plate. Copper tubing soldered to the underside of the plate collects and transfers heat to storage. The absorber plate is coated with black chrome and insulated beneath with fiberglass. Solar Tubes are lightweight and can be installed and retrofitted by the homeowner.

Heilemann also supplies a solar hot water kit, which includes Solar Tubes, storage tank with heat exchanger, expansion tank, differential thermostat, and circulating pump.

A solar-assisted hot water and space heater system allows a fan coil unit, controlled by a separate thermostat, to be installed in a hard-to-heat area. This kit includes 50 Solar Tubes, a 120-gallon storage tank with heat exchanger, and all other necessary parts.

**Intertechnology/Solar Corporation**
**276 Broadview Ave.**
**Warrenton, Virginia 22186**
**(703) 347-9500**

Intertechnology manufactures liquid-type, flat-plate collectors, single glazed with low-iron glass. The absorber is a fin tube assembly made with aluminum extruded fins and copper tubes painted black. It is mounted in a galvanized steel frame and insulated with fiber glass.

The ITC/Solar *Joule Box*™ Solar Water Heater, consists of solar collector(s), tank, pump, controls, piping, and fittings.

**Kalwall Corporation**
See Solar Furnaces.

**Lennox Industries, Inc.**
**200 South 12th St.**
**Marshalltown, Iowa 50158**
**(515) 754-4011**

Lennox manufactures the *LSC18-2S* flat-plate, liquid-type solar collector. It is single glazed with low-iron, tempered glass. Its steel absorber plate with copper tubes is coated with black chrome. It is insulated with fiber glass and housed in a galvalume steel frame.

The Lennox *LSHW2 Series Solarmate*® Hot Water Heating System combines one to five of these collectors with a solar hot water heater and a control module. This closed-loop system is intended for use with the existing hot water heater.

The solar hot water heater is stone-lined and is available in 40-, 65-, 85-, and 120-gallon capacities. It has an internal double-wall copper heat exchanger.

The control module includes pump, controller, expansion tank, and valves in a single, factory-installed package. It is designed to be mounted adjacent to the solar hot water tank.

**Mann-Russell Electric, Inc.**
See Collectors—High Temperature.

**Northrup, Inc.**
See Collectors—High Temperature.

**Park Energy Company**
**Box SR9**
**Jackson, Wyoming 83001**
**(307) 733-4950**

Park Energy manufactures *Type 8011 Thruflow*™ Solar Heat Collector. This flat-plate, air-type collector consists of a perforated aluminum absorber plate coated with flat black paint. Narrow slits cause air to pass very close to the aluminum plate, encouraging rapid and efficient heat transfer. It is single-glazed with a transparent polycarbonate cover made by GE.

Both absorber and cover are assembled on site as a replacement for standard roof coverings. When installed, the aperture is nearly 100 percent of the collector area; very little incoming sunlight is blocked by edges and gaskets.

PEC will size collector area and suggest suitable components for systems to meet the requirements of the individual application.

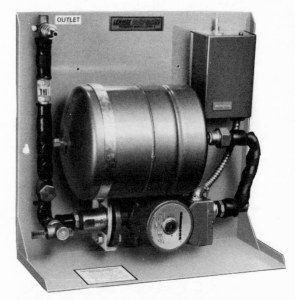

*Lennox solar system transport module LSHW2.*

*Lennox solar collector LSC18-2S.*

**Payne, Inc.**
**1933 Lincoln Drive**
**Annapolis, Maryland 21401**
**(301) 268-6150**

Payne, Inc., a multi-disciplinary engineering team, manufactures lightweight concrete collectors from cast or block. These flat-plate, air- or liquid-type collectors are coated with black paint and can be ground-mounted or incorporated into the structure of the roof. They are available with single or double glazing in *Tedlar*® and/or acrylic.

Payne has also developed a concrete block storage cube for forced hot air distribution systems that can be made into a structural part of the building. In addition, Payne is working on a multipurpose roof made of ceramic or concrete that can function as a rain catchment system, a solar still, and a domestic hot water preheater.

**PPG Industries**
**One Gateway Center**
**Pittsburgh, Pennsylvania 15222**

PPG Industries manufactures solar collectors and systems. Three types of flat-plate, liquid-type collectors are available. The Type III PPG collector consists of a black copper absorber plate with copper tubing and insulation beneath. It is single glazed with tempered glass.

PPG Type I and Type II collectors are double glazed and selectively coated. Type I collectors are designed to be mounted as part of a curtain wall or skylight; Type II collectors are supplied with mounting flanges for roof installations.

The PPG Solar Hot Water Heating System uses Type III collectors and operates on tap water. It includes a solar storage tank that stores heated water until it is needed, and then feeds it into the existing hot water heater. It is glass-lined and double-insulated and comes in 52-, 80-, and 120-gallon capacities. The circulating pump, controls, and valves are mounted on the top of the tank for easy access.

The system is self-draining for protection against overheating, freezing conditions, and power failure. It is sized by computer to meet the requirements of the homeowner and installed by PPG Industries.

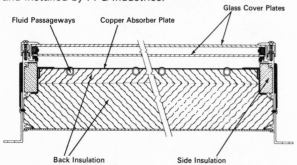

*PPG Type II solar collector—cross-section.*

**Rayosol**
**Apartado 81**
**Terremolinos (Malága)**
**Spain**

Rayosol makes a flat-plate, liquid-type solar collector with a copper absorber plate coated with black paint or copper oxide. It is enclosed in a fiber glass container with a glass cover.

**Reynolds Metals Company**
**Mill Products**
**Advertising Dept.**
**6603 W. Broad St.**
**Richmond, Virginia 23261**

Reynolds's liquid-type, flat-plate collector utilizes single or double plastic glazing and a one-piece aluminum absorber plate with integral tubes. It is mounted in an extruded aluminum frame with sandwich insulation. Extremely lightweight with adaptable mounting apparatus, it is easily installed and retrofitted by the homeowner.

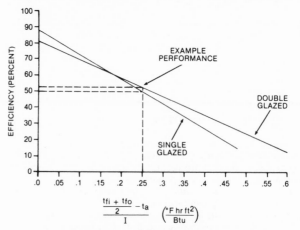

*Collector performances for Reynolds series 1400 and 1500 collectors.*

**Sekisui Chemical Co., Ltd.**
See Domestic Hot Water Systems.

**Solar Development Inc.**
**3630 Reese Ave.**
**Garden Industrial Park**
**Riviera Beach, Florida 33404**
**(305) 842-8935**

The *SD5* liquid-type, flat-plate collector can be used with space, hot water, and pool heating systems. It consists of an absorbent plate of formed copper with solder bond copper tubing, both coated with black paint. They are available with single or double glazing in Kalwall *Sunlite*® Premium and feature one to two inches Thermax insulation. They are encased in aluminum housing.

SDI's Solar Hot Water Heater combines SD5 collectors with the existing water heater, to which is attached a circulating pump and electronic controller. A special draindown system is available for cold climates.

SDI also manufactures *SD6*, a high-temperature collector for use in absorption air conditioning systems. This flat-plate, liquid-type collector consists of a copper tube-in-sheet absorber plate, coated with black chrome, and has a cover plate of tempered water-white glass. It is insulated with Celotex Thermax.

SDI also offers the California Model Collector for pool heating, which utilizes unglazed copper absorber plates with black paint coating. Pool water is run through the panels during the day to heat it; during the night to cool it.

**Solar Energy Products, Inc.**
**1208 N.W. 8th Ave.**
**Gainesville, Florida 32601**
**(904) 377-6527**

SEP's *Sunfired*™ *CU30-WW* flat-plate, liquid-type collector has an absorber plate of extruded aluminum with copper tubing. It is coated in flat black paint and single glazed with water white glass. Insulation is isocyanurate foam board and the frame is extruded aluminum. These collectors are used in SEP's *Sunfired*™ open and closed domestic water heating systems.

The *closed* system includes the *Solarstream*™ storage tank, which features a wrap-around steel heat exchanger and integral heating element. It is glass lined and insulated. The SEP *open* system offers automatic or manual drain-down for freeze protection.

SEP also manufactures unglazed collectors for pool heating, a copper *Roll-bond*® heat exchanger, and baseboard radiators. They carry a full range of circulating pumps, fluid handlers, mounting hardware, differential thermostats, and various accessories.

**Solar Energy Research Corporation**
**701 B South Main Street**
**Longmont, Colorado 80501**
**(303) 772-8406**

SERC manufactures *Thermo-Spray*™ trickle-type collectors. The copper absorber plates are selectively coated and single glazed with high-impact, UV-resistant thermoset plastic. A copper nozzle dispenses the heat transfer fluid in a free flow, circular spray pattern. The collector box is galvanized steel, is insulated with fiber glass, and will self-drain to prevent freezing.

SERC also provides complete systems. The *DHW-801* domestic hot water system includes collectors; 80-gallon, glass-lined water tank, stainless steel pump, and controls. Pipes, fittings, and valves are supplied by the homeowner.

The SERC *SH-500-830* forced-air heating system includes collectors, pumps, controls, heat exchanger, and the SERC spherical heat storage tank. This tank is made of high-density, cross-linked polyolefin coated with urethane and insulated with urethane foam. It is durable and lightweight and can be installed above or below ground.

*SERC hot water system collectors.*

**Solarator, Inc.**
**P.O. Box 277**
**Madison Heights, Michigan 48071**

Solarator makes an inexpensive collector out of 190 feet of tough, black PVC tubing welded into a metal panel. Its flexible accordion action prevents the formation of lime and scale. The *Solarator*™ is used for pool and domestic water heating, and for space heating and cooling in tandem with a reverse cycle heat pump. It can also be used for crop drying and crop storage. It can be installed and retrofitted by the homeowner for the additional cost of piping and valves.

**Solargizer® International, Inc.**
**P.O. Box 20142**
**Bloomington, Minnesota 55402**

The Solargizer® flat-plate, liquid-type collector has an absorber plate of *Roll-Bond*® copper coated with Nextel 101-C10 High Temperature black paint. It is single glazed with *Sunlite*® *Premium II* fiber glass and mounted in a one-piece fiber glass unit. It is insulated with isocyanurate foam.

Solargizer® also supplies complete domestic hot water kits, including insulated heat transfer storage tank in three sizes (66, 82, and 120 gallon capacity), pump, sensor control, expansion tank, and kit fittings.

**Solarkit™ of Florida, Inc.**
**1102 139th Ave.**
**Tampa, Florida 33612**
**(813) 971-3934**

The Solarkit™ *SolarQueen* is a flat-plate, liquid-type collector made with a solid-copper absorber plate and single glazed with tempered glass. It is framed in redwood and aluminum and features closed-cell insulation. Double glazing is optional for northern climates.

The *CopperQueen* absorber plate used in all Solarkit™ collectors (or available as a component) is made of copper tubing soldered on a grooved copper plate and coated with flat-black enamel.

Solarkit™ manufactures kits for domestic hot water heating, including collectors, circulating pump, controller with freeze protection and upper temperature limit, and all valves and fittings. Storage tanks, heat exchangers, and mounting frames are optional. The systems and components can be installed and retrofitted by the homeowner.

**Solaron Corporation.**
See Complete Systems.

**Solarsystems, Inc.**
507 W. Elm St.
Tyler, Texas 75702
(214) 592-5343

Solarsystems makes *Solarvak*® patented, vacuum-design solar collector. The flat-plate, liquid-type collector consists of a selectively coated copper absorber plate with copper tubing. It is held by compressive supports in an acrylic frame. The glazing is acrylic.

A low vacuum is created inside the frame that is equivalent to eight inches of fiber glass insulation; there is no need for external insulation. The vacuum level should be checked about every nine to twelve months with a vacuum gauge.

The *Solarvak*® is self-draining for freeze protection. The temperature of the housing is limited to a few degrees above the surrounding air by the vacuum.

It comes completely factory-assembled and must be installed by the homeowner, who supplies piping and connections. Upon contractual agreement, Solarsystems will design complete systems.

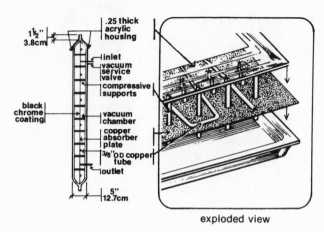

exploded view

*Solarvak*® *collector construction.*

**Sol Ray Division/Unit Electric Control, Inc.**
See Domestic Hot Water Systems.

**Sun Stone Solar Energy Equipment.**
See Domestic Hot Water Systems.

# Flat-Plate Collectors Compared—Air Type

| Manufacturer | Make | Glazing | Absorber | Coating | Emissivity |
|---|---|---|---|---|---|
| American Solarize Co. | Honeycomb collectors | Single or double: fiber glass, 3M Flexigard | Aluminum and carbon steel honeycomb; optional flat sheet beneath | | .14 |
| Future Systems, Inc. | Sun*trac portable collector | Single: fiber glass | | | |
| Kalwall Corp. | Solar-Kal Air Heater | Single: Sunlite® Premium | Flat or V-corrugated aluminum | Nonselective black paint | .95 |
| Park Energy Company | Type 8011 Thruflow™ Solar Heat Collector | Single: Lexan® | Perforated aluminum sheet | Nonselective black paint | .90 |
| Solaron Corp. | | Double: low-iron, tempered glass | Steel plate with channels beneath | Porcelain enamel | |
| Sun Stone Solar Energy Equipment | Flat plate collector | Single or double: low-iron, tempered glass | Porcelain enamel steel | Nonselective black paint | .85 |
| Sunworks, Inc. | Solector™ | Single or double: no-iron, tempered glass | Copper sheet | Selective | .07–.35 |

**Sunwater Energy Products**
**1488 Pioneer Way**
**Suite 17**
**El Cajon, California 92020**
**(714) 579-0771**

Sunwater manufactures flat-plate liquid-type solar collectors. Their collector for space and water heating features a metal absorber plate with silver soldered copper tubing. It is finished with flat black polyester coating. The collector is insulated with fiber glass and by a dead air space at the back. It is single glazed with glass. When left unglazed and uninsulated, it is suitable for pool heating.

Sunwater also makes a solar purification unit that consists of a fiber glass roof-mounted collector, storage tank, timer switch, and solenoid valve. It supplies drinking water through vapor distillation.

**Sunworks, Inc.**
**669 Boston Post Road**
**Guilford, Connecticut 06437**
**(203) 453-6191**

Sunworks manufactures liquid- and air-type flat plate collectors and packaged solar domestic water heaters. Their liquid-type *Solector*™ medium-temperature collector module consists of a copper absorber sheet, selectively coated, with solder bond copper tubing. It is single-glazed with tempered, no-iron glass and housed in an aluminum frame insulated with fiberglass. It is to be used with *Sunsol 60*, a nontoxic, nonflammable, antifreeze heat transfer fluid with special corrosive inhibitors.

The air-type collector is single or double glazed with no-iron, tempered glass and has a selectively coated copper absorber sheet. It is housed in aluminum and insulated with fiberglass and isocyanurate.

Sunworks's *Solector*™ *Pak* domestic water heater series comes complete with two collectors, storage tank, circulator, controls, sensors, fittings, valves, and instructions. Three types are available: a closed-loop system for cold climates, an open-loop system for warm climates, and an open-loop, automatic drain-down system for moderate climates. Sunworks also offers consulting services and publications covering solar energy system design. Include a stamped, self-addressed envelope when ordering booklets.

| Absorptivity | Dimensions | Price | Features |
|---|---|---|---|
| .95 | 4′ × 8′ × 5½″<br>4′ × 8′ × 4½″<br>4′ × 8′ × 3″<br><br>2½′ × 6′ × 5½″<br>2½′ × 6′ × 4½″<br>2½′ × 6′ × 3″ | $290<br>$225<br>$205<br><br>$150<br>$120<br>$ 98 | Honeycomb offers more reflective surfaces to catch radiation.<br>Honeycomb absorber plates and cover assemblies also sold separately. |
| | | | Can be mounted on trailer or permanently on roof or ground.<br>Flexible pipes duct heated air into desired area. |
| .95 | 4′ × 8′<br>5′ × 9′ | $384<br>$540 | To be used as a wall or mounted on existing wall or roof. |
| .97 | 22″ × 24″ sections interlock to create any size configuration | Example:<br>93.6 ft.²<br>= $1071<br>($11.44/ft.²) | Assembled on site as a replacement for roof covering.<br>Few edges or gaskets to obstruct entrance of solar radiation. |
| | 3′ × 6′6″ × 7″ | | |
| .98 | 78½″ × 34½″ × 11½″<br>or 76¼″ × 34⅜″ × 10″ | $289–<br>$344 | Two types for bracket or ground mounting. |
| .87–.92 | 3′ × 7′ × 4″ | About $420 | Factory-assembled. |

# Flat-Plate Collectors Compared—Liquid Type

| Manufacturer | Make | Glazing | Absorber | Coating | Emissivity |
|---|---|---|---|---|---|
| Advance Technology, Inc. | | Single or double: fiber glass and/or Tedlar® | Copper tubes between absorber and reflector sheet | Nonselective black paint | .88 |
| Alpha Solarco | Econosol-45 BC | Single or double: low-iron, tempered glass | Copper tubing | Selective black chrome | |
| Baker Bros. | | | Copper plate with copper tubing | Chem-Glaze Urethane | |
| Beasley Industries | | Single or double: glass | Copper tube-in-sheet | Selective | |
| Chamberlain Manufacturing Corp. | | Single or double: low-iron glass | Steel tube-in-sheet | Selective black chrome | .12 |
| | | | | Nonselective black paint | .92 |
| Columbia Chase Solar | RediMount® | Single or double: fiber glass reinforced polyester | Copper tube-in-sheet | Nonselective black paint | .97 |
| Daystar Corp. | 21-B | Double: low-iron, tempered glass and folded polymer heat trap | Copper plate; copper tubing | Nonselective black paint | .98 |
| | 21-C | Single: low-iron, tempered glass | Same as above | Same as above | .98 |
| Energy Converters, Inc. | | Single or double: low-iron glass; fiber glass; window glass | Aluminum or copper tube-in-sheet | Slightly selective black paint; moderately selective carbon particles | .60 |
| Energy Design, Inc. | Maxim I | Double: re-inforced fiber glass | Aluminum or copper tube-in-sheet | | |
| Fafco, Inc. | | None | Black plastic tube-in-sheet | None | .92 |
| Falbel Energy Systems, Inc. | Delta Model 31 | Single: acrylic | Copper tubes attached underneath aluminum fins; aluminized reflector panels | Nonselective black paint | |
| Halstead and Mitchell | Sunceiver® | Double: tempered glass | Copper tubes and aluminum fins | Nonselective black paint | .88 |
| Heilemann Electric | Solar Tube | Lexan tube | Copper plate with copper tubing soldered underneath | Selective black chrome | .10 |

| Absorptivity | Dimensions | Price | Features |
|---|---|---|---|
| .96 | 4' × 8' | $169–$189 | Advance Zerotherm insulation.<br>Available apart from Advance systems. |
| | | $325 | Can be used for space, domestic water and pool heating. |
| .95 | 46" × 76" × 1"<br>46" × 120" × 1½ | | Can be used glazed or unglazed. |
| | 24" × 54" × 2" | | |
| .94 | 84¼" × 36¼" × 4⅜" | | Factory-assembled. |
| .97 | 84¼" × 36¼" × 5¹/₁₆" | | |
| .95 | 107" × 44" × 4½" | | Factory-assembled.<br>Options include glass glazing and selective coating. |
| .98 | 72¾" × 44½" × 5¼" | | For space heating and cooling.<br>Includes temperature limiter to keep temperatures below 270° F. |
| .98 | 80¾" × 44½" × 5¼" | | For pool heating, hot water heating, and heat pumps.<br>No temperature limiter. |
| .98 | 3' × 8' | $268–$327 | Available separately from Energy Converters' systems. |
| | 36" × 97½" | | Available separately from EDI systems. |
| .97 | 4' × 8'<br>4' × 10' | $140 for 40 sq. ft. collector | For low temperature applications. |
| | 8' × 4' × 6" | $310–$320 | Available apart from Falbel systems. |
| .98 | 35⅜" × 77⅜" × 4" | $380 | Self-draining. |
| .93 | | | Patented.<br>Lightweight.<br>Provides directional flexibility.<br>Available apart from Heilemann systems. |

**Continued**

# Flat-Plate Collectors Compared—Liquid Type *(Continued)*

| Manufacturer | Make | Glazing | Absorber | Coating | Emissivity |
|---|---|---|---|---|---|
| Inter-technology | | Single: low-iron, glass | Extruded aluminum fins with copper tubing | Nonselective black paint; selective black paint | .8 .1 |
| Lennox Industries, Inc. | LSC18-25 | Single: low iron, tempered glass | Copper tubes on steel plate | Selective black chrome | .10 |
| Mann-Russell Electric, Inc. | Kopper Kettle Collector Module | Plexiglass | Copper sheet with under-mounted circulatory pipes | Selective black chrome | |
| Northrup, Inc. | | Single: glass; double: glass and Tedlar® | Extruded aluminum; copper tubes | Nonselective: black paint | |
| Payne, Inc. | | Single or double: Tedlar® and/or acrylic | Block or cast concrete | Nonselective black paint | |
| PPG Industries | Type I | Double: tempered glass | Copper plate; copper tubing | Selective | |
| | Type II | Same as above | Same as above | Same as above | |
| | Type III | Single: tempered glass | Same as above | Nonselective black paint | |
| Rayosol | | Single: glass | Copper plate | Black paint or copper oxide | .20 |
| Reynolds Metals Co. | | Single or double: plastic | Aluminum plate | | |
| Sekisui Chemical Co., Ltd. | Circulation System Flat Collector | Single: tempered glass | Copper plate; copper tubing | Selective | |
| Solarator, Inc. | Solarator™ | None | Black PVC tubing welded to metal panel | None | |
| Solar Development, Inc. | SD5 | Single or double: Kalwall Sunlite® Premium | Copper plate; copper tubing | Nonselective Selective | .9 .1 |
| | California Model Pool Heater | None | Copper plate; copper tubing | Nonselective black paint | .9 |
| Solar Energy Products, Inc. | Sunfired™ CU30-WW | Single: water-white glass | Aluminum plate; copper tubing | Nonselective black paint | .89 |
| Solar Energy Research Corp. | Thermo-Spray® | Single: thermo-set plastic | Copper plate | Selective | .10 |
| Solargizer® International, Inc. | Solargizer® | Single: Sunlite Premium II fiber glass | Roll-Bond® copper plate | Nonselective black paint | .89 |

| Absorptivity | Dimensions | Price | Features |
|---|---|---|---|
| .95 | 35⅜″ × 77⅜″ × 4¼″ | $223 | Also available with water-white glass glazing. |
| .94 | 35⅜″ × 77⅜″ × 4¼″ | $262 | |
| .94 | 71¹³/₁₆″ × 35⅞″ × 6¼″ | | Available apart from Lennox systems. |
| | 2′ × 6′ × 6″ | | May be mounted on roofs or walls.<br>May be used with heliostat. |
| | 103½″ × 37¼″ × 5⅝″ | | Factory-assembled.<br>Available apart from Northrup systems. |
| .95–.98 | 2′ × 8′ | $95.99 | Uses "trickle down" method.<br>Lightweight. |
| | | | Designed to be mounted as part of a skylight or curtainwall. |
| | | | Supplied with mounting flanges for roof installation. |
| | | | Supplied with mounting flanges for roof installation. |
| .90 | | About $447 | |
| | 4′ × 8′<br>4′ × 12′ | | Lightweight. |
| | 39.8″ × 61.4″ × 4.6″ | | For domestic hot water and air conditioning. |
| | 39″ × 75″ | $68.75 | Lightweight, easy to install. |
| .9 | 2′ × 10′<br>4′ × 10′ | $253.75<br>$420.50 | Self-draining.<br>Available separately from SDI systems. |
| .9 | 2′ × 10′<br>4′ × 10′ | $278.40<br>$471.25 | |
| .9 | 4′ × 10′ | $162 | For pool heating by day and cooling by night. |
| .98 | 98.5″ × 48.5″ × 2.57″ | $398 | Available apart from Sunfired™ systems. |
| .93 | 96″ × 23¾″ | $230.75–<br>$262.75 | Copper nozzle dispenses water in free-flow, circular spray.<br>Self-draining. |
| .98 | 101″ × 49″ | $795 | Can be purchased separately from Solargizer® systems. |

**Continued**

## Flat-Plate Collectors Compared—Liquid Type *(Continued)*

| Manufacturer | Make | Glazing | Absorber | Coating | Emissivity |
|---|---|---|---|---|---|
| Solarkit™ of Florida, Inc. | SolarQueen | Single: tempered glass | "CopperQueen"— copper sheet with copper tubing | Nonselective black enamel | |
| Solar-systems, Inc. | Solarvak® | Acrylic | Copper plate; copper tubing | Selective | |
| Sol-Ray Division/Unit Electric Control | | Single: tempered glass | Copper plate; copper tubing | Nonselective black paint | .89 |
| Sunearth Solar Products, Inc. | | Double: acrylic and Teflon® | Aluminum plate; copper tubing | Nonselective black paint | .88 |
| Sunwater Energy Products | | Single: glass | Metal plate; copper tubing | Nonselective black paint | |
| Sunworks, Inc. | Solector™ | Single: no-iron, tempered glass | Copper plate; copper tubing | Selective | .07–.35 |

# Collectors—High Temperature

**Alpha Solarco**
**1014 Vine St.**
**Suite 2230**
**Cincinnati, Ohio 45202**
**(513) 621-1243**

Alpha Solarco's *Suntrek-42 ATH* is an array of six liquid-type, high-temperature (250° to 500°F.) concentrating collectors with automatic tracking. Reflectors concentrate the sun's energy onto selectively coated steel pipe receivers (also available in copper, titanium, or stainless steel). Variations on the basic *Suntrek-42 ATH* include tubular glass envelopes for the receivers, vacuum-enclosures, and tempered glass collector covers for areas of snow damage or wind abrasion. Tracking and return to sunrise position are automatic in both single- and dual-axis arrays.

Sometimes used to preheat water for the concentrating collector, the *Econosol* liquid-type, flat-plate collector can be single or double glazed with low-iron, tempered glass. The absorber is copper tubing coated with black chrome; fluid passages are noncorrosive and insulation is built in. This collector is suitable for domestic space and water heating and for heating swimming pools.

The Alpha Solarco *SolAqua 58-2* is a self-contained solar heater with a built-in 75 cubic foot utility shed. It includes two *Econosol* collectors, water storage tank, controls, and pump. It is installed by Alpha Solarco at ground level. Larger sizes are available. Optional reflector shields cost $100 extra per collector.

Suntrek *high-temperature solar concentrators in production.*

88

| Absorptivity | Dimensions | Price | Features |
|---|---|---|---|
| | 3′ × 5′ × 3½″ | $205 | SolarQueen available apart from Solarkit™ systems.<br>CopperQueen also available separately. |
| | 4′ × 8′ × 5″ | | Low vacuum created inside the frame is equivalent to eight inches of fiberglass.<br>Self-draining.<br>Factory-assembled. |
| .98 | 35¼″ × 77¼″ × 2″ | $250 | Available separately from Sol-Ray systems. |
| .95 | 32.5″ × 97.5″ × 4″ | $289–$297 | Available apart from Sunearth systems. |
| | 2′ × 4′<br>4′ × 8′ | | Suitable for space and water heating.<br>Can be left unglazed and uninsulated for pool heating. |
| .87–.92 | 3′ × 7′ × 4″<br>3′ × 5′4″ × 4″ | about $336<br>about $200 | Factory-assembled. |

## Energy Design Corporation
1756 Thomas Road
P.O. Box 34294
Memphis, Tennessee 38134
(901) 382-3000

Energy Design Corporation manufactures the *XE-300* high-performance solar collector with a wide operating temperature range (140°–400°F.). It is a flat-plate, concentrating type, using glass vacuum tube receivers, aluminum reflectors, and copper tubing.

The glass vacuum tube receivers consist of an inner glass absorber tube with selective coating contained in an outer, permanently evacuated glass tube. Heat is conducted from these absorbers to the working fluid by cylindrical copper heat transfer fins at one end of the tube joined to U-shaped copper fluid tubes.

The collector is housed in an aluminum frame with glass weather cover. It comes completely assembled and is easily installed by the homeowner.

## Entropy Limited
5735 Arapahoe Ave.
Boulder, Colorado 80303
(303) 443-5703

Entropy manufactures *Sunpump®* Solar Collector Module, a nontracking, concentrating collector that converts solar heat to thermal energy through water vaporization. No electrical devices or backup heating systems are necessary. The double glazing is tempered glass; the absorber pipe is aluminum with corrosion-resistant finish and selective coating. The collector box is aluminum with a baked enamel finish, lined with high-temperature insulation. The collector can be mounted on flat or sloped roofs, vertical walls, or racks on the ground. It can be retrofitted and installed by the homeowner.

## Falbel Energy Corp.
P.O. Box 6
Greenwich, Connecticut 06830
(203) 357-0626

Falbel manufactures solar components: collectors, tanks, pumps, controllers, and heat exchangers. Two types of collectors developed by Gerald Falbel are available. *Delta Model 31* is a flat-plate, liquid-type collector in which copper tubes are attached to the underside of black aluminum fins. Aluminized reflector panels are mounted between the tubes. It is single glazed with acrylic.

*Delta Model 54* is a focusing, nontracking, liquid-type collector with an aluminum *Roll-Bond®* or copper absorber plate, blackened on both sides. Copper tubes are attached to the underside. It is mounted on the lower half of the collector behind a cover plate of Kalwall glazing. A curved, aluminized concentrating reflector serves as the back of the collector and allows heat to be gathered on both sides of the absorber.

Falbel also supplies complete hot water systems. The self-draining ones include collectors, mounting equipment, storage tank with heat exchanger, pump, and controller.

The antifreeze systems include collectors, accumulator tank, heat exchanger, pump, controller, and storage tank. Falbel will recommend space heating and cooling systems for specific applications upon request.

**General Electric Co./Solarquip Products**
**P.O. Box 13601**
**Philadelphia, Pennsylvania 19101**
**(215) 962–2112**

GE manufactures the *Model TC–100* vacuum tube collector, consisting of ten glass vacuum tubes mounted parallel in a V-trough aluminum reflector tray. To create the vacuum tubes, two glass tubes are placed one inside the other and vacuum sealed. The outer tube acts as the cover plate; the inner tube, which is selectively coated, acts as the absorber. Copper tubes carry water through the glass tubes to remove heat. Vacuum tube collectors are capable of generating high temperatures and are sensitive to both direct and diffuse sunlight. The collector can be installed and retrofitted by the homeowner.

**Mann-Russell Electronics, Inc.**
**1401 Thorne Road**
**Tacoma, Washington**
**(206) 383–1591**

Mann-Russell manufactures solar collectors and tracking devices. The *Mark IV* dual-axis heliostat rotates the carriage of a tracking collector to follow the sun during the day; it repositions itself after dark for sunrise. It includes three parts: a Solar Sensor for direct and diffuse sunlight, a logic and navigational module to move the carriage, and a hand-held manual remote control.

The *Sun Bucket IV* tracking collector utilizes the Mark IV heliostat and a heat pipe vacuum collector plate mounted on a lazy-susan rotational carriage. The collector consists of black-chrome-coated copper pipes that form a vacuum for the transference of water vapor. It can be double glazed with plastic or left unglazed depending upon the climate. It can also be ordered separately, as can the Sun Bucket carriage.

The less expensive *Kopper Kettle Module* consists of black-chrome-coated copper sheets with circulating pipes mounted beneath. It is glazed with Plexiglas and insulated with three inches of polystyrene foam. It can be placed on walls or on flat or tilted roofs and is compatible with either fixed or heliostat mountings.

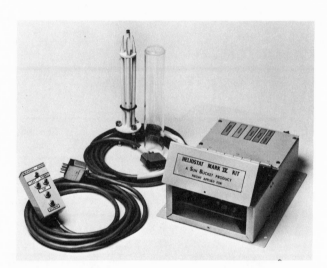

*Mann-Russell* Mark IV *heliostat, used with the* Sun Bucket *tracking collector.*

## High-Temperature Collectors Compared

| Manufacturer | Make | Glazing | Absorber | Coating | Emissivity |
|---|---|---|---|---|---|
| Alpha Solarco | Suntrek—42 ATH (concentrating) | | Steel pipes | Selective | |
| Energy Design Corp. | XE-300 (flat plate) | Glass weather cover | Glass vacuum tube receivers; copper heat transfer fins at end of tubes; aluminum reflectors | Selective coating on inner glass tube | .05 at 212°F. |
| Entropy Ltd. | Sunpump® Solar Collector Module (concentrating) | Double: tempered glass | Extruded aluminum pipe | Selective | .88 |
| Falbel Energy Systems Corp. | Delta Model 54 (concentrating) | Single: Kalwall fiber glass | Aluminum Roll-Bond® or copper plate; copper tubing attached underneath; aluminized reflector | Nonselective black paint | |

**Northrup, Inc.**
302 Nichols Drive
Hutchins, Texas 75141
(214) 225-4291

Northrup manufactures a tracking, liquid-type concentrating solar collector. Its Fresnel lens, made of extruded UV-resistant acrylic, concentrates the sun's rays onto a selectively coated copper absorber tube. The absorber tube is housed in a sturdy galvanized steel trough insulated with fiber glass. The collector is sold factory-assembled with frame and mounting. It can be retrofitted and installed by the homeowner.

Northrup's liquid-type, flat-plate collector is available with a first glazing of glass and an optional second glazing of Dupont *Teflon.®* The absorber plate is made of extruded aluminum mechanically connected to copper circulating tubes and coated with 3M Nextel® black paint. The housing is galvanized steel with a baked enamel finish on the sides and bottom.

The collectors are available as part of a domestic hot water heating package, which includes an 82-gallon or 120-gallon, porcelain-lined tank; circulating pump; and controls. The system is self-draining. Northrup also offers heat pumps, blowers, and air handlers.

*Suntec slats installation, Sandia laboratories, Albuquerque, New Mexico.*

**Suntec Systems, Inc.**
2102 Wooddale Drive
St. Paul, Minnesota 55119
(612) 735-7600

The Suntec *SLATS* collector is a line-focusing type consisting of a field of curved rectangular mirrors that track the sun to reflect its rays onto a linear absorber tube. It is capable of producing high temperatures and is especially suited to northern climates. It is designed for industrial/commercial space and water heating and air conditioning applications. It is supplied with a support structure and control system.

...Leading the Solar Industry

**Solar Development, Inc.**
See Collectors—Flat Plate.

| Absorptivity | Dimensions | Price | Features |
|---|---|---|---|
| | 2′ × 9′ | $4,995 | Array includes six collectors. Automatic tracking. Single and dual axis modules available. |
| .98 at 212° F. | 104″ × 47½″ × 6″ | $700 per module | Operating range from 140° F. to 400° F. Factory-assembled. |
| .93 | 80.5″ × 29.62″ × 15.7″ | $320 | Can be mounted on walls or roofs or on ground. No electrical devices or back-up systems necessary. |
| | 8′ × 7′ × 4″ | $360–$425 | Nontracking. Available apart from Falbel systems. |

**Continued**

## High-Temperature Collectors Compared *(Continued)*

| Manufacturer | Make | Glazing | Absorber | Coating | Emissivity |
|---|---|---|---|---|---|
| G.E. Co./ Solarquip Products | Model TC-100 Vacuum Tube Collector | Glass tube envelope | Copper tube | Selective | |
| Mann-Russell Electric, Inc. | Sun-Bucket IV | Double: plastic; unglazed | Copper tubes | Selective black chrome | |
| Northrup, Inc. | Concentrating Solar Collector | Single: acrylic lens | Copper tube | Selective | .12 |
| Solar Development, Inc. | SD6 (flat plate) | Single: tempered water-white glass | Copper plate; copper tubing | Selective black chrome | .01 |
| Suntec Systems, Inc. | SLATS Collector (concentrating) | Optional | Linear tube held by supports above curved rectangular mirror reflectors | | |

# Solar Furnaces

**Champion Home Builders Co.**
**Solar Division**
**5573 East North St.**
**Dryden, Michigan 48428**
**(313) 796-2211**

Champion's Solar Furnace consists of an air-type collector, rock bed storage, air handler, dampers, motors, and controls housed in an aluminum frame which is placed on the ground. A hinged reflector shield of mill-finished aluminum can be angled in the winter to focus the sun's rays on the collector and closed in the summer to reduce overheating.

The *VertaFin*™ collector is comprised of horizontal rows of two-inch-high, black-painted aluminum fins, which catch light normally reflected away from the collector. It is double glazed with low-iron glass and insulated with urethane foam. The *VertaFin*™ collector can also be installed separately on roofs or other structures.

A domestic hot water package can be added to the Solar Furnace to supply hot water in the off-demand space heating cycle. The package includes heat exchanger, pump, damper, controller, and 52- or 82-gallon, glass-lined preheat tank.

Champion also sells a solar monitor panel that can be installed in the home to indicate modes of operation, cycles, and temperatures. Special solar ductwork of molded urethane foam insulation with metal foil inside and *Mylar* outside is also available.

*Champion solar furnace.*

| Absorptivity | Dimensions | Price | Features |
|---|---|---|---|
| | 4′ × 4½′ | | Sensitive to direct and diffuse light. |
| | 5′ × 5′ | $7,500 | Includes lazy-susan rotational base and Mark IV Heliostat.<br>May be ordered separately. |
| .95 | | | Factory-assembled.<br>Sold with adjustable frame. |
| .90 | 76½″ × 36½″ | $295.80 | Self-draining.<br>For use in absorption cooling systems. |
| | | | For industrial/commercial use.<br>Supplied with support structure and control system. |

## Future Systems, Inc.
## Lakewood, Colorado 80228

The *sun\*trac* air-type, free-standing solar furnace incorporates collectors, air handler, and rock storage in one A-frame structure. It is mounted at ground level and connected to the forced air distribution system in the house. A hinged reflector directs the sun's rays onto the collectors. It is to be used with an auxiliary conventional heating system and is automatically controlled by a differential thermostat.

The *sun\*trac* air-type portable heater creates auxiliary heat for greenhouses, homes, cabins, barns and sheds, etc. It is mounted on a trailer but can also be permanently mounted on buildings or at ground level.

## Kalwall Corporation
## Solar Components Divison
## 88 Pine St.
## Manchester, New Hampshire 03103
## (603) 688–8186

Kalwall® manufactures passive and active solar systems utilizing their own glazing material (see Energy Conservation section). The Kalwall® Solar Furnace uses *Sunwall®* as the outside wall, behind which is positioned a row of water-filled, black-painted *Sunlite®* storage tubes. Air is filtered around these tubes and into the interior of the building through vents by means of natural convection or blowers.

Kawall's® Solar-Kal Airheater is a solar collector that can be roof-mounted or vertically-mounted on exterior

*Kalwall® solar furnace under construction.*

walls. In new construction it can function as the wall itself. The collector is covered with *Sunlite® Premium* and has an absorber plate of black-painted flat or V-corrugated aluminum. It can be insulated by the owner.

The Solar-Kal Airheater System consists of collectors, water storage tubes made from *Sunlite® Premium II*, an air mover with controls, and ductwork. Two basic ducting options are available. One allows heat to be delivered immediately to adjacent spaces; the other delivers it to storage. A system design guide is available for $15 to help the homeowner or architect size and plan a system.

Kalwall® sells their products and guide directly or by mail from their store and warehouse at the above address. The largest in the country, it carries not only Kalwall® but other brands of solar components and accessories as well. They will send a catalog upon request.

**Zomeworks Corporation**
**P.O. Box 712**
**Albuquerque, New Mexico 87103**
**(505) 242-5354**

Steve Baer and Zomeworks have developed a number of passive solar collection systems. Some of these devices are patented, but Zomeworks sells both plans and licenses at a reasonable price. In the Zomeworks *Airheater*, a bin of rocks, usually beneath or in front of the house, is heated by air flowing by convection through a collector. When heat is needed in the house, one opens a vent and the warm air rises into the room. In the sum-

## Solar Furnaces Compared

| Manufacturer | Make | Collector | Medium | Glazing | Absorber | Storage |
|---|---|---|---|---|---|---|
| Champion Home Builders | Solar Furnace | VertaFin™ | Air | Double: low-iron glass | Black aluminum fins | Rock bin |
| Future Systems, Inc. | Sun*trac Solar Furnace | Flat plate | Air | Single: tempered glass | Vertical vane | Rock bin |
| Kalwall Corp. | Solar Furnace | None | Liquid | Solar window: Kalwall Sunwall® | Black-painted Sunlite® storage tubes serve as both absorber and storage | |
| Zomeworks Corp. | Air Heater | Flat plate | Air | Single: glass | Six layers: expanded metal lath | Rock bin |

# Domestic Hot Water Systems

**Acorn Structures, Inc.**
See Complete Systems.

*Advance Energy's solar collector assists warehouse insulated with Advance Cooler's Zerotherm R-40 insulation.*

**Advance Energy Technology**
**Clifton Park, New York 12065**
**(518) 371-2140**

Advance makes *Homeside™* Solar Hot Water Systems, which include various components in increasing price ranges. Three *Homeside™* systems are available for use with an existing hot water tank and may include pumps, drain-down valves, differential thermostats, heat exchanger, and expansion tank. A fourth system comes complete with 82-gallon hot water tank. The collector, which is also available separately, utilizes Advance's *Zerotherm®* foam insulation. It has a patented absorber system of parallel copper tubing sandwiched between a primary absorber and a secondary reflective absorber. Glazing is single or double with insulated fiber glass and/or *Tedlar.®*

mer, the cool night air from the rock bin can be vented into the house during the day.

In *Drumwall®*, 55-gallon drums filled with water are set in racks behind south-facing glass walls. The outside-facing ends are painted black. The winter sun warms the water in the barrels through the glass and the heat radiates into the room. Large insulating doors are lowered on winter mornings; they allow the sun to shine in and warm the barrels and act as reflectors to intensify the heat from the sun. The doors are raised when the sun goes down to prevent heat loss. During the summer, the doors are kept closed and the cool water in the drums acts as a heat sink.

Zomeworks also offers three domestic hot water heaters. In one, a collector placed on the ground heats water treated with antifreeze. The water rises by convection to an 82-gallon storage tank placed above the collector level. Here, it is circulated through a heat exchanger jacket. This is primarily a preheater and is available with an electric back-up heat element.

In the *Pro Heater*, water is heated directly in a storage tank. An SDP acrylic double-skin cover is placed over the tank for optimum heating. A styrofoam cover is manually placed over the tank at night to prevent heat loss and removed in the morning.

The *Skylight Water Heater* is an 82-gallon, glass-lined tank fitted inside a skylight. An adjustable aluminum reflector is attached to it. The unit is glazed with double-skin acrylic and mounted on a steel frame.

| Size | Price | Features |
|---|---|---|
| 7'11" × 12'7" × 8'2" | | Automatic. Removable hinged reflector shield. Includes collector, storage, air handler, controls. Domestic hot water package optional. |
| 8' × 12' 8' × 16' 8' × 20' | $5000–$7000 | Automatic. Removable hinged reflector shield. To be used with auxiliary heating system. Includes collector, air handler, controls, storage. |
| 4' × 8' | $384 | Heated air distributed by natural convection or blowers. Optional heat control curtains between tubes and outside wall keep heat in at night. |
| | | Manually controlled. Heat distributed by natural convection from storage located beneath house. |

**All SunPower, Inc.**
**10400 S.W. 187 St.**
**Miami, Florida 33157**

All SunPower's closed loop domestic water heating system consists of collectors, heat exchanger, expansion tank, pump, differential control, copper piping, and all fitting. It can be adapted to a conventional hot water heater. The liquid-type, flat-plate collector has an anodized black aluminum absorber plate with flat integral fluid-carrying tubes over 90 percent of the surface. The plate is single-glazed with 1/8 inch glass. The collector has an aluminum frame and is insulated with polystyrene.

**Alpha Solarco.**
See Collectors—High Temperature.

**A.O. Smith**
**P.O. Box 28**
**Kankakee, Illinois 60901**
**(815) 933–8241**

A.O. Smith offers the *Conservationist*™ Solar Water Heater System, which includes collectors, a storage tank with built-in heat exchanger, pump, and controls. The liquid-type, flat-plate collector has a copper absorber sheet with soldered copper tubing coated in selective black. It is contained in an aluminum frame and insulated with fiber glass. Model NSC-19G is single glazed with low-iron glass; Models NSC-28 and NSC-40 are single glazed with Tedlar-coated fiber glass.

The A.O. Smith water heater includes a *Corona*™ heat exchanger, made of double-wall copper tubing, which is immersed in the tank. The *Phoenix*™ heating element, placed in the upper third of the tank, provides additional heat when required. The tank is glass lined and insulated with 3 inches of fiber glass. It is available in 82-, 100-, and 120-gallon capacities.

A.O. Smith also makes glass-lined storage tanks and electric heaters for separate sale. They are available in sizes of 66, 82, and 120 gallons. They include solar collector connections and 3 inches fiber glass insulation. The electric water heaters have the *Phoenix*™ heating element and automatic thermostat. Or they can function as conventional water heaters.

*A.O. Smith* Phoenix™ *heating element.*

**Bio-Energy Systems.**
See Absorber Plates.

**CSI Solar Systems Division, Inc.**
**12400 49th St.**
**Clearwater, Florida 33520**
**(813) 577-4228/4489**

For hot water heating with an existing hot water system, CSI manufactures *Sol-Heet* self-contained solar appliance. It consists of a solar collector, sensors, and pump housed in a stained redwood frame. It can be mounted on the roof or at ground level and comes with instructions for do-it-yourself installation.

The liquid-type, flat-plate collector is made of copper tubing with copper connections on an aluminum sink plate. It is insulated with fiber glass. Glazing is not included.

The centrifugal pump is housed at one end of the *Sol-Heet* unit and is run by a panel of solar batteries covering it. No additional power is needed.

The *Sol-Heet* appliance is completely automatic. Sensors provide freeze protection and overheating and overpressure protection with automatic reset.

Four models are available: *Model 250*, providing 30 gallons of water per day; *Model 500*, providing 50 gallons per day; *Model 750*, providing 75 gallons per day; and *Model 1000*, providing 100 gallons per day. All can be used with water or antifreeze solution for areas where freezing temperatures and power failures are likely.

**Energy Converters, Inc.**
See Collectors—Flat Plate.

**Energy Design, Inc.**
See Collectors—Flat Plate.

**Falbel Energy Systems Corp.**
See Collectors—High Temperature.

GRUMMAN ENERGY SYSTEMS, INC.
4175 VETERANS MEMORIAL HIGHWAY
RONKONKOMA, NEW YORK 11779

**Grumman Energy Systems, Inc.**
**4175 Veterans Memorial Highway**
**Ronkonkoma, New York 11779**

Grumman manufactures the *Sunstream*™ Solar Domestic Water Heating System. It is a closed-loop system using antifreeze for freeze protection. It preheats water for use in the existing water heater or can supply hot water itself.

Two *Sunstream*™ Model 60F collectors are provided with the system. They are housed in a white, baked enamel frame and glazed with an arched acrylic cover.

The system also includes the Model FST 80-gallon, glass-lined steel water storage tank with copper, wraparound heat exchanger. It is insulated with fiber glass. Expansion tank, differential controller, and circulating pump are mounted on the outside. Interconnection plumbing and wiring is factory installed.

**Halstead & Mitchell.**
See Collectors—Flat Plate.

**Heilmann Electric.**
See Collectors—Flat Plate.

**Intertechnology/Solar Corp.**
See Collectors—Flat Plate.

**Jackson Water Heater Division**
**W.L. Jackson Manufacturing Co., Inc.**
**P.O. Box 11168**
**Chattanooga, Tennessee 37401**
**(615) 867-4700**

The Jackson solar domestic water heating system includes liquid-type, flat-plate collectors, storage tank, differential thermostat, circulating pump, and other accessories. The self-draining solar collectors are made of a *Roll-Bond*® aluminum absorber sheet, selective coating and single fiber glass glazing. The 80-gallon storage tank with internal heat exchanger is glass lined, with an automatic auxiliary electric heating element.

# Jackson

A growing factor in the water heater business

**Lennox Industries, Inc.**
See Collectors—Flat Plate.

**National Solar Corp.**
**330 Boston Post Road**
**Old Saybrook, Connecticut 06475**
**(203) 388-0834**

NSC manufactures a liquid-type, flat-plate collector. The absorber plate is solid copper with flat integral tubes. The collector module contains two NSC collectors mounted on a redwood or aluminum frame. It is double glazed with tempered glass and insulated with fiber glass
NSC sells them as part of a domestic water heating system, including an 80-gallon, stone-lined preheat storage tank with built-in heat exchanger, circulating pump, differential thermostat, and expansion tank with air removal. The components come completely assembled and can be installed and retrofitted by the homeowner.

*Raypak* SG-18P *collector.*

**Raypak, Inc.**
**31111 Agoura Road.**
**P.O. Box 5790**
**Village, California 91361**
**889-1500**

Raypak manufactures *DHWS-2-T-80* solar domestic hot water system. It includes two Raypak *Model SG-18P* collectors, consisting of an aluminum absorber plate with copper waterways coated with flat black paint. They are single glazed with low iron, tempered glass and housed in an insulated steel frame. The package also includes an 80-gallon storage tank, pump, valves, and controls.

**Sekisui Chemical Co., Ltd.**
**2 Kinugasa-cho**
**Kita-ku, Osaka**
**Japan**

Sekisui manufactures a Gravity System Solar Water Heater and Circulation System Flat Collector. The water heater includes a collector and automatic water supply unit mounted on the roof. The collector consists of black plastic heating cylinders encased in a fiber-reinforced plastic box. It is single-glazed with high impact resistant, nonfading, transparent plastic and insulated with polystyrene foam. Its drain faucet for freeze protection must be manually operated.
The circulation system collector can be used in air conditioning as well as hot water heating. It consists of a selectively coated absorber plate with flow tubes bonded by continuous silver brazing. It is covered with tempered glass, housed in a galvanized steel frame, and insulated with rigid urethane foam.

*NSC flat-plate collectors mounted in new construction.*

**Northrup, Inc.**
See Collectors—High Temperature.

**PPG Industries.**
See Collectors—Flat Plate.

**Solar Development, Inc.**
See Collectors—Flat Plate.

**Solar Energy Products, Inc.**
See Collectors—Flat Plate.

**Solar Energy Research Corp.**
See Collectors—Flat Plate.

**Solargizer International, Inc.**
See Collectors—Flat Plate.

**Solarkit of Florida, Inc.**
See Collectors—Flat Plate.


**Solaron Corporation.**
See Complete Systems.


**Sol-Ray Division**
**Unit Electric Control, Inc.**
**130 Atlantic Drive**
**Maitland, Florida 32751**

The Sol-Ray domestic hot water heating system provides collectors, pump, controls, and storage tank. The flat-plate, liquid-type collector has a copper absorber sheet with copper tubing and is coated with Nextel 101-C10 matte black paint. It is single glazed with tempered glass; the aluminum housing is insulated with closed-cell polystyrene foam.

The storage tank is glass lined and is available in 82-, 100-, and 120-gallon capacities. A booster element is optional. A heat exchanger is necessary in cold climates where antifreeze is needed in the heat transfer fluid. The system comes complete with collectors, pump, controls, storage tank, and mounting equipment. It can be retrofitted and installed by the homeowner.

**Sunearth Solar Products Corp.**
**Progress Drive**
**Montgomeryville, Pennsylvania 18936**
**(215) 699-7892**

Sunearth manufactures domestic water heating systems that include collectors, glass- or stone-lined tank, controls, fittings, and instructions. Two liquid types are available: One uses water with motorized drain valves; the other uses an antifreeze solution with a heat exchanger. The flat-plate collector is double glazed with acrylic and *Teflon®*. The absorber plate is aluminum with copper tubing, coated with flat black paint. The frame is aluminum with thermal wool insulation. The insulated storage tank is glass lined for the drain-down system or stone lined for the antifreeze system.

# Domestic Hot Water Systems Compared

| Manufacturer | Make | Collector | Glazing | Absorber |
|---|---|---|---|---|
| Acorn Structures, Inc. | Sunwave® 70-2 Domestic Hot Water Heater | Sunwave® flat-plate: 4' × 10' | Single: polyester fiber glass | Aluminum plate; copper tubing; non-selective coating |
| Advance Energy Technology | Homeside® Solar Hot Water Systems | Flat plate: 4' × 8' | Double: fiber glass | Copper tubing between absorber sheet and reflector |
| | Same as above | Same as above | Same as above | Same as above |
| All SunPower, Inc. | | Flat plate: 8' × 5'1¼" × 4⅛" | Single: glass | Anodized black aluminum tube-in-sheet |
| Alpha Solarco | SolAqua-58-2 | Econosol flat plate collectors (2) | Single or double: low-iron, tempered glass | Copper tubing; selective black chrome coating |
| A.O. Smith | Conservationist™ Solar Water System | Flat plate: 35½" × 84" × 4" | Single: low-iron glass or Tedlar®-coated fiber glass | Copper sheet; copper tubing |

**Sun Stone Solar Energy Equipment**
**A Division of Sun Unlimited Research Corp.**
**P.O. Box 94**
**Sheboygan, Wisconsin 53081**
**(414) 452–8194**

Sun Stone offers a complete, packaged domestic water heating system. It includes a two, three, or four panel collector array to be bracket or ground mounted, a heat exchanger/blower/control unit, and an 82- or 120-gallon water storage tank. The flat-plate, air-type collector is single or double glazed with low-iron, tempered glass and has an absorber plate of porcelain enamel steel. It is fiber glass insulated.

The complete Sun Stone system for space and water heating includes collectors, blowers, controls, storage media, heat exchanger, pumps, storage tanks, and dampers. Three types of heat storage are offered: stone storage, a thermal storage medium that requires only ⅓ the space of stone storage, and water storage. The system features two-pass air flow heat collection, in which cold room air is returned to the collectors for heating, bypassing storage (pat. pend.).

The systems and collectors can be installed and retrofitted by the homeowner. Sun Stone will provide free on-the-job assistance to do-it-yourselfers.

**Sunwall, Inc.**
See Complete Systems.

*Sunstone solar energy system brings the log cabin into the solar age.*

**Sunworks, Inc.**
See Collectors—Flat Plate.

**Zomeworks Corporation.**
See Solar Furnaces.

| Storage | Size (Gallons) | Price | Features |
|---------|---------------|-------|----------|
| Stone-lined tank with internal heat exchanger and heating element | 120 | $2025 | Gravity drain-down.<br>Includes 2 collectors, storage tank, expansion tank, pump, controls. |
| Stone-lined tank with heat exchanger | 82 | $879 | Includes tank, collectors, differential thermostat, pump, expansion tank, heat exchanger, mounting equipment. |
| None | N.A. | $599<br>$495<br>$378 | Less expensive systems work with existing water heater tank and offer fewer components.<br>Drain-down system. |
| None | N.A. | | Adapted to existing water heater.<br>Includes collectors, heat exchanger, expansion tank, pump, differential control, copper piping, fittings. |
| Glass-lined tank | 52, 80, 120 | | Open-system.<br>Self-draining.<br>Sized by PPG computer to meet the requirements of the home.<br>Includes collectors, storage tank, circulating pump, controls, and valves. |
| Glass-lined, steel tank; internal heat exchanger and heating element | 82 | $1990–$2366 (2 or 3 collectors) | Includes collectors, storage tank, controls, expansion tank, circulating pump. |
| | 100 | $2426–$2880 (3 or 4 collectors) | |
| | 120 | $2646–$3100 (3 or 4 collectors) | |

**Continued**

# Domestic Hot Water Systems Compared (Continued)

| Manufacturer | Make | Collector | Glazing | Absorber |
|---|---|---|---|---|
| A.O. Smith | SolarSaver Solar Water Heating System | Flat plate:<br>48″ × 84″ × 3″<br>48″ × 120″ × 3″ | Single: Tedlar® coated fiber glass | Same as above |
| Bio-Energy Systems, Inc. | Domestic Hot Water Kit | N.A. | Tedlar® and fiber glass | BESI SolaRoll™ T-2 Tube Plate extrusion |
| CSI Solar Systems Division, Inc. | Sol-Heet | Flat plate | Not included | Aluminum with copper tubing |
| Daystar Corp. | Model HW2/NF-C | 21-C flat plate:<br>72¾″ × 44½″ × 5¼″ | Single: low-iron, tempered glass | Copper plate; copper tubing; nonselective black paint coating |
| | Model HW2/F-B | 21-B flat plate:<br>80¾″ × 44½″ × 5¼″ | Double: low-iron, tempered glass and a folded polymer heat trap | Same as above |
| | Model HW3/F-B | Same systems as above using 3 21-B collectors instead of 2 21-B collectors | | |
| | Model HW3/F-C | Same system as above using 3 21-C collectors instead of 3 21-B collectors | | |
| Energy Converters, Inc. | SolarSaver | Flat plate:<br>3′ × 8′ | Single: low-iron, tempered glass | Aluminum tube-in-sheet; selective coating |
| Energy Design, Inc. | Model-01 Water Heater | Maxim I flat plate:<br>36″ × 97½″ | Double: fiber glass | Aluminum or copper tube-in-sheet |
| Falbel Energy Systems Corp. | Basic Hot Water Systems | Delta Model 31 flat plate:<br>8′ × 4′ × 6″ | Single: acrylic | Copper tubes attached to aluminum fins; reflector shield; nonselective coating. |
| | | Delta Model 54 concentrating<br>8′ × 4′ × 4″ | Single: Kalwall® fiber glass | Aluminum or copper plate; copper tubes attached underneath; reflector shield; nonselective coating |
| | Direct Hot Water System | Delta Model 31 | See above | See above |

| Storage | Size (Gallons) | Price | Features |
|---|---|---|---|
| Same as above | 82 | $2156–$2032 (1 or 2 collectors) | Includes collectors and all components as in Conservationist™ system. |
| | 100 | $2116 (2 collectors) | |
| | 120 | $2156–$2672 (2 or 3 collectors) | |
| Not included | N.A. | $454—40 ft.² collector area $747—80 ft.² collector area | For do-it-yourself construction and installation. Includes T-2 Tube Plate, header set, SolaRoll™ extrusions for bonding, lock-strip system, thermosetting mastic, glazing, expansion tank, pump, valves, controls. Storage tanks cost extra. |
| Not included | N.A. | $496—2′ × 8′ $547—2′ × 11′ $661—4′ × 9′ $775—4′ × 11′ | Collector casing incorporates circulating pump run by solar batteries. Sensors provide protection from freezing, overheating, and overpressure; automatic reset. Used with existing water heater. Can be used as closed or open system. Can be installed on roof or ground by homeowner. |
| N.A. | N.A. | | For use with water in nonfreezing climates. Includes 2 collectors, pump, valves, controls, connections. |
| Water tank | 80 | | For use with antifreeze in freezing climates. Includes 2 collectors, expansion tank, storage tank, pump, valves, controls, connections, antifreeze. |
| Glass-lined steel tank | 80 | $1268 | Self-draining. Pre-assembled. Includes two collectors, storage tank, surge tank, pump, controls, auxiliary heat source. |
| Stone-lined, steel tank with built-in heat exchanger | 40 | | To be used with existing hot water heater. Includes storage tank, collectors, circulation pump, controls. |
| Plastic-lined tank with heat exchanger | 55 | $625 | Self-draining. Automatic. Includes collector, storage tank, mounting equipment, pump, controller. |
| Plastic-lined tank with heat exchanger | 55 | $670–$735 | Self-draining. Automatic. Includes collector, storage tank, mounting equipment, pump, controller. |
| Stone-lined tank | 80 | $1010 | Self-draining. Automatic. Includes two collectors, mounting equipment, tank, pump, controller. |

**Continued**

| Manufacturer | Make | Collector | Glazing | Absorber |
|---|---|---|---|---|
| Grumman Energy Systems, Inc. | Sunstream™ Solar Domestic Water Heating System | Sunstream™ Model 60F collectors (2): 113″ × 40¾″ × 9″ | Arched acrylic cover | Not specified |
| Halstead and Mitchell | Sunceiver® Solar Hot Water System | Sunceiver® flat plate: 35⅜″ × 77⅜″ × 4″ | Double: tempered water-white glass | Copper tube; aluminum fins; nonselective black paint coating |
| Heilemann Electric | Solar Water Heater System | Solar Tube 75″ × 4¼″ | Lexan tube | Copper plate with copper tubing soldered underneath; selectively coated |
| Inter-technology/ Solar Corp. | Joule Box™ | Flat plate: 35⅜″ × 77⅜″ × 4¼″ | Single: low-iron glass | Aluminum fins; copper tubes; nonselective black paint coating |
| Jackson Water Heater Division/ W.L. Jackson Manufacturing Co., Inc. | Jackson Solar Water Heating System | Flat plate: 8′2″ × 3′5″ × 5″ | Single: fiber glass | Roll-Bond® aluminum tube-in-sheet |
| Lennox Industries, Inc. | LSHW2 Series Solarmate® Hot Water Heating System | Flat plate: 71¹³⁄₁₆″ × 35⅞″ × 6¼″ | Single: low-iron, tempered glass | Copper tubes on steel plate; black chrome coating |
| National Solar Corp. | Domestic Hot Water Heating System | Flat plate: 3′ × 8′ | Double: tempered glass | Copper tube-in-sheet |
| Northrup, Inc. | Solar Hot Water Heating System | Flat plate: 103½″ × 37¼″ × 5⅝″ | Single: glass; second glazing of Teflon® optional | Aluminum plate; copper tubing |

| Storage | Size (Gallons) | Price | Features |
|---|---|---|---|
| Model FST glass-lined steel water tank with copper, wrap-around heat exchanger | 80 | $2190 | Includes collectors, tank, expansion tank, controls, circulating pump. |
| Tank with heat exchanger | 80 | $2545 (2 collectors) $2930 (3 collectors) $3310 (4 collectors) $3691 (5 collectors) | Includes collectors, storage tank, controls, valves, pumps, and expansion tank. |
| Tank with built-in heat exchanger | 42 52 66 82 120 | $580 (10 tubes) $680 (13 tubes) $790 (16 tubes) $950 (20 tubes) $1260 (30 tubes) | For use with the existing water heater. Includes collectors, storage tank, differential thermostat, circulating pump, expansion tank, valves. |
| Not specified | Not specified | $1750 | Includes collector(s), storage tank, pump, controls, piping, and fittings. |
| Glass-lined steel tank with internal heat exchanger | 80 | | Self-draining. Includes collectors, storage tank, differential thermostat, circulating pump. |
| Stone-lined tank with internal heat exchanger | 40, 65, 85, and 120 | | For use with existing water heater. Includes collectors, pump, storage tank, controls, most piping and wiring. |
| Stone-lined preheat tank; built-in heat exchanger | 80 100 120 | $1875 (2 collectors) $2695 (3 collectors) $3450 (4 collectors) | For use with existing hot water tank. Includes collectors, preheat tank, circulating pump, differential thermostat, expansion tank. |
| Porcelain-lined, steel tank | 82 and 120 | | Self-draining. Pre-assembled. Includes collectors, tank, circulating pump, controls. |

Continued

| Manufacturer | Make | Collector | Glazing | Absorber |
|---|---|---|---|---|
| PPG Industries | Solar Hot Water Heating System | Type III flat plate collector | Single: tempered glass | Copper with copper tubing; nonselective black paint coating |
| Raypak, Inc. | DHWS-2-T-80 Solar Domestic Hot Water System | Model SG-18P flat plate collectors (2): 37½″ × 79½″ × 4¼″ each | Single: low-iron glass | Aluminum with copper tubing; nonselective flat black paint |
| Sekisui Chemical Co., Ltd. | Gravity System Solar Water Heater | Flat plate: 90.6″ × 52″ × 8″ with tank | Single: plastic | Black plastic tubes |
| Solar Development, Inc. | Solar Hot Water Heater | SD5 flat plate: 2′ × 10′ or 4′ × 10′ | Single or double: Kalwall® Sunlite® Premium | Copper plate; copper tubing |
| Solar Energy Products, Inc. | Sunfired™ Closed Hot Water System | Sunfired™ CU30-WW flat plate: 98.5″ × 48.5″ × 2.57″ | Single: water-white glass | Aluminum sheet with copper flow tubes |
|  | Sunfired™ Open Hot Water System | Same as above | Same as above | Same as above |
| Solar Energy Research Corp. | DHW-801 Domestic Hot Water Kit | Thermo-Spray™ flat plate: 96″ × 23¾″ | Single: thermo-set plastic | Copper plate; selective coating |
| Solargizer™ International, Inc. |  | Solargizer™ flat-plate: 8′5″ × 4′1″ | Single: Sunlite® Premium II | Roll-Bond® copper plate; nonselective coating |
| Solarkit™ of Florida, Inc. | Solar Hot Water Heater | *SolarQueen* flat plate: 3′ × 5′ × 3½″ | Single: tempered glass | *CopperQueen* copper tube-in-sheet |
| Solaron Corp. | Domestic Hot Water Unit | Flat plate air-type: 3′ × 6′6″ × 7″ | Double: low-iron, tempered glass | Steel plate with channels beneath; porcelain enamel coating |
| Sol-Ray Division/Unit Electric Control, Inc. | Sol-Ray Water Heater | Flat plate: 35½″ × 77¼″ × 2″ | Single: tempered glass | Copper plate; copper tubing; nonselective coating |

| Storage | Size (Gallons) | Price | Features |
|---|---|---|---|
| Not specified | Not specified | $1578.61 | Self-contained in A-frame structure mounted at ground level.<br>Optional reflector shield.<br>Incorporates 75 cubic foot utility shed.<br>Includes collectors, water storage tank, controls, and pump.<br>Larger sizes available. |
| Water tank with electric element | 80 | | Includes collectors, tank, pump, valves, and controls. |
| Box located at top of collector | | | Water circulated by natural convection.<br>Manually operated drain-down. |
| None | | | Self-draining.<br>For use with standard storage tank.<br>Includes collectors, pump, controls. |
| Solarstream™ tank with wrap-around heat exchanger; heating element | 66<br><br>82<br><br>120 | $1655<br><br>$1757<br><br>$1889 | Includes collectors, storage tank, controls, pump, fluid handler, mounting hardware. |
| None | | $1338 | Includes collectors, fluid handler, controls, mounting hardware. |
| Glass-lined tank | 80 | | Includes copper heat exchanger, collectors, stainless steel pump, controls, surge tank. |
| Water tank with internal heat exchanger | 66<br><br>82<br><br>120 | $1750<br>(1 collector)<br><br>$2779.25<br>(2 collectors)<br><br>$3848<br>(3 collectors) | Includes collector(s), storage tank, expansion tank, pump, frame, controls, mounting kit. |
| None | | $395 | Includes collectors, pump, controls, valves, fittings.<br>Storage tank, heat exchanger, mounting hardware optional. |
| Stone-lined tank | 60 to 120 | | Includes collectors, heat exchanger, circulating pump, storage tank. |
| Glass-lined tank | 82, 100, and 120 | | Open or closed system available—heat exchanger optional.<br>Includes collectors, pumps, controls, storage tank, mounting equipment.<br>Heating element optional. |

**Continued**

## Domestic Hot Water Systems Compared *(Continued)*

| Manufacturer | Make | Collector | Glazing | Absorber |
|---|---|---|---|---|
| Sunearth Solar Products Co. | Domestic Hot Water Systems | Flat plate: 32.5″ × 97.5″ × 4″ | Double: acrylic and Teflon® | Aluminum sheet; copper tubing; non-selective coating |
| Sun Stone Solar Energy Equipment | Domestic Water Heater | Flat plate: 78½″ × 34½″ × 11½″ or 76¼″ × 34⅜″ × 10″ | Single or double: low-iron, tempered glass | Porcelain enamel steel |
| Sunwall, Inc. | Sunway HWPH-96C | Sunwall collection panels: air-type; 2′ × 6′ each | Double: Eastman Uvex® thermoplastic | Urethane foam; non-selective black paint coating |
| Sunworks, Inc. | Solector™ Pak 1000 | Solector™ flat-plate, liquid type: 3′ × 7′ | Single: no-iron, tempered glass | Copper plate; copper tubing; selective coating |
|  | Solector™ Pak 2000 | Same as above | Same as above | Same as above |
|  | Solector™ Pak 2200 | Same as above | Same as above | Same as above |
| Zomeworks Corp. | Domestic Water Heater | Flat plate |  | Copper |

| Storage | Size (Gallons) | Price | Features |
|---|---|---|---|
| Glass-lined for drain-down | 66 | $1247.78 (2 collectors) | Collector with "PFA" designation can be mounted in various positions for height adjustment. |
|  | 82 | $1588.88 (3 collectors) | Drain-down system includes collectors, pump, tank, differential thermostat and sensors, and all valves and piping. |
|  | 120 | $2050.73 (4 collectors) |  |
| Stone-lined with heat exchanger for anti-freeze | 65 | $1184.61 (2 collectors) | Antifreeze system includes collectors, pump, tank, heat exchanger, expansion tank, differential thermostat and sensors, and all valves and piping. |
|  | 80 | $1544.93 (3 collectors) |  |
|  | 120 | $1983.26 (4 collectors) |  |
| Water tank | 80 | $1626 (2 collectors) | includes bracket or ground mount collectors, heat exchanger/blower/control unit, and storage tank. |
|  |  | $1966 (3 collectors) |  |
|  |  | $2286 (4 collectors) |  |
|  | 120 | $1891 (2 collectors) |  |
|  |  | $2211 (3 collectors) |  |
|  |  | $2531 (4 collectors) |  |
| Glass-lined water tank | 120 |  | Potable water is heated by heated air flowing over finned tubing at top of collectors. Eight Sunwall panels are attached to or used as south-facing wall. Self-draining. Includes collectors, storage tank, controls, valves, pump, tubing. |
| Water tank with copper heat exchanger and heating element | 65 |  | Closed-loop system. Can be used as primary system or preheater. Includes 2 collectors, storage tank, expansion tank, pump, controls, valves. |
| N.A. | N.A. |  | Recirculation system. Manual drain-down. Used with existing hot water tank. Includes 2 collectors, pump, valves, controls. |
| N.A. | N.A. |  | Automatic drain-down. Used with existing water heater. Includes 2 collectors, pump, controls, valves. |
| Glass-lined, steel pre-heat tank with wrap-around heat exchanger and heating element | 82 | $660 | Tank placed, higher than collector to circulate water by convection. Closed system—uses anti-freeze. |

**Continued**

## Domestic Hot Water Systems Compared *(Continued)*

| Manufacturer | Make | Collector | Glazing | Absorber |
|---|---|---|---|---|
| Zomeworks Corp. | Pro Heater | None | SDP acrylic double-skin cover over tank | |
| | Skylight Water Heater | None | Skylight of double skin acrylic with adjustable reflector | |

# Complete Systems and Houses

**Acorn Structures, Inc.**
**Box 250**
**Concord, Massachusetts 01742**
**(617) 369–4111**

Acorn manufactures prefab solar houses and solar heating systems. Their "Solar Capes" have south-facing, double-glazed windows; internal chimneys; protected doorways; and weatherstripping on windows and doors. Certain models can be adapted to solar heating systems.

The *Acorn 420 Sunwave® Energy System* is used simultaneously and automatically with a backup heat source and water heater. It consists of a flat-plate, liquid-type collector, storage tank, preheat tank for domestic hot water, and warm air distribution system.

The collector is single glazed with polyester fiber glass and features an aluminum absorber plate with copper tubing coated with nonselective flat black paint. It is fiber glass insulated. The collector is self-draining to avoid freezing when not in use.

The 2000-gallon storage tank is made of vinyl-lined steel reinforced plywood. The homeowner supplies stan-

dard piping and wiring. The Acorn 420 System can be retrofitted. A six-collector system can heat a well-insulated 1500-square-foot home.

Acorn also offers the *Sunwave® 70-2* Domestic Hot Water Heating System, which consists of one or two *Sunwave®* solar collectors and a 120-gallon, stone-lined storage tank with integral heat exchanger. A gravity drain system eliminates the need for antifreeze.

**Arkla Industries, Inc.**
**P.O. Box 534**
**Evansville, Indiana 47704**

Arkla manufactures *Solaire* sun-powered air conditioning systems. *Solaire 36* is a three-ton absorption chiller whose full cooling capability is produced from 195°F. solar-heated water. The unit can operate on temperatures as low as 170°F.

*Solaire 300* is a 25-ton absorption chiller whose full cooling capability is produced from 195°F. The unit can operate on temperatures as low as 160°F. Both are to be installed indoors.

*Acorn's Solar Cape 2900.*

> **WHAT'S IT LIKE LIVING IN A SOLAR HOUSE?**
>
> Ever wondered just what it would be like to live in the solar houses you've read about? One way to find out is to travel around and ask the owners—if they welcome visitors.
>
> A faster way—and cheaper—is to read *At Home in the Sun: An Open-House Tour of Solar Houses in the United States,* by Norah Deakin Davis and Linda Lindsey (Charlotte, Vt.: Garden Way Publishing, 1979), $9.95. The authors did your traveling around and asking questions for you, and they share their findings, including photos, floor plans, and interviews with the owners, who explain exactly what they like (and don't like) about their homes.

| Storage | Size (Gallons) | Price | Features |
|---|---|---|---|
| Glass-lined steel tank | 42 | $288 | Water heated directly in tank. |
| | 82 | $390 | Insulated cover placed manually over tank at night. |
| Glass-lined tank | 82 | $462 | Storage tank fitted inside skylight. Water heated directly in tank. Seasonal adjustment of reflector twice a year. |

**Energy Converters, Inc.**
See Collectors—Flat Plate.

**Heilmann Electric.**
See Collectors—Flat Plate.

**Kalwall Corp.**
See Solar Furnaces.

**Skytherm Processes, Inc.**
**2424 Wilshire Blvd.**
**Los Angeles, California 90057**

Harold Hay has developed a simple, passive space heating and air conditioning system for new constructions. The system utilizes "thermoponds," polyethylene bags of water mounted on the roof of the building. In *Skytherm Southwest* moveable insulation panels are opened during the day to allow the thermoponds to absorb heat and closed at night so that the heat radiates into the house. Cooling is accomplished by reversing the process.

In *Skytherm North* the thermoponds are mounted in the attic under a glazed, south-sloped roof. The Skytherm process is very inexpensive compared to the cost of many solar heating and cooling systems and maintains a high comfort level. A small, one-time patent license fee is charged to the builder or homeowner. Skytherm Processes also provides reasonably priced consulting services and publications.

**Solar Energy Research Corp.**
See Collectors—Flat Plate.

**Solar Room Company, Inc.**
**Box 1377**
**Taos, New Mexico 87571**
**(505) 758-9344**

The *Solar Room®* is a combination solar collector/greenhouse that can be installed and retrofitted by any homeowner on any house with at least twelve feet of south-facing wall. It can be easily removed and refitted at a new location.

The *Solar Room®* collects heat through a double-skinned plastic sheet stretched over a galvanized steel frame. This Twin-Skin™ glazing is kept inflated by a small blower to create an insulating space that retains collected solar heat within the structure. This heat can be circulated through the rest of the home by natural convection or by fans.

In addition to supplying 100,000 Btu per day when the sun shines, the *Solar Room®* functions as additional living space and/or as a greenhouse. It is available in lengths from 12 to 39 feet in 3-foot increments. A solar circulator and 36-watt blower is included.

*Solar Room solar collector/greenhouse.*

## Solar Technology Corp.
2160 Clay St.
Denver, Colorado 80211
(303) 455-3309

Soltec's *SunUP*™ air-type, flat-plate collector is double glazed with thermoglass or single glazed with acrylic. It has an absorber plate of black anodized aluminum and is insulated with fiber glass duct board and polystyrene foam. The collector box is galvanized steel.

Soltec provides complete systems for space and domestic water heating, including air handler, concrete rock-storage bin, heat exchanger, preheat tank, pump, ducting, and piping. Operation is automatic with thermal controls and thermostat.

Soltec also manufactures the *Solera*™ solar structure—a prefabricated, modular walk-in collector. With sloping or vertical solar windows, it can be used as residential "sunspace" and supplemental passive heating. Adding a blower system to thermal storage located inside the structure can improve its heating capacity. The *Solera*™ structure can be modified to be a domestic water heater, a sauna, or a *Solar Garden*™ greenhouse, which provides for heat collection, storage, and food-production. The structures can be installed and retrofitted by the homeowner.

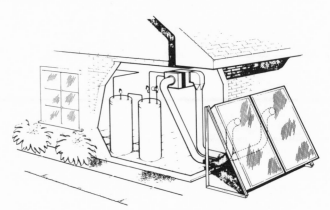

## Solaron Corporation
300 Galeria Tower
720 South Colorado Blvd.
Denver, Colorado 80222
(303) 759-0101

Solaron Corporation manufactures air-type solar energy systems based on the designs of Dr. George Löf, whose home in Denver has been heated by a similar system for over 20 years, troublefree. The collector consists of a steel absorber plate with channels running beneath the plate. It is double-glazed with low-iron, tempered glass and housed in a steel frame. Solaron also offers a new domestic hot water heater utilizing an air-type collector, solar hot water storage tank, heat exchange unit, and circulating pump.

## Solartran Corporation
Escanaba, Michigan 49829
(906) 789-0050
(906) 786-4550

Solartran Corporation cooperates with American Timber Homes, Inc. (also of Escanaba, Michigan) in the manufacture of maintenance-free, energy efficient homes. The American Timber homes feature treated cedar exteriors, thermal-insulated doors and windows, hand-hewn log trusses, and optional interior panelling.

Four different solar homes are available. Two have incorporated a total solar design concept; the other two are traditionally styled homes fitted with appropriate solar equipment. Solar heating systems are either air- or water-circulating.

Each of the houses includes a fireplace with water-to-air heat exchanger for extra heating and a backup heat source or heat pump for energy during cloudy periods.

Solartran supplies all components for the solar system and for the basic house package. A local contractor builds the house and supplies plywood, felt, roof shingles, bulky insulation, drywall, plumbing, wiring, and conventional heat source.

Prices range from $25,930 to $48,308, including delivery. Optional interior panelling costs about $2000 extra. Solar equipment can be added later for a lower initial cost.

*Solartran air collector with heat exchanger and storage tanks.*

## Sun Stone Solar Energy Equipment.
See Domestic Hot Water Systems.

---

### SOLAR INDEX

The Solar Index, like the windchill factor or the air quality index, is becoming a standard feature in the weather reports of newspapers and broadcasts around the country.

The Index is a number between 0 and 100 which gives the percentage of heat that could be supplied on a given day by a solar water heating system. If the Solar Index were 83, 83 percent of the hot water for a household could have been provided by a solar system that day.

A computer program calculates the figure for a water heating system for a family of four, using 80 gallons of hot water a day, and having a collector area of between 50 and 80 square feet. Of course, different-sized collectors would produce different figures, but the index serves as a general indicator for solar use that day.

DOE and local weather bureaus provide the Solar Index to interested media at no charge. If you would like to obtain the Solar Index for your area, contact the Solar Index Project Manager, Department of Energy, Washington, D.C. 20545.

## Sunwall, Inc.
## Box 9723
## Pittsburgh, Pennsylvania 15229

Sunwall makes solar collection panels for medium-temperature applications. They are designed to be mounted vertically on a south-facing wall or to be employed as a substitute building material for new construction. They can be installed by the homeowner or by an authorized contractor.

*Sunwall* collection panels provide for a passive, air-type solar energy system. Brick, concrete block, or other masonry or cementitious building walls behind the panels act as thermal storage. Openings in the wall allow heated air to pass through the wall into the interior of the house by natural convection or blowers.

The collection panels are constructed of an absorber/insulator (patent pending) of black-painted polyurethane foam. Double glazing of Eastman *UVEX®* thermoplastic is easily and tightly secured to the outside building wall after the absorber/insulator has been installed. A check valve is included to stop reverse heat flow at night. Differential temperature controls and fan units are also available for use with *Sunwall* systems.

The *Sunway HWPH-96C* system is a domestic hot water heating system consisting of eight *Sunwall* panels, a 120-gallon, glass-lined storage tank, differential control, control valve, and pump. Potable water is heated as rising warm air generated by the panels flows over finned tubing at the top of the collector. This tubing carries the heated water to the storage tank. A drain-down system is used to protect the collectors from freezing and power failure.

## Thomason Solar Homes, Inc.
## 609 Cedar Ave.
## Fort Washington, Maryland
## (Washington, D.C.) 20022
## (301) 839-1738
## (301) 202-5122

The patented Thomason *Solaris®* Jr. system includes 96 or 128 square feet of Solaris liquid-type, flat-plate trickling collectors. The absorber plate is black-painted, corrugated aluminum and is single glazed with window glass. It is insulated with fiber glass and housed in a wooden frame.

Heated water is stored in a 280-gallon tank embedded in a ton of stones. Air is blown through the heated stones and used in a forced-air distribution system. A smaller tank immersed in the storage tank preheats domestic hot water. Auxiliary heat can be taken when necessary from a conventional water heater.

*Solaris®* Jr. can be installed easily in existing homes. Additional units can be added to take on increased amounts of the home-heating load. Advanced systems include air conditioning and back-up heat.

*Sunwall collector panels mount on south wall.*

## Wormser Scientific Corporation
## 88 Foxwood Road
## Stamford, Connecticut 06903
## (203) 329-2001

Wormser manufactures and installs Gerald Falbel's patented Pyramidal Optical Collector System. The focusing collector is a liquid-type that uses Plexiglas skylights as the aperture. A movable reflective surface within the attic follows the sun's angle changes during the year to change the size of the aperture. Stationary and movable reflective surfaces form a pyramid shape that focuses the sunlight onto selectively coated, copper *Roll-Bond®* absorber plates at the back of the attic. It operates with tap water because there is no danger of freezing.

The Optical Collector System can be retrofitted. It can be used for space heating and air conditioning and for hot water heating. Wormser supplies all components, including collection apparatus; 850-gallon, rubber-lined concrete storage tank; heat exchanger; hot water heater; pumps; heat pumps; controls; and back-up heat system.

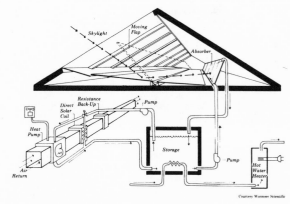

*Wormser Scientific's Pyramidal Optics system. The collectors are inside, protected from wind and weather.*

## Zomeworks Corporation.
See Solar Furnaces.

# Complete Systems Compared

| Manufacturer | Make | Functions | Collector | Medium | Glazing |
|---|---|---|---|---|---|
| Acorn Structures, Inc. | 420 Sunwave® Energy Systems | Space heating; domestic water pre-heating | Flat plate: 4′ × 20′ × 5″ | Liquid | Single: polyester fiber glass |
| Arkla Industries Inc. | Solaire Sun-Powered Air Conditioning | Absorption chillers | Lithium bromide as absorbent; water as refrigerant | | N.A. |
| Daystar Corp. | MOD10/XRH-B | Hydronic space and hot water heating | 21-B flat plate: 80¾″ × 44½″ × 5¼″ | Liquid | Double: low iron, tempered glass and a folded polymer heat trap |
| | MOD10/XR-B | Forced air space heating and hot water heating | Same as above | Same as above | Same as above |
| Energy Converters | The 460-Gallon Residential Solar Energy System | Space and water heating | Flat plate: 3′ × 8′ | Liquid | Single: low-iron glass |
| Heilemann Electric | Solar-assisted Hot Water and Space Heater | Space and water heating | 50 Heilemann Solar Tubes | Liquid | Lexan cover tube |
| Kalwall Corp. | Kalwall Air-heater System | Space heating | Kalwall Airheater | Air | Sunlite® Premium |
| Skytherm Processes, Inc. | Skytherm North and Skytherm Southwest | Space heating and air conditioning | "Thermo-ponds"—black polystyrene bags | Liquid | None |
| Solar Energy Research Corp. | SH500-830 Forced Air Space System | Space heating | Thermo-Spray® flat plate: 96″ × 23¾″ | Liquid | Single: thermoset plastic |
| Solaron Corp. | Air Heater | Space heating | Flat plate: 3′ × 6′6″ × 7″ | Air | Double: low-iron, tempered glass |
| Solar Room Company, Inc. | Solar Room® | Space heating | N.A. | Air | Twin-Skin™ double-skin plastic sheet stretched over steel frame |

| Absorber | Storage | Price | Features |
|---|---|---|---|
| Aluminum plate; copper tubing; nonselective black paint | 2000-gallon tank: vinyl-lined plywood; steel reinforcers | $7250 | Self-draining.<br>Works with backup heat source and water heater.<br>Piping and wiring not supplied. |
| N.A. | N.A. | | Indoor installation. |
| Copper plate; copper tubing; nonselective black paint coating | Hot water tank<br><br>2 storage tanks | | Includes ten collectors, storage tanks, expansion tank, valves, controls, connections, antifreeze. |
| Same as above | Same as above | | Includes ten collectors, storage tanks, expansion tank, valves, controls, connections, antifreeze, and heat exchanger. |
| Copper tube-in-sheet; moderately selective coating | Glass-lined steel tank | $5,206–$5,616 | Self-draining.<br>Includes collectors, storage, pump, controls. |
| Copper plate with copper tube soldered underneath | 120-gallon tank with heat exchanger | $2480 | Used with existing heating equipment.<br>Fan coil unit with separate thermostat heats only one area. |
| Flat or V-corrugated aluminum; nonselective black paint | Water storage tubes made from Sun-lite ® Premium II | Not specified | Includes collectors, storage tubes, air mover, and two basic ducting options—for direct delivery of heat or delivery to storage. |
| Water bags (see collectors) | Water bags (see collectors) | | Thermo-ponds on roof heat and cool house by radiation.<br>Panels close at night to hold warmth.<br>New construction. |
| Copper plate; selective coating | Spherical polyolefin tank:<br>530 gallons<br>830 gallons<br>1100 gallons | <br>$ 5,450.00<br>$ 8,337.50<br>$10,693.95 | Automatic.<br>Used with existing forced air distribution system.<br>Includes collectors, pump, controls, heat exchanger tank. |
| Steel plate with channels beneath; coated with porcelain enamel | Pebble-bed | $25–$35 per sq. ft. | Includes collectors, air handler, controls, and storage. |
| N.A. | N.A. | $899–$1394 | Removable addition to house.<br>To be used as greenhouse, living area, for supplemental heat.<br>Blower keeps Twin-Skin inflated for extra insulation.<br>Collected heat is circulated through house by natural convection or fans.<br>Installed and retrofitted by homeowner on south-facing wall.<br>Includes glazing, frame, solar circulator, fittings, and blower. |

**Continued**

**Complete Systems Compared** *(Continued)*

| Manufacturer | Make | Functions | Collector | Medium | Glazing |
|---|---|---|---|---|---|
| Solar Technology, Inc. | SunUP™ Solar Collector System | Space and water heating | SunUP™ flat plate: 3′ × 6′ 4′ × 8′ | Air | Double: thermo-glass or Single: acrylic |
| | Solera™ Walk-in Solar Collection System | Space heating and water heating | SunUP™ collectors optional | Air | Insulated wall panels; solar windows |
| | Solar Garden™ | Space and water heating; food production | SunUP™ collectors optional | Air | Solera™ shell with double windows |
| Sun Stone Solar Energy Equipment | | Space and water heating | Flat plate: 78″ × 34″ × 10″ | Air | Single or double: low-iron, tempered glass |
| Sunwall, Inc. | | Passive forced air space heating | Sunwall collection panels: 2′ × 6′ each | Air | Double: Eastman Uvex® thermo-plastic |
| Thomason Solar Homes, Inc. | Solaris® Jr. | Space heating and water preheating | Solaris® flat plate: 4′ × 16′ | Liquid | Single: window glass |
| Wormser Scientific, Inc. | Pyramidal Optical Collector System | Space and water heating and air conditioning | Pyramidal Optical focusing collector | Liquid | Plexiglass skylights |
| Zomeworks | Drumwall® | Space heating | None | Liquid | Glass walls |

| Absorber | Storage | Price | Features |
|---|---|---|---|
| Black anodized aluminum plate | Concrete rock bin | $7500–$9000 plus $1000 for water heating per 1500 sq. ft. home; $2000 for water heating only | Automatic.<br>Includes collectors, storage, air handler, heat exchanger, preheat tank, pump, controls, ducting, and piping. |
| Black-painted barrels filled with water | | $1,499–$5,500 | Permanent addition to home.<br>Expandable, modular.<br>Works passively to heat itself or actively to heat home.<br>With collectors, can be used to heat water. |
| Black-painted barrels filled with water | | $2099–$7000 plus $250 for water heating | Permanent addition to home.<br>Expandable, modular.<br>Works like Solera™ for space heating.<br>Can also heat domestic water.<br>Includes blower, fan, lights, and grow beds. |
| Porcelain enamel steel | Stone, water, or special thermal medium; water tank | | Two-pass air flow heat collection allows cold room air to be returned to the collector for heating.<br>Includes collectors, blowers, controls, storage, heat exchanger, pumps, water storage tank, and dampers.<br>Free on-the-job assistance for do-it-yourselfers. |
| Urethane foam; black paint coating | N.A. | | Absorber added to south-facing wall.<br>Glazing attached over it.<br>Masonry wall acts as thermal storage.<br>Openings in wall allow heated air to be vented into house.<br>Controls and fan units available. |
| Black-painted corrugated aluminum | 280-gallon water tank in rock bed | $1900 | "Trickle-down" method.<br>Includes collectors, storage, air handler, preheat tank, heat exchanger.<br>Advanced system includes air conditioning and backup heat functions for $4000–$8000. |
| Copper Roll-Bond® plate; selectively coated | 850-gallon rubber-lined concrete tank | $9,000–$12,000 | Absorber placed in attic behind skylights.<br>Stationary and mobile reflective surfaces focus sun's rays onto absorber.<br>Includes collectors, pumps, heat pumps, storage, heat exchanger, hot water heater, backup system.<br>Most suited to new construction.<br>Installed by Wormser. |
| Black-painted 55-gallon drums behind glass | | | Built as south-facing walls in new or existing construction.<br>Insulating panels on inside operated manually—lowered in mornings in winter to act as reflector to heat drums; raised at night to let heat in.<br>In summer, insulating panels are kept closed; cool water in drums acts as heat sink. |

# Solar Controls

**Contemporary Systems, Inc.**
**68 Charlonne St.**
**Jaffrey, New Hampshire 03452**
**(603) 532-7972**

Contemporary System's Logic Control Unit is a differential thermostat designed for use in air-type solar space heating systems. It controls the total operation of collection, distribution, and storage as well as switching on backup energy. It monitors collector, storage, and room temperatures and chooses the appropriate mode for most efficient heating. It can be surface-mounted or recessed in the wall, operating automatically or manually.

The Universal Switching Unit is a combination fan and air valving box that operates all air handling and valving requirements in the solar heating system.

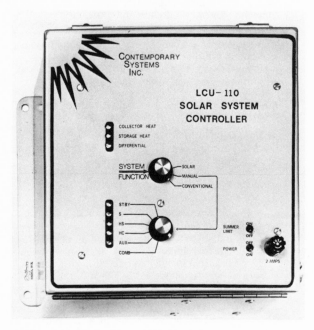

*Contemporary Systems controller.*

**del Sol Control Corporation**
**11914 U.S. 1**
**Juno, Florida 33408**
**(305) 626-6116**

The del Sol Control differential thermostat is designed to be used in combination with the March pump and motor Model 809-115 VAC, though it can control any motor using 115 volt AC up to 2 amps. Heat is added to storage as soon as—and so long as—any collector is slightly warmer than the water in the storage tank. Accessories for the thermostat are available.

**Hawthorne Industries, Inc.**
**Solar Energy Division**
**1501 South Dixie**
**West Palm Beach, Florida 33401**
**(305) 659-5400**
**Toll Free—1-800-327-2280**

Hawthorne's line of solar energy controls includes the *Actovator*, a solid-state switch that senses absolute temperatures. It can be used to bring in back-up systems, estimate limits of operation, and drain collector for freeze protection.

The *Fixflo* control is a differential thermostat that controls circulating pumps and blowers. Optional sensors monitor absolute temperature for freezing or overheating and automatically start drain-down or stop circulation as needed. A *Fixflo* with a "frost override" is available that overrides the freeze protection and fills the collector when there is energy to be gained.

The *Variflo* proportional control enables pumps and blowers to produce optimum flow conditions. Upper-limit sensors and frost protection sensors can be added. The *Variflo* is only to be used with pumps and blowers that have been approved by Hawthorne.

| MODEL NUMBER | CONTROL TYPE | Domestic Hot Water | Swimming Pools | Relays/Solenoids | Differential Control | Absolute Temperature Control | Space Heating | Backup Control | Shaded Pole Motors | Permanent Split Capacitor Motors | Universal Motors | Motors with Starting Windings | Heat Recovery Systems | Precision Thermostat Control | Spas/Tubs |
|---|---|---|---|---|---|---|---|---|---|---|---|---|---|---|---|
| H-1500-A | Actovator Control | | x | | | x | | x | x | x | x | x | | | |
| H-1503-A | Fixflo Control | x | x | x | x | | x | | x | x | x | x | x | x | x |
| H-1503-B | Fixflo Control — Board Only | x | x | x | x | | x | | x | x | x | x | x | x | x |
| H-1504-A | Fixflo with Frost Control | x | x | x | x | x | x | x | x | x | x | x | x | x | x |
| H-1505-A | Fixflo with Dual Outlet | x | x | | x | | x | | x | x | x | x | x | x | x |
| H-1506-A | Fixflo with Frost Override | x | | x | x | x | x | x | x | x | x | x | x | x | x |
| H-1510-A | Variflo Control | x | | x | | x | | x | x | x | | x | | | |
| H-1510-B | Variflo Control — Board Only | x | | x | | x | | x | x | x | | x | | | |
| H-1511-A | Variflo with Frost Control | x | * | x | x | x | x | | x | x | x | | x | | |
| H-1512-A | Variflo with Dual Outlet | x | | x | | x | | x | x | x | | x | | | |

*Use in Frost Control output ONLY*

*Uses of Hawthorne controls.*

## Heliotrope General
**3733 Kenora Drive
Spring Valley, California 92077
(714) 460-3930**

Heliotrope General's *Delta-T*™ differential temperature thermostat is an automatic motor control that turns on and off circulation pump/blowers in solar heating and hot water systems. The *DTT–9, 290,* and *690* series can be installed by the homeowner. The *DTT–100* series automatically turns the pump off when the collector temperature is below 80°F. Thus, the pump will not turn on at night to replenish depleted reserves in the storage.

The *DTT–200* series features an automatic freeze control circuit that protects the collector from freezing by circulating warmer storage water through it.

The *DTT–400* limits stored water to a temperature of 160°F., eliminating the fear of scalding. A feature of the *DTT–690* series is the *Freeze-Fail-Safe*™ system that drains the collector in case of power failure or 32°F. temperatures. The *DTT–690* series is warranted for five years. Adjustable modifications of these series are also available for even more accuracy or versatility.

The *Helio-Matic I*™ Solar Pool Heat Controller includes valves and venting that regulate the flow through any solar collector. The owner can adjust high temperature limit to his or her own specifications.

The *Solar Spa/Pump Controller* accomplishes the same thing as the *Helio-Matic I*™ by turning on and off the circulation pump. An *FS–1 Freeze Sensor* is available for both of these controllers; it causes the pump to turn on at 32°F. to prevent the collector from freezing.

Heliotrope General also offers an electronic thermometer that can sense temperatures from eleven different locations. The read-out dial is calibrated in Fahrenheit and Celsius, from 0° to 350°. Also available is the *Hydro-Rain*™ *Solar Valve*, a solenoid valve for use with the *Helio-Matic I*™ pool heat controller.

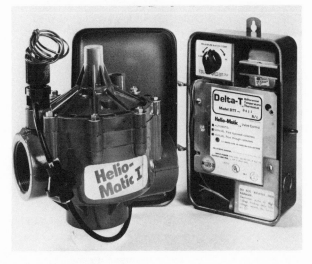

*Heliotrope General's differential thermostat and pool heat controller.*

## Honeywell Solar Energy
**Honeywell Plaza
Minneapolis, Minnesota 55408**

Honeywell manufactures a special line of controls for solar energy systems. The *Solarvisor Differential Controller Series* offers automatic control of circulating pumps, valves, dampers, motors, and other accessories. Some models include freeze protection, auxiliary relay drivers, and over-temperature protection alone or in combination, and some are adjustable.

Honeywell also offers room temperature controls, outdoor thermostats, liquid-type flow controls, air-flow controls, and the *Economizer*, which allows for the use of outdoor air as a cooling agent wherever possible. Honeywell can also supply all individual equipment needed for the control of solar energy systems, such as relays and contactors, transformers, and timers.

## Natural Power, Inc.
**Francestown Turnpike
New Boston, New Hampshire 03070
(603) 487-5512/5513**

All Natural Power solar controls are automatic and adaptable to complex as well as simple systems. They are adjustable by the owner or installer and feature system self-test, meter monitoring of temperatures and temperature differentials, and status indicator lights. They are complete with sensors.

Natural Power products include the *Series S10* Automatic Solar Controls, providing all control and monitoring functions for any system ($500). The *Series S25* and *S26* Differential Thermostats activate pumps or blowers based on temperature differentials ($200). They are optionally available with storage over-temperature control and/or collector freeze control.

The *S27* and *S28* Proportional Controllers are provided with eight speeds for collection under marginal conditions. The *S30* Outdoor Reset Control lowers the temperature at which the system switches from storage to the back-up heat source. The *S35* and *S36* Temperature Monitors display in Fahrenheit and Celsius temperatures or temperature differentials from sensors located at various parts of the system.

Natural Power products can also be leased for a minimum of three months for a deposit of 50 percent of the purchase price.

## Rho Sigma
**11922 Valeria St.
North Hollywood, California 91605
(213) 982-6800**

Rho Sigma manufactures a line of solar energy controls. For space heating, they offer differential thermostats providing pump or fan control ($91.87). Additional circuits on some models control drain-down valves for freeze protection or can be used to switch from solar energy to auxiliary heating. A Proportional Pump Speed Control senses small temperature differentials and changes pump speed accordingly ($107.30). Additional circuits provide overheating and freeze protection.

Rho Sigma also makes Automatic Valve Controls for pool and spa heating ($114.61). These controls can also shut off the heater when pool temperature reaches a preset upper limit. A Differential Pump Control allows direct switching of pumps in solar systems used in heating large pools ($132.05). It also can shut off the heating systems to prevent pool overheating.

Rho Sigma also has an Integrated Solar/Conventional Heating System Control ($289.62) and a Btu Meter ($338.94).

**Richdel**
**Solar Division**
**P.O. Drawer A**
**Carson City, Nevada 89701**

Richdel Pool-Spa Differential Thermostat Control ($87.50) provides for a turn-on and a turn-off differential and an adjustable temperature cut off. It can be operated automatically or manually. The Solar Domestic Hot Water Differential Temperature Control ($87.50) provides control of a valve used for collector drainage during freezing conditions or power failure. It also turns on or shuts off a recirculation pump.

Richdel also manufactures a centrifugal Solar Recirculation Pump ($60.00). It is used to supply hydraulic flow from storage tank to collectors in domestic hot water systems and responds to a differential temperature controller.

Richdel's Solar Hot Water Control Valve ($49.50) protects collectors in case of freezing or power failure. It responds to messages from a differential temperature control.

*Solar Control air and water probes.*

**Solar Control Corp.**
**5595 Arapahoe Road**
**Boulder, Colorado 80302**
**(303) 449-9180**

Solar Control's *Solar Air Mover* (SAM) controls solar air heating systems—both air flow and various operational modes. It contains a blower and all necessary power dampers and has solid-state logic and switching controls. It operates in seven modes: heat storage, direct solar heating, storage heating, auxiliary heating, domestic hot water preheating, continuous air circulation with auxiliary heater, and domestic hot water supplied from the coil in summer. It automatically closes the storage inlet duct during noncollection periods to eliminate heat loss.

The *Homemaster Solar System Controller* (Model SCC-77-620) is a multichannel differential thermostat with logic and control circuits. It operates in five modes: heat storage, direct solar heating, solar storage heating, auxiliary heating, and solar domestic water preheating. It can be used in air or water space heating systems and operates collection and distribution channels with an unlimited number of pumps, blowers, valves, and dampers.

Solar Control Corp. also sells monitors and controllers for solar home heating and swimming pools—the *Solarstat* (Model 77-180) and controller (Model 77-171).

**West Wind Electronics, Inc.**
**P.O. Box 542**
**Durango, Colorado 81301**
**(303) 884-9709**

West Wind offers a temperature differential switch that can be used to activate solar system pumps or blowers. It features integrated circuitry and heavy-duty relay. Optional freeze and upper temperature limit sensing is available. Temperature differential is adjustable to any collector. It costs $35.

*Richdel solar recirculation pump.*

# Solar Accessories

**Berry Solar Products**
**A Division of the Berry Group**
**Woodbridge-at-Main**
**P.O. Box 327**
**Edison, New Jersey 08817**
**(201) 549-3800**

Berry offers *Solarstrip* selective surface coating, made of continuously electroplated black chrome on copper. It can be applied to liquid- or air-type absorber plates or be used directly as the absorber itself. It can also be spiral-wrapped on tubing and formed or soldered without damage to the coating. It can be retrofitted and installed by the homeowner.

Prices range from $1.30 to $2.30 per square foot (depending upon metal thickness) for 100 to 1999 square feet. Prices decrease significantly with applications over 1999 square feet.

**Daniel Enterprises, Inc.**
**P.O. Box 2370**
**La Habra, California 90631**
**(213) 943-8883**

Daniel Enterprises offers a computing service to calculate the performance of any solar collector in any location. The computation is based on the collector's thermal efficiency test curve developed by ASHRAE, incident angle modifier curve, ambient air temperatures supplied by the National Climatic Center, and an "Available Insolation" print-out that must be ordered together with the performance computation.

The print-out restates the input information and provides a table that presents, for each month of the year, average collector efficiency, daily and monthly useful heat collected per square foot, monthly useful heat collected by the specified system area, and system yield per year. Any number of performance runs can be made to compare the performance of different collectors in the same system or one collector under varying conditions.

The cost of the preliminary "Available Insolation" three-page print-out is $12 for nontracking, flat-plate or focusing collectors, $20 for collectors using tilt and/or orientation optimization, and $15 for tracking collectors. The first performance computation costs $5; additional runs cost $4. Each order is accompanied by a data sheet explaining the mathematics.

Other services provided by Daniel Enterprises include "Life Cycle" Economic Analysis and computation of spacing between solar arrays to determine the position for least shading.

**Dow Corning Corporation**
**Solar Energy Division**
**Midland, Michigan 48640**

Dow Corning manufactures *Syltherm*™ *444* silicone heat transfer liquid designed to be used with closed systems operating at temperatures of −50° to 400°F. with intermittent exposure to collector stagnation temperatures up to 450°F. It is noncorrosive, virtually nontoxic, and it will neither freeze nor boil. It generates no vapor pressure,

eliminating the need for automatic drain-down systems and pressure relief valves. It is nonflammable up to 500°F. One fill will last the life of the system.

Dow Corning also makes *Silastic®* *RTV* Silicone Adhesive/Sealants for use in bonding and sealing air- or liquid-type collectors. These sealants do not crack, dry, or shrink. They are leak-tight, permanently flexible, and resist weathering, moisture, aging, and vibration.

**Energy Applications**
**Route 5**
**Box 383**
**Rutherfordton, North Carolina 28139**
**(704) 287-2195**

Energy Applications manufactures *Sun-Track* Systems for tracking collectors. The Sun-Track Systems work on single- or dual-axis tracking devices; a single sensor with a stable glass filter element reduces background effects. The tracking device must be equipped with an electrically operated reversing drive system. Sun-Track also makes a power module to operate the sensors, with solid state relays for directional control of the motor. A day-night sensor returns the collector each night to the point of sunrise. Available in north-south or east-west orientation. All are completely automatic.

Sun-Track sensor units run from $50 to $150. Interface modules cost $60. Complete systems cost from $100 to $235.

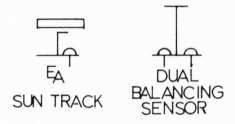

**Ford Products Corporation**
**Ford Products Road**
**Valley Cottage, New York 10989**

Ford Products manufactures a water heater whose internally-placed heat transfer coil of finned copper allows for direct and efficient heating of domestic hot water. Because the tank is stone lined, electrolytic corrosion presents no problem. The stone lining also serves as extra insulation and as a heat sink. The heater is made of steel with a baked enamel finish and is heavily insulated with fiber glass. It is available in four sizes.

An optional heating element in the upper third of the tank maintains water temperature when solar energy is insufficient; no backup heating system is necessary. "E" models come with a separate thermostat for controlling the electric heating element. The heaters are completely factory-assembled and can be installed and retrofitted by the homeowner.

**The Heliodon Co. of Los Angeles**
**14654 Moorpark Ave.**
**Sherman Oaks, California 91403**

The *Heliodon* is a device for precisely simulating solar exposure on scaled models. Made of cast aluminum and varnished birch, it is a one-piece device that visually supplies profile angle and angle of incidence in the correct relationship at any hour, latitude, or season.

It can be used to determine location and type of glazing; positioning of overhangs and other projections; location of skylights, solar collectors, and clerestories; necessity of shading devices; placement of landscaping; and use of daylighting.

Its base is 12 inches by 12 inches and its platform, 18 inches square, is capable of handling large scale models. It costs $159.

**The Natural Energy Centre**
**161 Clarence St.**
**Kingson-Upon-Thames**
**Surrey KT1 1QT**
**England**
**01-549-5888/9**

The Natural Energy Centre (formerly Conservation Tools and Technology Limited) is the leading European distributor of alternative energy equipment. They supply solar panels, heat pumps, wind generators, wind-driven pumps, wood-burning stoves, and so on. They publish a very useful handbook/catalog at about $3.50. They also run The Natural Energy Association, giving members quarterly newsletters and the handbook/catalog. (Subscription about $14.)

**Natural Heating Systems**
**2417 Front St.**
**West Sacramento, California 95691**
**(916) 372-2993**

Natural Heating Systems offers installation, sales, design, consulting, and proposal preparation for solar energy applications.

**Nuclear Technology Corporation**
**P.O. Box 1**
**Amston, Connecticut 06231**
**(203) 537-2387**

Nuclear Technology makes Nutek corrosion-inhibitors for solar collector systems. They also protect systems against scaling. All are neutral, biodegradable, and require no special handling.

The Nutek 800 Series consists of five compounds chemically formulated to give optimum corrosion protection in multimetal systems of copper, aluminum, steel and their alloys:

*Nutek–800* is an ethylene-glycol based compound formulated to provide corrosion protection in mild temperature zones where freeze protection to 0° F. is adequate.
*Nutek–830* is an ethylene-glycol based compound similar to Nuteck–800 but is recommended for systems requiring freeze protection to −30°F.
*Nutek–805* is a propylene-glycol based compound that provides corrosion and freeze protection to 0°F. in systems that may come in contact with potable water systems.
*Nutek–835* is a propylene-glycol based compound similar to Nutek–805 but is recommended for use in systems requiring freeze protection to −30°F.
*Nutek–876* is a water-based compound that offers corrosion protection in systems where freeze protection is not a factor.

With the exception of *Nutek–800* and *Nutek–830*, all are nontoxic.

Nuclear Technology also makes *Nutek–70* for precleaning aluminum or steel collector solar hot water systems and *Nutek–80* for precleaning copper solar hot water and heating systems.

Nutek products are also marketed by NPD Energy Systems under the name of *Sunsafe*™. NPD Energy Systems, Inc./Chemical Division is located at 2050 North Broad Street, Lansdale, Pennsylvania 19446. Telephone: (215) 362-1178.

**Ram Products**
**1111 Centerville Rd.**
**Sturgis, Michigan 49091**

Ram Products produces *Plexi-View* acrylic mirrors in standard sizes 1/8 inch thick, useful for reflectors or parabolic focusing collectors.

**Solar Energy Company**
**P.O. Box 151**
**Barker, Texas**

SEC manufactures *Suncharger*™ battery panels that convert light to electricity by means of silicon solar cells. The panels are designed to be flat-mounted and are weather resistant. They can charge any kind of battery and can power electric equipment directly. Direct sunlight is not necessary.

*Suncharger*™ panels range in price from $36 to $2500 depending on voltage and panel size. SEC also sells individual silicon cells for from $6.50 to $14.50 each depending on size.

**Solar Masters**
**719 Haddon Avenue**
**Collingswood, New Jersey 08108**
**(609) 854-2690**

Solar venetian blinds like those illustrated in Figure 2-13 are now offered by this company. Blinds are blackened on one side to absorb heat in winter, reflect it in summer. Cost for complete, painted blinds is $2.25 per square foot.

**Solar Sunstill, Inc.**
**Setauket, New York 11733**
**(516) 941-4078**

Solar Sunstill manufactures products for the control of
condensation and light on solar collectors, solar structures, and greenhouses. *Sun Clear* is a nontoxic,
sprayable coating that makes nonwettable surfaces of all
plastics and many metals permanently wettable. Dripping, which can promote fungus diseases, is eliminated
from the roofs of greenhouses and other structures. Up
to 50 percent more light is transmitted through the
treated surface. A similar coating for glass, *Sun Clear-G*,
also has been developed.

*Varishade* is a coating that shades when dry but is
practically transparent when wet. This variable shade
coating can be applied to glass or to plastic and, when
dry, will reduce excess solar heat and light. It also
eliminates dripping.

*Thermoshade* is a temperature-sensitive film that is
transparent below a certain temperature but becomes
cloudy above that predetermined temperature (80–100 F.).

**Sensor Technology, Inc.**
**21012 Lassen St.**
**Chatsworth, California 91311**
**(213) 882-4100**

Sensor Technology manufactures solar electric power
generators consisting of solar cells selected and connected to deliver a specific power output. The solar cells
are silicon semiconductor devices that convert the energy
of the sun to electricity. Sensor Technology's solar electric generators come in five sizes and generate varying
amounts of power. Entire systems are available that include a solar panel array on a rigid frame, a solid-state
regulator and battery overload protection, a control panel,
and storage battery. With care, the panels last an unlimited period of time.

Sensor Technology's attic fan is powered by a solar
cell panel mounted on the roof. The fan consists of a
12-inch aluminum blade driven by a motor. The attic cooling system can be retrofitted and installed by the homeowner.

**Spiral Tubing Corp.**
**533 John Downey Drive**
**New Britain, Connecticut 06051**
**(203) 224-2409**

Spiral Tubing manufactures *Turbotec* spiral metal tubes,
which can be used in solar collectors and water storage
tanks. The increased surface per foot and the turbulence
created by the spiralled flutes allows less tubing to be
used for heat transfer. It can be easily bent to the user's
specifications without distortions. Turbotec tubing is
available in copper, 90/10 CuNi, aluminum, carbon steel,
and 304 or 316 stainless steel.

Copper tubing costs from 50¢ for ½ inch diameter to $1
for 1⅛ inch diameter per foot in lengths of 10 to 20 feet.

*Sensor Technology's solar-powered attic fan—using the
sun to cool your sun-heated home.*

# Solar Information Sources

**Brace Research Institute**
**McGill University**
**Ste. Anne De Bellevue**
**Quebec, Canada**
**HOA 1CO**

Brace Research Institute of McGill University publishes a
wide range of cheap, do-it-yourself pamphlets on simple
solar technologies and greenhouse design.

*How to make a Solar Still (Plastic Covered)*, by A.
Whillier and G.T. Ward. $1.25.

*How to Make a Solar Steam Cooker*, by A. Whillier.
$1.25.

*How to Heat Your Swimming Pool Using Solar Energy*,
by A. Whillier. 75¢.

*How to Build a Solar Water Heater*, by D.A. Sinson and
T. Hoad. $1.25.

*Instructions for Constructing a Simple 8 Sq. Ft. Solar
Still for Domestic Use and Gas Stations*, by T.A. Lawand.
$1.25.

*Plans for a Glass and Concrete Solar Still*, by T.A.
Lawand and R. Alward. $4.50.

*The Status of Solar Refrigeration and Air Conditioning*,
by R.K. Swartman. $2.

*Production Drawing for Solar Cabinet Dryer*, by O.
Goldstein. $2.50.

*Storage of Solar Energy—A Review*, by J. Grace and
Y.W. Li. $2.

*Survey of Solar Agricultural Dryers*, by Brace Research
Institute. $9.

*Plans for the Construction of Solar Steam Cooker.* $7.
*Plans for the Construction of a Brace Greenhouse*—2 sizes, 20′ x 20′ and 20′ x 60′ (please specify). $2.50.
*Description of Some Solar Heated Houses in Canada*, by T.A. Lawand and B. Saulnier. $2.25.
*The Development and Testing of an Environmentally Designed Greenhouse for Colder Regions*, by T.A. Lawand, R. Alward, B. Saulnier and E. Brunet. $1.25.
*Solar Energy Greenhouse: Operating Experiences*, T.A. Lawand, et al. $1.25.
*Experimental Testing of a Solar Pond*, by B. Saulnier, S. Savage, and N. Chepuirney. $1.50.
*Systems of Solar Distillation*, by T.A. Lawand. $1.50.

Send money order or check with order. Include 25¢ extra with checks and if ordering only one leaflet. Mail to the attention of the Publication Department.

## Edmund Scientific Co.
## Edscorp Building
## Barrington, New Jersey 08007

For over 36 years, Edmund Scientific Co. has been selling scientific equipment from its store in New Jersey and by mail. Its detailed catalog lists countless items of use to hobbyists and experts alike. It costs $1.
A sampling of solar energy products includes a lightweight, all-plastic solar collector; silicon solar cells, panels, and demonstrator units of all sizes; fresnel lenses; solar cookers, furnaces, and heaters.
Publications sold by Edmund Scientific include:

*Your Home's Solar Potential*, by Irwin Spetgang and Malcolm Wells. $9.95.
*Solar Dictionary.* $20. Over 600 pages of reference material. Listings of architects, engineers, manufacturers, contractors, researchers, and information services.
*Solaria*, by Edmund, Homan, Thomason, and Wells. $12.95. The story of the first solar-heated, earth-covered house designed by Malcolm Wells incorporating the Thomason Solaris system. Includes plans.

Edmund Scientific also sells Thomason House Plans and guides to solar heating:

*Solar House Plans 11A.* $24.95.
*Solar House Plans. The Basic Concept.* $10.
*Solar Greenhouse and Swimming Pool.* $5.

## Helion, Inc.
## Box 445
## Brownsville, California 95919

Helion sells books and plans about solar energy. Their plans and study guides include the following:

*Provider Greenhouse.* $10. Plans for a year-round, detached greenhouse.
*Helarium.* $10. Plans for an expandable, add-on greenhouse for supplemental solar heating.
*Solar Greenhome.* $6. Study drawings and photos of a home heated by a Helarium.
*Small Solar Greenhouses.* $10. Set of 12 color slides with descriptive pamphlet.

Books on solar energy include these well-known titles:

*The Food and Heat Producing Solar Greenhouse*, by Rich Fisher and Bill Yanda. $6.
*The Solar Home Book*, by Bruce Anderson and Michael Riordan. $8.50.
*Homegrown Sundwellings*, by Peter van Dresser. $5.95.

*Other Homes and Garbage. Designs for Self-Sufficient Living*, by Jim Leckie, Gil Masters, Harry Whitehouse, and Lily Young. $9.95.
*From the Ground Up*, by John Cole and Charles Wing. $7.95.

In addition to offering books and plans, Helion conducts workshops and lectures and provides consulting services.

## National Solar Heating
## and Cooling Information Center
## P.O. Box 1607
## Rockville, Maryland 20850
## (800) 523-2929

A national clearinghouse for solar information, the center provides the following free pamphlets and lists, among others:

"Solar and Energy-Related Associations." A sourcelist.
"Put the Sun to Work Today." 28 pp., U.S. Dept. of Energy.
"Solar Energy and Your Home." 20 pp. U.S. Dept. of Housing and Urban Development.
"Solar Hot Water and Your Home." 16 pp. Gives a short introduction to solar heating, glossary, references.

The center also publishes bibliographies of technical books and articles relating to solar technology, fact sheets on solar heating principles, lists of alternative energy information sources, and names of solar equipment manufacturers around the country.

## The Bookstore at Natural Power, Inc.
## New Boston, New Hampshire 03070
## (603) 487-5512

In addition to manufacturing controls and instruments for solar and wind energy applications, Natural Power, Inc. sells books on alternate energy at their bookstore and by mail.
Their solar energy titles include the following:

*Direct Use of the Sun's Energy*, by Farrington Daniels. $1.95.
*Solar Energy and Shelter Design*, by Bruce Anderson. $7. Includes charts, tables, and bibliographies.
*Directory of the Solar Industry*, by Solar Data. $7.50. Lists over 550 domestic organizations in all phases of the solar industry. Quarterly supplements will be issued.
*Solar Age Catalog: A Guide to Solar Energy Knowledge and Materials*, from the editors of *Solar Age*. $8.50. Includes product descriptions, listings of solar professionals, and articles by solar experts.
*Solar Energized Food Dehydrator Plans*, by Solar Survival. $6.
*Solar Heated Buildings, A Brief Survey*, by W.A. Shurcliff. $12.
*The Solar Home Book*, by Bruce Anderson, $8.50. Covers the fundamentals of solar heating, history, technology, and design of the solar home. Includes do-it-yourself projects.
*Solar Water Heater Plans*, by Zomeworks. $5. A do-it-yourself system for $150.
*Sunspots*, by Steve Baer. $4. Covers the principles and basic technology of solar energy in a lighthearted format.

*Tilly's Catch a Sunbeam Coloring Book,* by Tilly Spetgang and Friends. $1.50. Explains solar energy principles for youngsters.

*Solar Energy Home Design in Four Climates,* by TEA. $12.75. Designs for four air-heated solar homes. Includes drawings, charts, tables, bibliography, listing of resource material, and solar component manufacturers.

*Solar Heated Houses for New England and other North Temperate Climates,* by Massdesign Architects and Planners. $7.50. Award-winning designs for solar applications on Cape Cod and Saltbox style houses.

*The Fuel Savers,* by Dan Scully, Don Prowler, Bruce Anderson with Doug Mahone. $2.75. Eighteen ideas for solar energy applications on existing homes.

*The Nicholson Solar Energy Catalogue and Building Manual.* $9.95. Pictures and drawing of seven solar homes built by Nick Nicholson in Quebec, Canada.

*Solar Energy,* by Bruce Anderson. $21.50. Written by an architect/engineer for the building-trade professional. Profusely illustrated.

When ordering, please enclose payment with 75¢ postage. Make checks payable to The Bookstore at Natural Power, Inc.

### The New Alchemy Institute
### P.O. Box 432
### Woods Hole, Massachusetts 02543

The New Alchemy Institute is an international, nonprofit organization founded in 1969 by Dr. John Todd. It was formed for the purpose of researching efficient low consumption technologies, powered by the renewable resources of sun, wind, and biological systems.

Their first project was the creation of the ARK, by definition a structure that provides protection and safety. The ARK attempts to solve the problems of energy demand, food production and resource conservation through a combination of a number of approaches: solar energy systems, both passive and active; a wind power installation; aquaculture; greenhouse production; and prudent waste handling.

Erected on Prince Edward Island, Canada, the ARK has been functioning adequately since 1976, surviving several severe winters. This first experimental ARK will continue to be tested and modified as funds are available to further the development of bioshelters of this kind.

For as little as $10, anyone can be a Pauper Patron of the Institute. Membership includes a subscription to *The Journal,* the New Alchemists' periodical stressing a wholistic approach to ecological planning. *The Journal* includes design information, research, and scholarly papers. Membership also includes a subscription to the New Alchemy newsletters.

Send to the New Alchemy Institute for details about joining and for a complete bibliography listing their publications and other energy-related articles and books.

### *Solar Age* Magazine
### SolarVision, Inc.
### Church Hill
### Harrisville, New Hampshire 03450

*Solar Age* is published monthly by SolarVision, Inc. It has articles and editorials by experts about the practical, theoretical, philosophical, and historical aspects of alternate energy sources, such as solar, wind, water, and wood. Included are reviews of books, buildings, systems, and products, plus interviews with prominent personalities on the energy scene. Subscription is $20 for one year, $32 for two years, $40 for three years; back issues cost $2.50 each.

The editors of *Solar Age* have also published product descriptions, lists of solar professionals, and articles by solar experts in the *Solar Age Catalog: A Guide to Solar Energy Knowledge and Materials,* $8.50. It will be supplemented by a regular "New Products and Catalog Supplement" section of the monthly *Solar Age* magazine.

### SOLAR ENERGY DIGEST
POST OFFICE BOX 17776 · SAN DIEGO, CALIFORNIA 92117

### Solar Energy Digest
### P.O. Box 17776
### San Diego, California 92117

*Solar Energy Digest* is a monthly newsletter founded in 1973, blending practical applications of solar energy with news about the frontiers of this new science and industry. In addition to feature articles, it carries regular features such as book reviews, letters to the editor, and a solar energy calendar, which lists solar conferences, seminars, and short courses. A full year subscription costs $28.50; a sample costs $1.

SED's editor, William B. Edmondson, has been active in solar energy research and development since 1944. He holds a patent on his *SolarSan* flat-plate and sells a license and construction/installation manual for $25.95.

SED also supplies solar energy publications such as the following:

*Solar Heated Buildings of North America: 120 Outstanding Examples,* by William A. Shurcliff. Quality paperback, 8½ x 11, 304 pages. $9.80. Descriptions of solar buildings in alphabetical order by state. Amply illustrated with drawings and photos.

*The Performance of Flat-Plate Solar Heat Collectors,* by H.C. Hottel and B.B. Woertz. Paperback, 8½ x 11, 14 pages. $3.40. Classic paper by MIT solar pioneers. Includes charts, tables, drawings, bibliographical references.

### Solar Energy Research Institute
### 1536 Cole Boulevard
### Golden, Colorado 40801
### (303) 234-7171

The Solar Energy Research Institute (SERI) was created by Congress through the Solar Energy Research, Development, and Demonstration Act of 1974. The institute actually began operations in July, 1977. Its purpose is to support "at the earliest possible time," solar applications that are commercially attractive and environmentally acceptable.

Among SERI's goals is to develop and implement the Solar Energy Information Data Bank (SEIDB), which, SERI explains, "will assure that those individuals who are making decisions concerning the solar option receive needed information . . . in an understandable and usable format" promptly and efficiently.

This may mean you.

The data bank will contain a National Library of Solar Energy, computerized, with a data system and "dissemination services."

To find out how SERI can help you, write to them for their free little booklet, "Solar Energy Information Locator." Though short, the booklet is chock full of names, lists, and indexes that can lead you to the organizations or publications you want.

## SolarVision, Inc.
## Church Hill
## Harrisville, New Hampshire 03450

The publishers of *Solar Age* magazine offer a series of videotape programs covering many solar issues.

*The Solar Age.* An overview of the subject with leading solar architects, builders, engineers, and historians.
*A Community Approach.* An account of the approach of an inner-city community towards solar retrofitting and partial self-sufficiency.
*Moving Towards Mass Production.* Shows the adaptation of industry to solar manufacturing. With George Löf.
*The Karen Terry House: Architecture, Building and the Sun.* An account of the conception, construction, and performance of a passive solar house. With Karen Terry, builder; David Wright, architect; and B.T. Rodgers.
*Solar Law.* Discussion of legal implications and problems facing the solar industry. With William Thomas, research attorney for the American Bar Foundation.

## Total Environmental
## Action, Inc.
## Church Hill
## Harrisville,
## New Hampshire 03450

TEA offers professional and consulting services in research, design, engineering, planning and education in the field of alternate energy.

Founded in 1973 by Bruce Anderson, it serves a wide range of clients, from individual homeowners and builders to government agencies and large corporations.

Of most interest to the homeowner is TEA's information services, which include workshops and training seminars and lectures with slide and videotape presentations. TEA also runs a bookshop at its offices. Catalogs are available.

In the field of solar energy, TEA offers plans for its *Goosebrook Solar Home*, which combines passive solar heating features with the builder's choice of active system. Eight construction sheets and Bill of Materials cost $75. Extra sets cost $10 each at the time of ordering.

## TWR Enterprises
## 72 West Meadow Lane
## Sandy, Utah 84070

Tom W. Rentz runs this information and consulting service providing books and plans for alternate energy systems. Publications concerning solar energy include *Low-Cost Solar Heaters for Your Home* ($3), which gives plans for a passive solar heater and the Rentz combination passive solar concentrator, as well as outlining many simple solar energy techniques. Send 50¢ and a stamped, self-addressed envelope for more information.

## Volunteers In Technical Assistance
## VITA Executive Offices
## 3706 Rhode Island Ave.
## Mt. Rainier, Maryland 20822
## (301) 277-7000

VITA is a private, nonprofit organization based in the United States. It provides information and assistance by mail to individuals and groups seeking help with technical problems.

As part of their service, they publish books and manuals on alternate energy. Their solar energy titles include the following:

*Solar Cooker Construction Manual.* VITA, 1967. $2.25. Plans for a low-cost solar cooker of wood. Detailed, illustrated, easy-to-use instructions.
*Evaluation of Solar Cookers,* by the VITA Research Team. VITA, 1962. $5.95. Reports on solar cookers evaluated for applicability in developing countries. Test results and methodology included.
TB#6 *Solar Oven.* $1.
TB#12 *Solar Water Heater.* $1. Small (18 gallon) heater for clothes washing.

VITA's periodicals, *VITA News* and *Vis-A-Vis*, contain updates on VITA programs, notices of important events, technical abstracts, profiles of VITA volunteers, and lists of problems requiring solutions. They are available upon request from VITA Communications Department. Donations are accepted.

When ordering books, please enclose payment. Make checks payable to VITA Publications Service.

## Zomeworks Corporation
## P.O. Box 712
## Albuquerque, New Mexico 87103
## (505) 242-5354

Zomeworks manufactures several unique passive and active solar systems and energy conservation devices (see product descriptions). In addition, they publish a number of plans and books.

*Sunspots,* by Steve Baer. $4. Articles and solar fiction, construction and design tips, social commentary.
*Solar Water Heater Plans.* $5. Plans for both warm and cold climates; shower regenerator.
*Bread Box Water Heater Plans.* $2.50. Plans for water heater using tank as collector.
*Drumwall® Plans.* $5.
*Solar Slide Set.* $15. 24 slides showing different types of solar heating installations in New Mexico. Explanatory sheet included.
*Beadwall® System—Plans and License.* $15.

Please add 50¢ postage and handling when ordering.

# 3
# Wind Power

Throughout recorded history humans have used the wind to grind grain, pump water and transport goods across the seas. Windmills using sails or blades to rotate a shaft (Figure 3–1) were common in ancient Greece, and they may have been in use before then. Local variations in materials, skills and requirements created a variety of designs. Many have horizontal shafts with the sails in the form of a propeller facing the wind. Others have vertical shafts, and sails that accept the wind from any direction.

These traditional windmills, as well as the multibladed props of the American Midwest, are designed for mechanical work like grinding or pumping. Because of their slow speeds, they do not produce electricity very efficiently. During the last fifty years, modern wind turbines have been developed that achieve the high rotational speeds necessary to run an electrical generator. With advances in efficiency and economy, wind power has become an attractive source of home energy.

# Principles

A wind-electric system comprises four basic components: a propeller, a generator, a means of controlling the output of current, and usually some means of storing the energy. The rotational force of the propeller, transferred by the shaft, turns the armature of the generator. To produce a continuous and usable supply of electric current, the armature must be turning at a very high and fairly constant speed, in excess of 18,000 rpm. A modern propeller-type wind machine spins at about 300 to 400 rpm; this means that step-up gears are usually required between the shaft and the armature. It also means that the mill must generate the maximum rotational force, or *torque*, at any windspeed to capture as much of the wind's power as possible.

# Propellers and Turbines

Aerodynamically shaped blades of propeller design produce more torque at high speeds than do the traditional sails. The first reference to propeller-type blades for a windmill occurs in Belidor's *L'Architecture Hydraulique*, written in 1737. Most wind-electric generators are still

Source: John Reynolds, *Windmills and Watermills* (Praeger, 1970).

**Eighteenth-century English mill.**

**Figure 3–1. Traditional windmills. Mills for pumping water, Cyprus.**

based on this design. The airfoil section of each blade develops its own rotational force as it moves around, much as a sailboat uses the wind passing around it to propel itself forward.

For efficient generation of electricity, a high *tip-speed ratio* is important. This is the ratio of the speed of the tip of the blade to the speed of the wind, and should be as high as possible to achieve maximum torque at high wind speeds. Traditional slow-speed windmills had tip-speed ratios of about 1:1; modern state-of-the-art propeller machines achieve tip-speed ratios as high as 8:1. (See Figure 3–3.)

Large-diameter propellers produce more power than smaller props. The power output is proportional to the square of the diameter, so a twelve-foot propeller produces four times the power of a six-foot prop. Large propellers are also better able to make use of slower wind speeds, increasing the system's efficiency.

Windmills with high *solidity ratio* (ratio of blade area to swept area) are able to produce more power at slow wind speeds. But because of their low tip-speed ratio, they are less able to make use of high winds. And high winds carry most of the available power, even if they only blow occasionally. This is because the wind's power is proportional to the *cube* of the velocity—the power of a 12 mph wind is *eight times* that of a 6 mph wind. Most electricity-generating wind machines

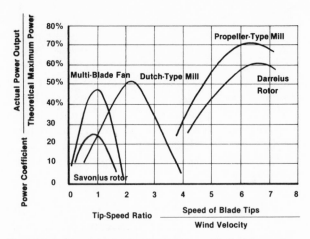

Figure 3-3. Tip-speed ratio vs. power coefficient for various windmills. Note that each type of mill operates most efficiently at a particular windspeed.

are designed to exploit the high winds (in excess of 20 mph) and neglect the gentle winds (under 10 mph). Clearly, a wind generator that can operate efficiently over a wide range of wind speeds is the best choice.

The theoretical maximum *transfer efficiency* (from wind power in the swept area of the blades to rotational power in the shaft) has been calculated at 59.3 percent. In practice, however, most mills of good design achieve 40 to 45 percent efficiencies. Table 3–4 illustrates the relation

Table 3–4. Propeller Diameter vs. Generator Output in Watts.
70% aerodynamic efficiency,
70% transmission & generator efficiency

| Propeller Diameter in feet | Wind Velocity in mph | | | | | |
|---|---|---|---|---|---|---|
| | 5 | 10 | 15 | 20 | 25 | 30 |
| 2 | .6 | 5 | 16 | 37 | 72 | 125 |
| 4 | 2 | 19 | 62 | 150 | 290 | 500 |
| 6 | 5 | 42 | 140 | 335 | 650 | 1100 |
| 8 | 9 | 75 | 250 | 590 | 1150 | 2000 |
| 10 | 14 | 115 | 390 | 930 | 1800 | 3100 |
| 12 | 21 | 165 | 560 | 1350 | 2600 | 4500 |
| 14 | 28 | 225 | 770 | 1800 | 3550 | 6100 |
| 16 | 37 | 300 | 1000 | 2400 | 4650 | 8000 |
| 18 | 47 | 375 | 1270 | 3000 | 5900 | 10000 |
| 20 | 58 | 465 | 1570 | 3700 | 7250 | 12500 |
| 22 | 70 | 560 | 1900 | 4500 | 8800 | 15000 |
| 24 | 84 | 670 | 2250 | 5350 | 10500 | 18000 |
| 26 | 98 | 785 | 2650 | 6300 | 12000 | 21000 |
| 28 | 115 | 910 | 3075 | 7300 | 14000 | 24500 |
| 30 | 130 | 1040 | 3500 | 8350 | 16000 | 28000 |
| 32 | 150 | 1190 | 4000 | 9500 | 18500 | 32000 |

From Henry Clews, *Electric Power From the Wind.*

Figure 3-2. A modern three-bladed Zephyr Wind Dynamo at Kittery Point, Maine.

between propeller diameter and electrical output for different wind speeds, assuming typical efficiencies. Most systems are sized to take advantage of maximum wind speeds of 25 mph or higher. For example, a wind system with a twelve-foot propeller should have a maximum generating capacity of 2600 watts (2.6 kw) or more. Since the wind seldom blows this hard, the actual output will be less than the full rated 2600 watts. Table 3–5 allows a very rough estimation of monthly output for a given average windspeed. Remember that gusts carry most of the wind's power, so the average windspeed is not an accurate indication of available energy. More on this subject later.

**Table 3–5. Average Monthly Generator Output vs. Windspeed, in Kilowatt-Hours per Month.**

| Nominal Output Rating of Generator in Watts | Average Monthly Wind Speed in mph | | | | | |
|---|---|---|---|---|---|---|
| | 6 | 8 | 10 | 12 | 14 | 16 |
| 50 | 1.5 | 3 | 5 | 7 | 9 | 10 |
| 100 | 3 | 5 | 8 | 11 | 13 | 15 |
| 250 | 6 | 12 | 18 | 24 | 29 | 32 |
| 500 | 12 | 24 | 35 | 46 | 55 | 62 |
| 1000 | 22 | 45 | 65 | 86 | 104 | 120 |
| 2000 | 40 | 80 | 120 | 160 | 200 | 235 |
| 4000 | 75 | 150 | 230 | 310 | 390 | 460 |
| 6000 | 115 | 230 | 350 | 470 | 590 | 710 |
| 8000 | 150 | 300 | 450 | 600 | 750 | 900 |
| 10,000 | 185 | 370 | 550 | 730 | 910 | 1090 |
| 12,000 | 215 | 430 | 650 | 870 | 1090 | 1310 |

From Henry Clews, *Electric Power From the Wind.*

Figure 3-6. Three-bladed propeller.

## HORIZONTAL SHAFT MILLS

The most common commercially available wind generator uses a *horizontal shaft* with a two- or three-bladed propeller. Two-bladed props can achieve greater tip-speed ratios in high winds, but tend to vibrate in a noisy and/or destructive manner. Three-bladed propellers make less vibration, and because of their higher solidity ratio they tend to have lower starting speeds. Blades are made of wood, metal or fiber glass. Metal blades may cause radio and television interference. Fiber glass blades are relatively new on the market, and long-term performance has not been proven. Wood is an excellent material for propellers, combining lightness, strength and resilience. Choose blades of the highest aircraft-quality wood, and be sure that the edge is reinforced with fiber glass or a comparable protection.

The propeller, of course, must be kept facing the wind. To do this, most windmills have a vane perpendicular to the prop that causes it to turn back into the wind whenever the wind direction shifts. Others have no vane, but turn freely about the main support post until the propeller is perpendicular to the wind direction—downwind of the post. This design requires a careful balancing of the motor equipment on top of the support post to insure that rotation is very easy.

## VERTICAL SHAFT MILLS

Vertical shaft mills have the great advantage of accepting the wind from any direction. They are also easier to construct, which would explain why they were in use long before the horizontal-shaft machines. In the 1920's, the Finnish engineer S.J. Savonius developed a more efficient version of the simple vertical shaft machine, using airscoops instead of sails (Figure 3–7). Lately, this design has been used for water pumping, particularly in underdeveloped countries, but with a tip-speed ratio of only 1:1.5, it is not particularly suitable for generating electricity. A few homebuilt systems do generate a small current, taking advantage of gentle breezes with the Savonius rotor's high solidity ratio.

**129**

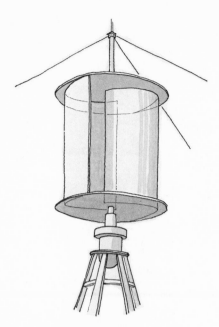

Figure 3-7. A vertical-axis Savonius rotor.

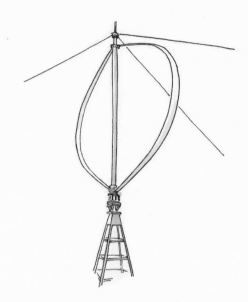

Figure 3-8. A Darreius rotor, developed in the Thirties.

Another modification of the vertical axis mill, the *Darreius rotor*, uses aerodynamically shaped blades that curve up and around the central shaft, giving the mill the appearance of a large egg-beater (Figure 3–8). Although slightly less efficient (20 to 40 percent) than a horizontal shaft machine, the Darreius rotor offers several advantages. In high winds, the rotor simply stalls, eliminating the need for variable-pitch blades or governors to protect the machine from damage. The rotor's design allows the heavy generating equipment to sit on the ground. And it could potentially be manufactured very cheaply, which makes the Darreius rotor particularly attractive for small-scale power generation.

The main disadvantage of the Darreius rotor is that it needs a push to start turning. This can be done manually or be motor assisted. The latest Sandia mills use the generator as a starter motor. The starter may be activated by a wind-pressure switch or may be operated periodically by a timer (somewhat more wasteful). The Darreius tends to run at lower rpm than horizontal-axis machines, requiring a more costly transmission. But if it can be produced inexpensively, the Darreius rotor still may prove to be the best buy for home power generation.

A relative of the Darreius machine is the *cyclogyro*, a three-bladed egg-beater that uses straight, variable-pitch blades, permitting the extraction of more power at low speeds (Figure 3–9). The straight blades also may prove cheaper to manufacture. The Cycloturbine, manufactured by Pinson Energy Corporation, has three eight-foot

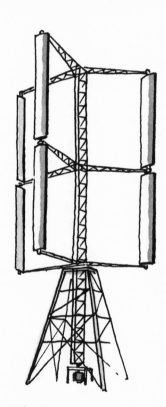

Figure 3-9. A cyclogyro.

blades with a total diameter of twelve feet. It is currently rather costly ($5500 plus $1000 for the tower), but can produce four kilowatts in a 30 mph wind, and two kilowatts at 24 mph. Other manufacturers have cyclogyro designs under development; as with all wind machines, economy is the biggest hurdle.

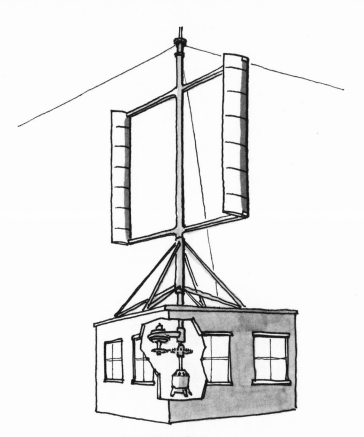

Figure 3-10. Circulation-control.

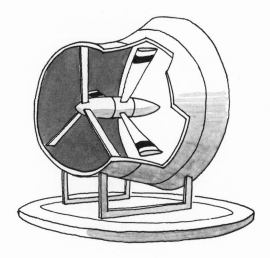

Figure 3-11. The diffuser-augmenter.

A further advancement on the cyclogyro takes advantage of an aircraft wing design known as the *circulation-control* wing (Figure 3-10). In this system, high-pressure air is blown over the trailing edge through slots in the blade. The trailing edge is rounded instead of the traditional knife-edge, and the high-pressure air adheres to the

Figure 3-12. The dynamic inducer.

downward-curving edge, giving increased lift. The same principle applied to a cyclogyro rotor is expected to increase the torque and to allow the turbine to operate at a lower speed. Overall efficiency may be 40 to 60 percent, operating at about half the speed of a conventional cyclogyro. The lower speeds allow more economical construction because structural stresses are lessened.

OTHER APPROACHES TO
WINDMILL EFFICIENCY

*Augmenter windmills* present another approach to efficiency. The idea is to focus or enhance the power of the wind to get more out of the propeller, allowing the prop to be smaller and more economical. Grumman Aerospace Corporation is developing a machine of this type called the *diffuser-augmenter* (Figure 3-11). In this design, a flared shroud is placed behind the propeller. The shroud expands as it extends back, creating a low-pressure area immediately behind the rotor blades. Airflow is increased through the propeller. Recent tests indicate that the diffuser may increase power by 350 percent. But the shroud is costly, and must be strong enough to withstand high winds. Turbulence has also been a design problem.

The *dynamic inducer* design improves on the

131

diffuser-augmenter by reducing the shroud to a few small segments and mounting them on the blade tips (Figure 3–12). Like the shroud system, these T-shaped segments push air away from the blades, causing more air to be drawn in, and increasing overall efficiency. But because of increased drag, more wind power is required to drive the prop.

Another augmenter-type design, the *vortex augmenter* (Figure 3–13), makes use of the high-energy whirlwinds, or *vortices*, created when wind passes over a wing shape. Two small rotors are mounted on a delta wing, which deflects high-speed vortices into the blades. Wind speed is controlled by manipulating the wing angle, eliminating the need for variable-pitch blades on the propellers.

Grumman Aerospace is also working on a *tornado wind turbine* (Figure 3–14) that may be able to augment wind power by up to 1000 percent. In this system, operable vents in the side of a tall tower create an artificial tornado, with its low-pressure eye over a small high-performance rotor. Intake vents below the rotor allow air to be sucked in and through the rotor at very high speed.

As futuristic as these systems may sound, other wind energy systems, some of them even more fantastic, may hold serious promise. One design based on *electrofluid dynamics* uses no moving parts; instead, electrically charged water droplets are blown by the wind into a charged grid, creating a current. This method (Figure 3–15) is similar to the way in which lightning is produced. Another approach uses *humid air* to create natural convective drafts that drive a rotor

power plant in a convection tower or chamber (Figure 3–16).

The *Madaras rotor* (Figure 3–17) uses the wind blowing past a rotating cylinder to propel a train car around a circular track. A continuous string of such cars, powered by this curious phenomenon, could generate electrical power by their motion.

Researchers at the University of Texas at Dallas are experimenting with a *lift translator*, consisting of a series of airfoil wings mounted on an

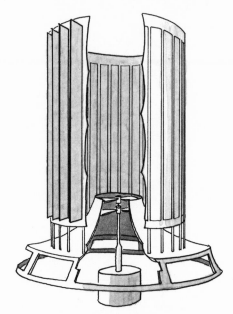

Figure 3-14. The tornado wind turbine.

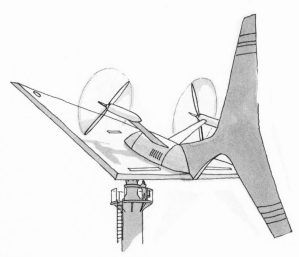

Figure 3-13. The vortex augmenter.

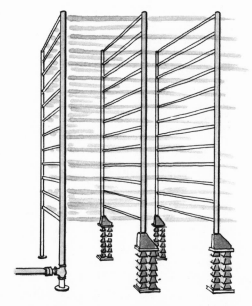

Figure 3-15. Electrofluid dynamics: the charged grid.

endless belt (Figure 3-18). The system has been likened to a cyclogyro on its side. It is unlimited in size, and can accept winds of any speed and from nearly any direction. A forty-five foot high prototype ran for nine months, generating up to fifteen kilowatts of power.

# Generators and Alternators

A *generator* is a machine which converts rotational force into electrical current. There are two general types: units which produce AC current are called *alternators*; units producing DC current are simply referred to as *generators*.

The size of the generator depends on the wind speed available and on the size of the propeller, as demonstrated in Table 3-4. Commercial windmills can generate 200 to 6000 watts, and a windmill was once operated with a capacity of 1250 kilowatts (Figure 3-19). Just as automobile electric systems now use alternators instead of generators, so most commercially produced wind electric systems now employ alternators.

An *alternator* is merely a generator with the magnetic field in the armature rather than in the coil. It produces alternating current (AC), though it can be rewired easily to produce direct current (DC) if required. The most suitable alternators for wind electric systems have permanently magnetized armatures that require no excitation from an existing current. This eliminates the need for brushes to supply the current to the electromagnetic armature, and thus eliminates one of the weakest parts of a conventional generator. As you can imagine, replacement of worn brushes can present a real problem if the windmill sits atop a ninety-foot tower.

Alternators are also lighter, smaller and cheaper than generators; but they require a high rotation speed. Several manufacturers have developed slow-speed alternators for direct-drive use.

DIRECT VS. ALTERNATING
CURRENT

Using an alternator rather than a generator allows the choice of generating AC or DC current. There are advantages and disadvantages to both

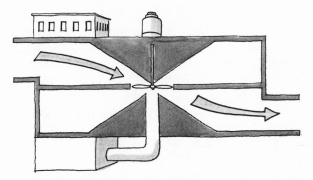
Figure 3-16. Humid air currents drive a subterranean rotor.

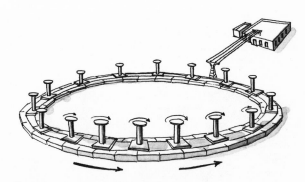
Figure 3-17. The Madaras rotor.

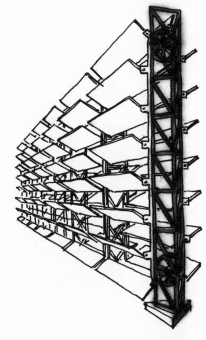
Figure 3-18. Airfoil wings of the lift translator.

systems. Almost all domestic electrical equipment uses AC. This is because the utility companies choose to generate AC, which is transmitted much more efficiently over long distances. Direct current wired over long distances tends to dissipate energy in the form of heat. The alternating cycles of AC current are used to regulate clocks and other electric motors, and to power televisions, stereos and large power tools and appliances. The current alternates at sixty cycles per second; any variation in this frequency causes televisions and stereos to "brown out," and clocks to keep incorrect time.[1] But DC current has the advantage that it can be stored in batteries.

Often *both* AC and DC are used in different parts of a wind electric system. Lights, heaters, toasters and hand power tools can be operated on DC current. Radios, tape decks, clocks and other

appliances that use DC can be obtained. Automobile equipment uses twelve volts DC; boats and trains use thirty-two-volt DC equipment. Electric resistance heating can use either AC or DC.

The cost and efficiency of conversion becomes critical. AC can easily convert to DC at virtually 100 percent efficiency by using a simple and cheap *rectifier*. To produce AC from DC, however, requires some form of inverter. A *rotary inverter* is inexpensive but inefficient, consisting of a DC motor that drives an AC alternator. It inverts power at 50 to 75 percent efficiency, but draws a "no-load" current of 15 to 20 percent, greatly reducing overall performance. A 1.5 kilowatt rotary inverter will waste up to 7.2 kwh per day unless switched off. A *static inverter* is more efficient, inverting power at about 85 percent efficiency, with a no-load current of only 2 to 4 percent. These solid-state electronic inverters seem to be a better solution. They are more efficient and produce a steadier current. But they cost $800 or more for a 400-watt model suitable for a home.

When closely matched to their loads, there is no great difference in efficiency between a rotary and a static inverter. But if they operate at less than their full capacity, heavy losses are incurred. So it is imperative that AC power needs be minimized and controlled. To accommodate motors that require an instantaneous surge of power when starting but less power once running, you can install a *load sequencer* to stagger operation of large motors in the house (water pump, furnace fan, refrigerator compressor) to avoid high demand peaks and even out the load. If you will operate electronic equipment such as stereos, choose an inverter that produces a sine-wave signal. Match the inverter to the system; in general, its capacity should be ¼ to ½ the rated output of the windmill.

## Regulation and Storage

Regulating the unsteady output of energy from a wind turbine and storing of the power produced are the two most difficult problems with a wind electric system. Since they often can be solved together, they will be discussed together.

Figure 3-19. The 1250 kw gargantuan windmill built during World War II on Grandpa's Knob, Rutland, Vermont.

1. Some televisions with no transformers can operate on 110 volts DC. Philco is one manufacturer. But check with a television expert before plugging in.

## GOVERNORS

Most commercially available windmills have some kind of *governor* to control maximum blade speed for safety. One type of governor is a system of weights attached to the blades, altering their pitch by centrifugal force when the prop spins too fast. In a second system, the prop may be mounted slightly off center, so that it turns away from a high wind. A third system uses air flaps or spoilers activated by centrifugal force. One promising concept being developed by United Technologies is the *bearingless rotor*, a flexible rotor with a centrifugal weight attached to each blade that bends it to the desired pitch (Figure 3–20). The blade connection is made of highly flexible carbon epoxy. The bearingless rotor eliminates the need for mechanical pitch control, significantly reducing the cost of the turbine.

In addition, most mills need to be equipped with a *brake* or a means of turning the blade completely out of the wind, either for servicing or for an emergency. Many manufacturers offer an automatic brake that is activated by a wind pressure switch when wind speeds exceed sixty miles per hour.

The alternator needs to be equipped with an appropriate *voltage regulator* that will maintain a steady voltage and avoid overcharging the battery. The current output of the voltage regulator will vary greatly as the wind changes.

## STEADYING THE CURRENT

To obtain a steady current for household use, some kind of "energy sink" is needed, where the fluctuations in the output of the mill can be absorbed. A battery bank is one way of achieving this; the electrolysis of water into hydrogen for fuel cells is another. Both of these are electro-chemical processes, but mechanical methods using pumped water, compressed air, or flywheels also can be considered. Or the energy can be converted directly to house and hot-water heat, eliminating the need for storage, conversion, inversion, *or* voltage regulation.

## BATTERIES

At the moment, *batteries* are the most readily available and easily installed form of electricity storage. Conventional *automobile batteries*, designed to give a high charge for a short period, may not have a long life, particularly when the chemical storage process (the eroding and depositing of lead on the plates) goes through a complete discharge cycle in a very short time. Heavy-duty houselighting batteries, called *stationary batteries*, have a longer lifetime (fifteen to twenty years), and are not as affected by total discharge. They are designed to give a steady output over a long period. They store energy at 65 to 85 percent efficiency, though they drop in efficiency when they are cold. Stationary batteries are costlier and bulkier than auto batteries. Other types, including nickel-cadmium and sodium-sulphur batteries, are even more expensive but they give excellent performance. Nickel-cadmium batteries weigh less than stationary batteries, are unaffected by repeated total discharge, and will last twenty years or longer.

One factor that limits battery storage is the number of batteries needed and their size. The

Figure 3-20. The bearingless rotor.

135

number of cells in a battery bank must be equal to the required voltage output. If the appliances running off the batteries use 115-volt current, the number of cells must then be 115 (or a multiple of 115). In a single-family house, it is economical to carry about four to seven days worth of storage capacity, supplemented by auxiliary power generation when necessary. A storage system with a capacity of six days average demand would occupy about eighty cubic feet (Figure 3-21).

Another limiting factor is that the batteries must not be charged too quickly. The charging rate should not exceed 14 amps per 100 amp-hours of capacity. For example, Table 3-4 indicated that a ten foot diameter propeller could generate as much as 1800 watts in a 25-mph gust. Amps times volts equals watts; so 1800 watts of power equals 15 amps in a 120 volt system. So we know that if 25 mph winds are anticipated, the system needs slightly more than 100 amp-hours of battery capacity. Thus even if your house's storage demands are small, a large battery bank may be necessary to absorb the windmill's charging capacity in a strong wind.

Finally, lead-acid batteries emit small amounts of flammable hydrogen gas, which must be allowed to escape confined spaces through a small vent or window. Keep small children away from the storage room; the high voltage may be dangerous. And avoid freezing or overheated temperatures.

Figure 3-21. A battery bank capable of storing 12 kwh.

## ELECTROLYSIS

Another energy storage system uses the current produced by the mill to *electrolyze water* into hydrogen and oxygen. The electrolytic process is relatively simple and can operate on AC or DC current. The hydrogen gas must be stored for later use to power a fuel cell or internal combustion engine to generate a steady current of electricity when needed. Or it simply could be burned to produce heat. But this is an inefficient use of wind power. If it were necessary to produce heat from the wind, it would be simpler and more efficient to run AC current direct from the mill to a hot water tank, rather than to generate hydrogen for heat.

## FLYWHEEL

Of the mechanical means of storing wind energy, the *flywheel* seems to be the most promising for future use. A flywheel operates on the principle that a large rotating mass with very careful balancing and low friction will store for a very long time most of the energy required to rotate it. To be economically feasible, the storage capacity of the flywheel must be very large in relation to its weight, its volume, and its cost. By enclosing the wheel in a vacuum-sealed container, the drag and danger of failure can be minimized, while the efficiency is greatly improved.[2] Recent experiments on a "superflywheel," consisting of an array of steel rods radiating from a metal hub, have resulted in storage capacities of 6 kilowatt-hours per pound in a 1400-pound flywheel. This rating is a great improvement on past performances, and it compares very favorably with batteries, which can store only 0.04 kilowatt-hours per pound. But it is a very expensive piece of high-technology equipment that is not yet practical for a single household.

## PUMPED-WATER STORAGE

This method is used at present by utility companies for storing electricity at off-peak periods. It could also be used on a smaller scale with rea-

2. David Rabenhorst, "The Superflywheel," *Scientific American*, December 1973.

sonable efficiency. A water-pumping windmill (averaging around 50 percent efficiency) used in conjunction with a water turbine (modern turbines are about 90 percent efficient) could provide a practical system for generating electricity, as well as storing power. The windmill would pump water into a storage pond when the wind was blowing. The water turbine, equipped with an automatic governor, could use the stored water to generate electricity when needed.[3]

The main drawback would be the very high initial cost of the water turbine and governor, the pumping mill and the water storage dam. If one or more of these components already were present it might be worth adding the rest. Otherwise the installation probably would cost too much.

### SYNCHRONOUS INVERTER

Finally, there is the possibility of using the electric utility network itself as a kind of storage system. When a surplus of electric power is being produced by the mill, it would simply pass into the utility company's system, running the electric meter backwards. During periods without wind, the utility company would provide electricity in the usual way. The house owner pays only for the *net* amount of electricity used, if any. This ingenious system is made possible by a recent invention, the *synchronous inverter*, which synchronizes the alternating current output of the wind generator to the frequency of the utility line, permitting compatible power exchange without risk of damage or signal degradation. The synchronous inverter is costly, but it eliminates the need for battery storage or DC home appliances.

To use a synchronous inverter system, you must have a line connection to the utility company available—and permitted. The difficulty here is that the period when an excess amount of wind power is being produced is often at night, when there is less house load on the wind-electric system. At that time there would also be a much smaller load on the utility companies, which have indicated that this off-peak power might be difficult to use. In addition, utility companies are

3. Figures taken from manufacturer's data on Aermotor mills, and the James Leffel & Co. Water Turbines. The latter is a domestic manufacturer of good small-scale water turbines, and provides useful information for anyone considering installing a water turbine to generate electricity. See Water Power section.

wary of low-grade signals that might adulterate their own high-quality AC signal, or might damage company equipment. Nonetheless, utility companies are becoming gradually more receptive, and have been known to spend thousands of dollars on monitoring equipment to examine the actual performance of utility-grid wind power storage so that an equitable rate structure may be determined.

If a utility line hookup is *not* available, the electric power storage will probably need to be equipped with a *back-up generator*. As with solar power, it is usually not economical to try to supply 100 percent of your house's power needs; that last increment of storage capacity may only be needed a few times a year. It makes more sense to purchase an inexpensive generator to get you through those infrequent sustained windless periods. Such a generator typically supplies less than 3 percent of the house's total annual energy needs. Generators may be fueled with gasoline, LP or propane gas, and may be manual or automatic.

# Available Energy

The selection of a site for generating electricity from the wind involves a series of complex and accurate measurements of wind speed and direction over a long period of time. Five years of research, for example, went into the choice of Grandpa's Knob near Rutland, Vermont as the site for a 1250 kilowatt generator. In assessing the suitability of sites for smaller mills, however, several estimations can be made that give a fairly accurate picture of the patterns of air movement.

Table 3–22 shows some yearly average windspeeds throughout the United States. These figures are related to global patterns of air movement, which are caused by pressure differences between the equator and the polar regions, by the rotation of the earth, and by the shifting seasonal temperatures of the earth's surface.

More detailed estimations of wind speed and direction are available from local meteorological stations throughout the country. These stations provide accurate measurements of monthly and annual wind speed and direction, as well as maximum and minimum wind speeds over periods of many years. If the nearest weather station is

# Table 3-22. Annual Percentage Frequency of Wind by Speed Groups and the Mean Speed for Selected Cities.

| STATE AND STATION | 0-3 m.p.h. | 4-7 m.p.h. | 8-12 m.p.h. | 13-18 m.p.h. | 19-24 m.p.h. | 25-31 m.p.h. | 32-38 m.p.h. | 39-46 m.p.h. | 47 m.p.h. and over | Mean speed m.p.h. |
|---|---|---|---|---|---|---|---|---|---|---|
| ALA. Birmingham | 27 | 22 | 30 | 17 | 3 | 1 | * | * | * | 7.9 |
| Mobile | 7 | 28 | 38 | 20 | 6 | 1 | * | * | * | 10.0 |
| Montgomery | 31 | 29 | 27 | 12 | 2 | | * | * | | 6.9 |
| ALASKA, Anchorage | 28 | 35 | 25 | 11 | 2 | | * | * | | 6.8 |
| Cold Bay | 4 | 9 | 18 | 27 | 21 | 14 | 5 | 2 | * | 17.4 |
| Fairbanks | 40 | 35 | 19 | 5 | 1 | * | * | * | | 5.2 |
| King Salmon | 11 | 20 | 30 | 24 | 10 | 4 | 1 | * | * | 11.4 |
| ARIZ. Phoenix | 38 | 36 | 20 | 5 | 1 | * | * | * | | 5.4 |
| Tucson | 18 | 35 | 30 | 14 | 3 | 1 | * | * | | 8.1 |
| ARK. Little Rock | 12 | 30 | 39 | 16 | 2 | * | * | * | | 8.7 |
| CALIF. Bakersfield | 35 | 30 | 24 | 10 | 1 | | * | * | | 5.8 |
| Burbank | 52 | 26 | 18 | 4 | 1 | * | * | * | | 4.5 |
| Fresno | 30 | 41 | 22 | 7 | 1 | | * | * | | 6.1 |
| Los Angeles | 28 | 33 | 27 | 11 | 1 | | * | * | | 6.8 |
| Oakland | 26 | 28 | 28 | 16 | 2 | 1 | * | * | * | 7.5 |
| Sacramento | 15 | 28 | 31 | 18 | 5 | 1 | * | * | * | 9.3 |
| San Diego | 28 | 38 | 28 | 6 | | * | * | * | | 6.3 |
| San Francisco | 16 | 21 | 26 | 22 | 11 | 3 | * | * | * | 10.6 |
| COLO. Colorado Springs | 9 | 27 | 38 | 19 | 6 | 2 | * | * | * | 10.0 |
| Denver | 11 | 27 | 34 | 22 | 5 | 2 | * | * | * | 10.0 |
| CONN. Hartford | 13 | 26 | 32 | 24 | 6 | 1 | * | * | * | 9.7 |
| D.C. Washington | 11 | 26 | 35 | 22 | 5 | 1 | * | * | * | 9.7 |
| DEL. Wilmington | 15 | 31 | 30 | 19 | 4 | 1 | * | * | * | 8.8 |
| FLA. Jacksonville | 10 | 33 | 35 | 18 | 3 | | * | * | * | 8.9 |
| Miami | 14 | 30 | 34 | 20 | 2 | | * | * | * | 8.8 |
| Orlando | 18 | 28 | 32 | 17 | 4 | | * | * | * | 8.6 |
| Tallahassee | 33 | 36 | 23 | 7 | | * | * | | | 6.1 |
| Tampa | 9 | 31 | 40 | 16 | 2 | * | * | * | * | 8.8 |
| West Palm Beach | 9 | 22 | 36 | 27 | 6 | 1 | * | * | | 10.5 |
| GA. Atlanta | 13 | 24 | 36 | 21 | 6 | 1 | * | * | * | 9.7 |
| Augusta | 36 | 29 | 25 | 9 | 1 | | * | * | | 6.3 |
| Macon | 10 | 26 | 46 | 16 | 2 | * | * | * | | 8.9 |
| Savannah | 12 | 34 | 37 | 14 | 3 | * | * | * | | 8.4 |
| HAWAII, Hilo | 7 | 34 | 43 | 15 | 2 | * | * | * | | 8.7 |
| Honolulu | 9 | 17 | 27 | 32 | 12 | 2 | * | * | * | 12.1 |
| IDAHO, Boise | 15 | 30 | 32 | 18 | 4 | 1 | * | * | | 8.9 |
| ILL. Chicago (O'Hare) | 8 | 22 | 33 | 27 | 8 | 2 | * | * | * | 11.2 |
| Chicago (Midway) | 7 | 26 | 36 | 25 | 5 | 1 | * | * | * | 10.2 |
| Moline | 14 | 23 | 32 | 24 | 7 | 2 | * | * | * | 11.2 |
| Springfield | 7 | 22 | 28 | 27 | 12 | 3 | 1 | * | * | 12.0 |
| IND. Evansville | 19 | 23 | 32 | 21 | 5 | 1 | * | * | * | 8.9 |
| Fort Wayne | 9 | 23 | 33 | 25 | 8 | 2 | * | * | * | 10.9 |
| Indianapolis | 9 | 22 | 34 | 26 | 7 | 2 | * | * | * | 10.8 |
| South Bend | 7 | 21 | 35 | 30 | 7 | 1 | * | * | * | 10.9 |
| IOWA, Des Moines | 3 | 17 | 38 | 29 | 10 | 3 | 1 | * | * | 12.1 |
| Sioux City | 10 | 20 | 31 | 25 | 10 | 4 | 1 | * | * | 11.7 |
| KANS. Topeka | 11 | 19 | 30 | 27 | 10 | 2 | * | * | * | 11.2 |
| Wichita | 4 | 12 | 30 | 31 | 16 | 5 | 1 | * | * | 13.7 |
| KY. Lexington | 8 | 25 | 39 | 22 | 6 | 1 | * | * | | 10.1 |
| Louisville | 17 | 28 | 31 | 20 | 3 | 1 | * | * | | 8.8 |
| LA. Baton Rouge | 17 | 29 | 34 | 17 | 3 | * | * | * | | 8.3 |
| Lake Charles | 19 | 31 | 29 | 17 | 4 | 1 | * | * | * | 8.5 |
| New Orleans | 16 | 27 | 32 | 19 | 5 | 1 | * | * | * | 9.0 |
| Shreveport | 12 | 26 | 37 | 21 | 4 | 1 | * | * | * | 9.5 |
| MAINE, Portland | 10 | 30 | 33 | 22 | 4 | 1 | * | * | * | 9.6 |
| MD. Baltimore | 7 | 24 | 39 | 22 | 6 | 2 | * | * | * | 10.4 |
| MASS. Boston | 3 | 12 | 33 | 35 | 12 | 4 | 1 | * | * | 13.3 |
| MICH. Detroit (City AP) | 8 | 23 | 37 | 26 | 5 | 1 | * | * | * | 10.3 |
| Flint | 16 | 26 | 32 | 22 | 3 | 1 | * | * | * | 9.0 |
| Grand Rapids | 14 | 23 | 32 | 25 | 5 | 1 | * | * | * | 9.8 |
| MINN. Duluth | 6 | 15 | 33 | 31 | 11 | 4 | 1 | * | * | 12.6 |
| Minneapolis | 8 | 21 | 34 | 28 | 9 | 2 | * | * | * | 11.2 |
| MISS. Jackson | 33 | 25 | 26 | 14 | 2 | * | * | * | | 7.1 |
| MO. Kansas City | 9 | 29 | 35 | 23 | 5 | 1 | * | * | | 9.8 |
| St. Louis | 10 | 29 | 36 | 21 | 3 | 1 | * | * | * | 9.3 |
| Springfield | 4 | 13 | 34 | 32 | 13 | 3 | 1 | * | * | 12.9 |
| MONT. Great Falls | 7 | 19 | 24 | 24 | 15 | 9 | 3 | 1 | * | 13.9 |
| NEBR. Omaha | 12 | 17 | 29 | 28 | 11 | 3 | * | * | * | 11.6 |
| NEV. Las Vegas | 18 | 26 | 25 | 20 | 8 | 3 | 1 | * | * | 9.7 |
| Reno | 52 | 20 | 13 | 10 | 4 | 1 | * | * | * | 5.9 |
| N. J. Newark | 11 | 25 | 34 | 24 | 5 | 1 | * | * | * | 9.8 |
| N. MEX. Albuquerque | 17 | 36 | 26 | 13 | 5 | 2 | * | * | * | 8.6 |
| N. Y. Albany | 23 | 24 | 27 | 21 | 4 | 1 | * | * | * | 8.6 |
| Binghamton | 11 | 23 | 35 | 25 | 5 | 1 | * | * | * | 10.0 |
| Buffalo | 5 | 17 | 34 | 27 | 13 | 3 | 1 | * | * | 12.4 |
| New York (Kennedy) | 6 | 15 | 30 | 31 | 12 | 4 | 1 | * | * | 12.0 |
| New York (La Guardia) | 6 | 15 | 30 | 31 | 12 | 4 | 1 | * | * | 12.9 |
| Rochester | 8 | 22 | 34 | 25 | 9 | 2 | 1 | * | * | 11.2 |
| Syracuse | 14 | 27 | 30 | 23 | 5 | 1 | * | * | * | 9.7 |
| N. C. Charlotte | 20 | 32 | 31 | 14 | 2 | * | * | * | | 8.7 |
| Greensboro | 20 | 32 | 31 | 14 | 2 | * | * | * | | 8.0 |
| Raleigh | 18 | 33 | 34 | 14 | 2 | * | * | * | | 7.7 |
| Winston-Salem | 19 | 22 | 33 | 21 | 4 | 1 | * | * | | 9.0 |
| N. DAK. Bismarck | 14 | 20 | 27 | 24 | 12 | 3 | 1 | * | * | 11.2 |
| Fargo | 4 | 13 | 28 | 31 | 15 | 7 | 2 | * | * | 14.4 |
| OHIO, Akron-Canton | 7 | 25 | 35 | 26 | 5 | 1 | * | * | * | 10.4 |
| Cincinnati | 11 | 27 | 36 | 22 | 4 | 1 | * | * | * | 9.6 |
| Cleveland | 7 | 18 | 35 | 29 | 9 | 2 | * | * | * | 11.6 |
| Columbus | 26 | 23 | 29 | 18 | 4 | 1 | * | * | | 8.2 |
| Dayton | 8 | 25 | 36 | 23 | 6 | 2 | * | * | * | 10.3 |
| Youngstown | 7 | 26 | 36 | 24 | 6 | 1 | * | * | * | 10.3 |
| OKLA. Oklahoma City | 2 | 11 | 34 | 34 | 13 | 6 | 1 | * | * | 14.0 |
| OKLA. (Cont.) Tulsa | 9 | 24 | 34 | 26 | 7 | 1 | * | * | * | 10.6 |
| OREG. Medford | 47 | 31 | 14 | 6 | 2 | * | * | * | * | 4.6 |
| Portland | 28 | 27 | 25 | 16 | 4 | 1 | * | * | * | 7.7 |
| Salem | 25 | 32 | 28 | 13 | 2 | * | * | | | 7.1 |
| PA. Harrisburg | 28 | 31 | 25 | 13 | 3 | 1 | * | * | | 7.3 |
| Philadelphia | 11 | 27 | 35 | 21 | 5 | 1 | * | * | * | 9.6 |
| Pittsburgh | 12 | 26 | 34 | 22 | 4 | 1 | * | * | | 9.4 |
| Scranton | 11 | 33 | 35 | 18 | 2 | * | * | * | | 8.8 |
| R. I. Providence | 11 | 20 | 32 | 28 | 7 | 2 | * | * | * | 10.7 |
| S. C. Charleston | 12 | 28 | 35 | 19 | 4 | 1 | * | * | | 9.2 |
| Columbia | 25 | 35 | 26 | 12 | 2 | * | * | | | 7.0 |
| S. DAK. Huron | 10 | 18 | 29 | 29 | 10 | 3 | 1 | * | * | 11.9 |
| Rapid City | 15 | 22 | 28 | 21 | 10 | 4 | 1 | * | * | 11.0 |
| TENN. Chattanooga | 39 | 25 | 24 | 11 | 1 | * | * | | | 6.1 |
| Knoxville | 29 | 29 | 25 | 12 | 4 | 1 | * | * | * | 7.5 |
| Memphis | 14 | 26 | 34 | 20 | 5 | 1 | * | * | * | 9.4 |
| Nashville | 27 | 31 | 25 | 14 | 2 | * | * | * | | 7.2 |
| TEX. Amarillo | 5 | 15 | 32 | 32 | 12 | 4 | 1 | * | * | 12.9 |
| Austin | 13 | 25 | 34 | 23 | 5 | 1 | * | * | | 9.7 |
| Brownsville | 10 | 17 | 25 | 30 | 14 | 3 | * | * | * | 12.3 |
| Corpus Christi | 11 | 16 | 26 | 33 | 12 | 2 | * | * | * | 12.6 |
| Dallas | 9 | 21 | 32 | 28 | 9 | 1 | * | * | | 11.0 |
| El Paso | 10 | 22 | 32 | 22 | 9 | 4 | 1 | * | * | 11.3 |
| Ft. Worth | 4 | 14 | 34 | 34 | 10 | 3 | * | * | * | 12.5 |
| Galveston | 4 | 13 | 39 | 33 | 10 | 2 | 1 | * | * | 12.5 |
| Houston | 6 | 18 | 36 | 28 | 10 | 2 | * | * | * | 11.8 |
| Laredo | 6 | 15 | 32 | 34 | 13 | 5 | 1 | * | * | 12.3 |
| Lubbock | 4 | 11 | 33 | 34 | 13 | 5 | 1 | * | * | 13.6 |
| Midland | 9 | 22 | 38 | 26 | 4 | 1 | * | * | * | 10.1 |
| San Antonio | 18 | 23 | 32 | 22 | 4 | 1 | * | * | | 9.2 |
| Waco | 3 | 14 | 36 | 35 | 10 | 2 | * | * | * | 12.5 |
| Wichita Falls | 5 | 22 | 41 | 27 | 5 | 1 | * | * | * | 10.5 |
| UTAH, Salt Lake City | 12 | 33 | 36 | 14 | 4 | 1 | * | * | * | 8.7 |
| VT. Burlington | 24 | 24 | 28 | 22 | 2 | * | * | * | | 8.3 |
| VA. Norfolk | 14 | 23 | 30 | 25 | 6 | 1 | * | * | * | 10.2 |
| Richmond | 14 | 37 | 36 | 11 | 1 | * | * | * | | 7.8 |
| Roanoke | 31 | 22 | 23 | 17 | 5 | 2 | * | * | * | 8.3 |
| WASH. Seattle-Tacoma AP | 13 | 16 | 35 | 26 | 8 | 2 | * | * | * | 10.7 |
| Spokane | 17 | 38 | 27 | 14 | 3 | 1 | * | * | | 8.1 |
| W. VA. Charleston | 29 | 37 | 25 | 8 | 1 | * | * | | | 6.2 |
| WIS. Green Bay | 8 | 22 | 32 | 26 | 10 | 2 | * | * | * | 11.2 |
| Madison | 15 | 22 | 30 | 23 | 7 | 2 | * | * | * | 10.1 |
| Milwaukee | 8 | 17 | 31 | 30 | 11 | 3 | 1 | * | * | 12.1 |
| WYO. Casper | 8 | 16 | 27 | 27 | 13 | 7 | 2 | * | * | 13.3 |
| PACIFIC, Wake Island | 1 | 6 | 27 | 48 | 17 | 2 | * | * | * | 14.6 |
| P. R. San Juan | 15 | 28 | 27 | 25 | 4 | * | * | * | * | 9.1 |

Source: Climatography of the United States Series 82; Decennial Census of the United States Climate—Summary of Hourly Observations, 1951-60 (Table B).

close by, these statistics could provide you with a fairly accurate idea of wind patterns for a given site.

## CALCULATING WIND SPEED

Wind speed is very much affected by local geographical conditions, such as terrain, vegetation and height above ground. Figure 3-25 illustrates the increase in wind speed with height over different types of terrain. Above the sea, or on any flat, open land, the speed increases very rapidly with height. Obstructions near the ground, such as buildings and trees, will cause turbulence and reduced wind speeds. Over undulating terrain there generally is a concentration of wind power on exposed hilltops and ridges (Figure 3-26). On steep-sided hills, however, the wind current often breaks away from the edge of the slope, causing turbulence that will lead to excessive wear on a windmill placed there. To avoid this turbulence, a windmill should be placed at least twenty to thirty feet higher than the nearest obstruction

within 300 to 500 feet in any direction. A windmill placed atop a hill should be on a tower that will raise it above the turbulence occuring at the peak.

Once a promising site has been chosen, on-site measurements are necessary for more accurate estimation of wind power. These measurements can be made intuitively by visiting the site often; Figure 3-28 shows how to estimate wind speed. Simple *anemometers* (instruments to measure wind speed) can be obtained cheaply from hobby shops and used to make more accurate readings. A number of readings over a period of a few weeks can be compared to the local weather station data to establish a local correction factor for the site. The data may be corrected further to take into account the height of the proposed tower, using Figure 3-29. A streamer attached to a long pole can be used to detect turbulent wind currents at the tower site. *If average wind speeds are found to exceed ten miles per hour with no turbulence, the site is suitable for wind electric power generation.*

Increasing the tower height is the most cost-effective way to increase power output from the system. Towers may be either self-supporting, with substantial footings and an elaborate structure, or braced with guy wires (this is simpler and less expensive). The tower should be corrosion-resistant, lightning-protected, climb-proof, and sturdy. A ninety-foot tower is tricky to erect and install, so obtain good advice from the manufacturer before risking your windmill—or your neck.

CHOOSING A WINDMILL

When information on the wind speeds at the site is available, you must choose or design a windmill to operate most efficiently under those conditions. Figures 3–4 and 3–5 will help you to select the proper size machine; suppliers also will be glad to advise you if you wish. Most mills available for generating electricity are designed to put out maximum power in a 25-mph wind (Figure 3–30). This means that at 9 or 10 mph the output of the mill is negligible. Moreover, at wind speeds above 25 mph, this type of mill rapidly declines in efficiency: the power available in the wind is increasing, but the mill already has reached its fixed maximum output. Consequently, for any particular site it is worth knowing not only the average and maximum wind speeds, but also the standard deviation from the mean. By looking at

**Table 3-24. Wind Data Recorded at Bridgeport, Connecticut. Similar records are available from weather stations throughout the United States.**

| | Mean Hourly Windspeed mph | Prevailing Direction | Fastest Recording mph |
|---|---|---|---|
| January | 12.7 | NW | 67 |
| February | 13.2 | NW | 52 |
| March | 13.1 | NW | 51 |
| April | 12.7 | N | 55 |
| May | 11.7 | E | 50 |
| June | 10.2 | SW | 38 |
| July | 9.6 | SW | 36 |
| August | 9.6 | SW | 42 |
| September | 11.0 | NE | 47 |
| October | 11.7 | NE | 51 |
| November | 12.5 | NW | 58 |
| December | 12.5 | NW | 53 |

the variation in output of standard models with changes in wind speed, you can estimate the suitability of these machines at various locations. One company, North Wind Power Company of Warren, Vermont, even offers a wind assessment survey service for those who want accurate data before making the investment in wind power.

The selection of the whole wind-electric system also depends on the amount of electricity and storage you will require. You should make an accurate study of the estimated consumption of

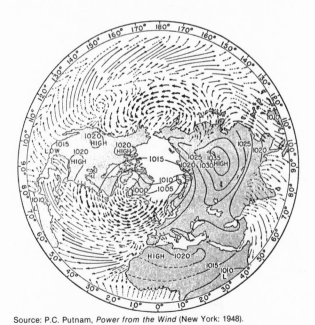

Source: P.C. Putnam, *Power from the Wind* (New York: 1948).

**Figure 3-23. Air currents above the oceans in the Northern Hemisphere. Thickness of arrows indicates strength of wind.**

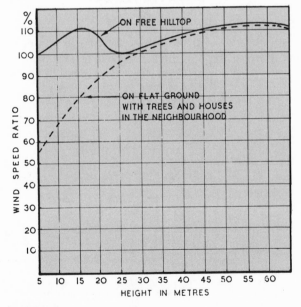

Source: E.W. Golding, *The Generation of Electricity by Windpower* (London: Electrical Research Association, 1955).

**Figure 3-25. The concentration of windspeed over a hilltop.**

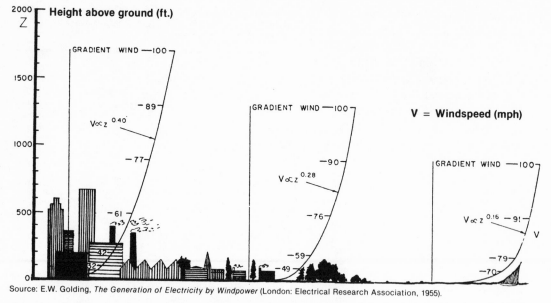

Source: E.W. Golding, *The Generation of Electricity by Windpower* (London: Electrical Research Association, 1955).

**Figure 3-26. Windspeed varies with height for different kinds of terrain.**

various household appliances to determine the demand on the wind power plant and the size of the generator required. Table 1–21 on page 17 lists typical electrical consumption of many household appliances; Table 3–31 illustrates a sample energy-demand calculation for a small self-sufficient homestead.

# Economics

To compete with the utility companies, windmills must be able to produce electricity over a twenty-year investment period at a cost of around nine cents per kilowatt-hour. This cost is based on the initial investment amortized over the twenty-year period at a given interest rate, plus the maintenance costs if any. The projected rise in fuel costs must also be taken into account—electric rates have been increasing at *15 to 20 percent per year* since 1971. So wind power at nine cents per kilowatt-hour may be very attractive in twenty years; in many parts of the country it already is.

The table in the Wind Power Catalog (p. 152) compares many commercially available windmills for producing electricity. The table gives the cost of each mill and its output as given by the manufacturer. From it, you can estimate the cost of the electricity it produces. This last figure can be derived by taking the cost of the equipment

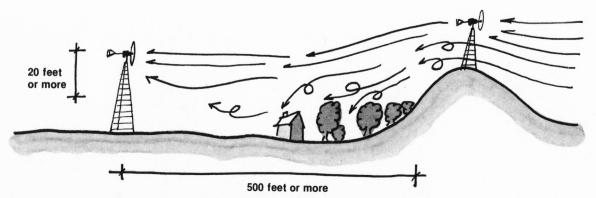

**Figure 3-27. For best performance, a windmill should be at least 20 to 30 feet higher than any obstruction within 500 feet. A windmill atop a hill should be raised above the air turbulence that usually occurs at the summit.**

**Table 3-28. You can estimate windspeed by comparing conventional descriptions of the wind with the Beaufort Scale number, windspeed in mph, and wind force.**

| Beaufort Number | Windspeed (mph) | Mean Windforce ($lb/ft_2$) | Qualitative Description of Wind |
|---|---|---|---|
| 0 | 0–1 | 0 | Calm. Smoke rises vertically. |
| 1 | 1–3 | 0.01 | Light air. Smoke drifts but wind vanes do not turn. |
| 2 | 4–7 | 0.08 | Light breeze. Wind vane turns. Leaves rustle. |
| 3 | 8–12 | 0.28 | Leaves and twigs in constant motion. |
| 4 | 13–18 | 0.67 | Moderate breeze. Raises dust and loose paper. |
| 5 | 19–24 | 1.31 | Small trees in leaf begin to sway. Small crested waves form. |
| 6 | 25–31 | 2.3 | Strong breeze. Large branches move. Telephone wires whistle. |
| 7 | 32–38 | 3.6 | Moderate gale. Large trees in motion. Walking is difficult. |
| 8 | 39–46 | 5.4 | Strong gale. Extreme difficulty in walking against wind. |
| 9 | 47–54 | 7.7 | Light roofs liable to blow off houses. |
| 10 | 55–63 | 10.5 | Hurricane. Even the strongest mills liable to be damaged. |

**Figure 3-29. Increased tower height produces increased windspeed and power output.**

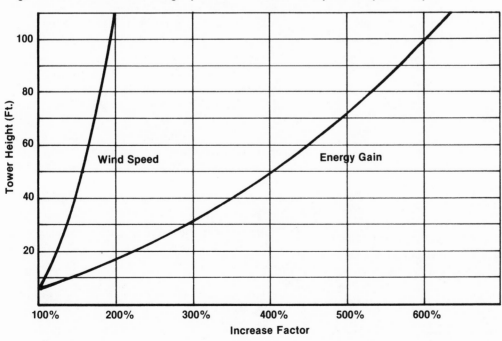

141

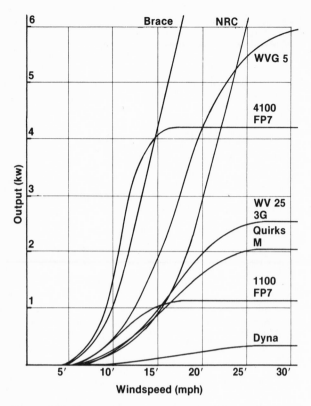

Figure 3-30. Power output vs. windspeed for various commercially available electricity-generating mills.

**Table 3-31. Sample Calculation of Power Requirements.**

| Appliance | Rating (in watts) | Avg. Monthly Use (in hours) | Avg. Monthly Power Req. (in watt hrs.) |
|---|---|---|---|
| Light Bulbs (8) | 75 × 8 | 116 | 69,600 |
| TV Set | 55 | 182 | 10,100 |
| Furnace | | | |
| Burner | | | |
| Motor | 270 | 210 | 56,700 |
| Hot Water | | | |
| Circulator | 120 | 250 | 30,000 |
| Toaster | 1100 | 3 | 3,300 |
| Coffee Maker | 600 | 12 | 7,200 |
| | | Total: | 116,900 |

Average Daily Requirements in KWH = 3.9
Average Monthly Requirement in KWH = 117

*Source:* Enertech, *Planning a Wind-Powered Generating System,* 1977.

necessary for a complete wind-power plant and the installation costs. For a larger installation, sample estimated additional costs can be computed as follows:

| | |
|---|---|
| Solid-state inverter, 2 kw | $1400. |
| Batteries: 19 6-volt units, 15-kwh storage | 550. |
| 70-foot steel tower | 700. |
| Miscellaneous (wiring, control panel, etc.) | 500. |
| Installation costs | 1200. |
| Total costs (minus windmill) | $4350. |

The total cost of the installation should be amortized over twenty years at a 10 percent interest rate and the result divided by the total amount of electricity the machine will produce over twenty years at an average wind speed of 15 mph. The overall power efficiency can be taken as 50 percent, to account for inefficiencies in the mill, the transmission, and the inverter.

There is a great variation in the cost of electricity from different installations. One of the best investments appears to be the *Elektro WVG 50,* a windmill that produces electricity at eight cents per kilowatt hour (to which must be added the costs of maintenance, which will vary according to the type of mill). At that price, wind-generated electricity seems like a sound investment. This figure is very much dependent on wind speed: At 10 mph the cost of electricity from the Elektro mill goes up to 26 cents per kilowatt-hour. Costs could be cut, however, by eliminating the need for an inverter (by using DC in all appliances) and by installing the mill yourself.

If the house is located far from the utility company's power lines, then the installation of a wind-power plant becomes even more feasible. In Connecticut, for example, there is a charge of $250. plus $.50 per foot for buried cable over 150 feet from the utility lines. This figure does not include the cost of digging the trench and laying a bed of sand in it, which would probably add another dollar per foot. For a house 200 feet from the power line, the installation of a supply line would cost around $500. For distances over 250 feet overhead cables are generally installed. The material costs then become $220. per pole and $1.00 per foot for the cable. Including labor costs, this amounts to over $3.50 per foot—$1750. for a 500-foot installation, or as much as $20,000 per mile.

In very remote locations the cost of bringing a power cable to the house is often greater than the cost of a large power plant. In Happytown,

Maine, Henry Clews installed a two-kilowatt power plant himself for $2790—less than the $3000 the power company would have charged to install a power cable. Clews has managed to run his household appliances on the 120 kilowatt-hours per month that his Quirks mill produces in 8.6 mph average wind speeds.

## COMPARING SYSTEMS

The economy of a wind system is highly dependent on the availability of power line electricity, the need for storage, and the life style of the users. For a house already hooked up the utility lines, it may make sense to employ a synchronous inverter system, making use of existing 115-volt AC appliances and wiring, and avoiding the need for energy storage. For a remote site or a new house, it could be more feasible to choose a DC system with batteries and save on the purchase of an expensive inverter. Listed below are typical costs for various systems, assuming an average local windspeed of twelve miles per hour.

### 1. Wind for Heating

| | |
|---|---|
| Elektro Wind Generator, 10 kw (FOB Switzerland) | $5600. |
| Importation, tower & erection | 3500. |
| | $9100. |

This is a high-capital-cost, low-maintenance way to use wind energy. Such a system will produce 15,000 to 30,000 kwh per year, or 33 percent to 100 percent of the annual heating requirement of an average house, paying for itself in about ten years. Except in very windy or cloudy regions, solar heating might be a better investment.

### 2. Low-Voltage DC System

| | |
|---|---|
| Winco Wincharger, 12 volts, 200 watts, with 10-ft. tower | $450. |
| 2 heavy-duty, 125 amp-hr. batteries | 140. |
| Voltage regulator | 70. |
| | $660. |

This system combines low cost with low maintenance. The tower may need to be higher for better power. Output is approximately 300 kwh per year, enough to power several lights, a radio and a small television. Cost per kilowatt-hour is high, but the low total cost may make such a system attractive to the self-sufficient home-steader.

### 3. Higher-Output DC System

| | |
|---|---|
| Sencenbaugh 1000-14 wind generator with control panel | $2650. |
| Rohn guyed tower, 70 ft. plus top section | 820. |
| 900 amp-hour 12-volt battery bank | 1200. |
| | $4670. |

Several other machines offer higher output, at a higher price. This system assumes that all appliances can run on DC current. Output will be about 1800 kwh per year, costing around fifteen cents per kilowatt-hour over twenty years.

### 4. Synchronous Inverter System

| | |
|---|---|
| Jacobs 2 kw wind generator | $3500. |
| 60-foot self-supporting tower, second-hand | 500. |
| Gemini Inverter | 1250. |
| Installation | 650. |
| | $5900. |

No storage is required, since the utility company is the "storage." All appliances may use AC current. Output is about 4200 kwh per year, reducing total costs to around seven cents per kilowatt-hour over twenty years.

### 5. Large AC Domestic System

| | |
|---|---|
| Elektro 6 kw wind generator | $ 5000. |
| 50-foot Rohn guyed tower with top section | 675. |
| Battery bank (540-amp-hour, 115-volt, DC) | 3000. |
| Delatron inverter, 115VDC to 115VAC, rated at 6 kw, sine wave output | 4000. |
| Stand-by generator, 2 kw | 400. |
| Installation | 1000. |
| | $14,075. |

This is a very expensive system; you should carefully reassess your total energy needs before considering such an investment. A system like this can be expected to provide about 6000 kwh per year, costing around 11½ cents per kilowatt-hour over twenty years.

Six thousand dollars may seem discouragingly costly, especially to a young family building a new house. As with solar power, however, *life-cycle costing* is the key to understanding the advantages of wind power. An additional $800 to $1200 down payment on a $40,000 house (to add a wind power system) will produce a savings of $100 to $200 per year in energy costs. And any of several other contingencies (rapid energy cost increases, remoteness or unavailability of electric utility hookup, blackout, economic depression or energy crisis) could make wind energy even more attractive.

HOMESTEADERS' LAYAWAY PLAN

For the homesteader building from scratch, a wind system can be purchased piecemeal, using a kind of layaway plan:

1. At the start of construction, buy a 115-volt or 115/230-volt backup generator with remote start capability. The generator can be used to power the tools used in construction.

2. When construction is finished, purchase an AC/DC rectifier, generator control, batteries for the planned wind system, and a DC/AC inverter, if you require AC current. The generator can be operated periodically to charge the battery bank, from which house power is drawn as needed.

3. When you can afford it, add a windplant and tower. Use the backup generator for occasional supplementary power during windless periods.

If each component is bought with an eye toward eventual wind-system use, the Homesteaders' Layaway Plan allows the opportunity to invest gradually in a system that is useful and efficient at every stage in its growth, and one that can place the power of the wind within economic reach of nearly everyone.

# References

Clews, Henry. *Electric Power From the Wind.* Norwich, Vt.: Solar Wind Publications, 1972, updated 1974. $2.00. Buy this 40-page booklet if you plan to install a wind system. Simple, readable and comprehensive, it contains plenty of how-to information and the fruits of a fair amount of do-it-yourself research by the author and other wind pioneers.

*Climatic Atlas of the United States.* Environmental Data Service, National Climatic Center, Federal Building, Asheville, North Carolina 28801. Gives wind averages, the strongest wind, and wind direction. Monthly wind reports for each state are also available from EDS.

Golding, E.W. *The Generation of Electricity by Wind Power.* New York: Halsted Press. 1955. The best textbook available on wind power. Technical, but readable. 318 pages.

Hackleman, Michael. *The Homebuilt, Wind-Generated Electricity Handbook.* Mariposa, Ca.: Earthmind Press. $8.00. Excellent guide to rebuilding and installing old Jacobs or Wincharger machines, or any old wind generators.

Leckie, et al. *Other Homes and Garbage.* San Francisco: Sierra Club Books. 1975. $9.95. Good explanations of electrical theory as it relates to alternative energy.

McGuigan, Dermot. *Harnessing the Wind for Home Energy.* Charlotte, Vt.: Garden Way Publishing, 1978. $4.95. A valuable little book, stuffed with information especially useful to those just getting started. Plenty of resource and product information.

McGuiness, William J. and Stein, Benjamin. *Mechanical and Electrical Equipment for Buildings.* New York: John Wiley & Sons, Inc., 1975. $23.95. A technical textbook used by architects, this book covers the topics of basic electricity, conductors and raceways, service and utilization equipment, wiring design, and electric space heating in detail. Though residential construction is considered, the emphasis tends toward large buildings.

*Simplified Electrical Wiring.* Chicago: Sears Roebuck & Co., 1974. 50¢ At the other end of the scale, this little booklet tells you how to wire a house, with plenty of illustrations and simplified explanations. Buy it if electricity scares you; you will be cured.

*Wind Energy Report.* P.O. Box 14, Rockville Centre, New York 11571. International, 16-page monthly newsletter devoted exclusively to wind energy. $75 for one year subscription.

*Wind Power Digest.* 54468 CR31, Bristol, Indiana 46507. $6.00, quarterly issues. Essential and enjoyable reading for the wind enthusiast.

"Synchronous Inverters—Windpower Without Batteries." *Popular Science,* October 1975.

"Thirteen Wind Machines." *Popular Science,* September 1978.

"Windmills." *Popular Science,* November 1972.

"Windmills: New Developments." *Popular Science,* July 1974.

# Wind Power Catalog

The following pages show products and companies that are currently active in the field of wind power. Naturally, this is not a complete catalog—many excellent products are not represented here, and more are coming on the market all the time.

All information in this catalog section was supplied by the various manufacturers or organizations; we have briefly summarized what is available from each. Our goal is to help you, the reader, locate the products and information that will allow you to evaluate for yourself the feasibility of a home wind power system.

In using the wind generator comparison chart, keep in mind that prices are constantly changing. If you need more information about any of the products described in the catalog section, we ask that you write directly to the companies you are interested in, *not* to Garden Way Publishing.

# Wind Generators

**Aermotor/Division
of Valley Industries, Inc.
Industrial Park
P.O. Box 1364
Conway, Arkansas 72032
(501) 329-9811**

Aermotor manufactures windmills for water pumping. Their multi-bladed mills are available with diameters of 6, 8, 10, 12, 14, and 16 feet. They feature a positive oiling system, adjustable stroke, and automatic regulation.

Aermotor also makes four-post standard and widespread towers from 21 to 47 feet high and three- or four-post stub towers from 3 to 20 feet high for use with existing towers.

**AeroLectric
13517 Winter Drive
Cresaptown, Maryland 21502**

The portable *Edmund Wind Wizard* is manufactured by AeroLectric. Listed in the Edmund Scientific Co. catalog (No. 85,262), the wind plant is a nine-foot, three-bladed propeller unit, delivering 600 watts at 25 mph. It starts charging at wind speeds of 9 mph and has a 26 mph factory-set fold-back. It generates 12 volts DC suitable for motor homes, campers, cabins, boats, and so on. An adjustable output voltage control is included.

*Happiness is a wind machine—even homemade.*

**Aero Power Co.
2398 4th St.
Berkeley, California 94710**

Aero Power manufactures the *SL1000 Windpowered Electric System*. The wind generator is a three-bladed spruce propeller with stainless steel leading edge. Blades automatically feather at high wind speeds. A tail vane controls the position of the propeller and prevents damage from gusts and turbulence. The weather-sealed, three-phase alternator and step-up gear box, both housed in heavy cast aluminum, provide 1000 watts in 20 mph wind.

The system also includes a fully charged set of 350 amp hour batteries, solid state automatic voltage regulator, and control equipment with overcharge protection. Guyed towers in sizes from 30 to 80 feet and ATR and Best inverters cost extra.

**Aerowatt
37, Rue Chanzy 75011
Paris, France**

Aerowatt wind generators come in five different sizes from 28 to 4100 watts. Designed to operate in very low wind speeds and to withstand very high ones, these machines are primarily for industrial applications.

*Models 24 FP7, 150 FP7, 300 FP7,* and *1100 FP7* utilize a two-bladed propeller made of wood. In the three smaller generators, the propeller direct drives a brushless alternator. In *Model 1100 FP7*, a speed-increasing gear is used.

The largest generator, *Model 4100 FP7*, uses extruded aluminum blades finished with a urethane paint. Its brushless alternator is also gear-driven.

All Aerowatt generators cut in at 6 mph winds; full output occurs at 16 mph. The propeller speed is regulated by a centrifugally operated pitch control system—generators are safe in winds up to 125 mph. Specifications are as follows:

| Model | Blade Diameter | Rated Output at 16 mph |
|---|---|---|
| 24 FP7 | 3.3 feet | 28 watts |
| 150 FP7 | 6.7 feet | 130 watts |
| 300 FP7 | 10.7 feet | 350 watts |
| 1100 FP7 | 16.7 feet | 1125 volt-amperes |
| 4100 FP7 | 30.7 feet | 4100 volt-amperes |

Automatic Power will also supply controls, batteries, and towers sized to fit their wind generators.

American distributor:

Automatic Power, Inc./Division of Pennwalt Corp.
213 Hutcheson St.
Houston, Texas 77023
(713) 228-5208

**Ampair Products
Aston House
Blackheath
Guildford
Surrey GU4 8RD
England**

Ampair manufactures the *Ampair 50* wind driven alternator for marine applications. It is designed for permanent installation on cruising yachts.

The wind turbine has 14 individually replaceable polypropylene blades, mounted in an aluminum hub. It can be used with 14 blades for low windspeed environments or 7 for higher windspeed environments. It is 26 inches in diameter and includes a 30 inch long mounting tube.

The alternator is capable of operation at very low speeds. It includes a permanent magnet rotor and remotely located rectifier for converting AC to DC.

The Ampair 50 can produce up to 50 watts of 12 or 24 volt DC electricity. Voltage limiter and read-out unit are optional. A special mounting bracket kit costs extra.

Ampair 50

**Chalk Wind Systems
(formerly American Wind Turbine)
P.O. Box 446
St. Cloud, Florida 32769
(305) 892-7338**

Tom Chalk's recently-invented, multi-blade windmill is custom-built for specific applications. Its aluminum blades are attached at the outer perimeter to an aluminum rim. Aluminum wire spokes like those of a bicycle run from the hub to the rim to create a strong framework for the mill. Its airfoil profile allows it to run at winds as low as 3 mph. It is protected against high winds by a tail vane.

It can be used to pump water (82 gallons per minute in 16 mph wind) or to generate electricity by means of an alternator run from a belt on the rim. It can provide 700 watts in 20 mph winds. Chalk claims it exceeds 50 percent efficiency.

## CHALK WIND SYSTEMS

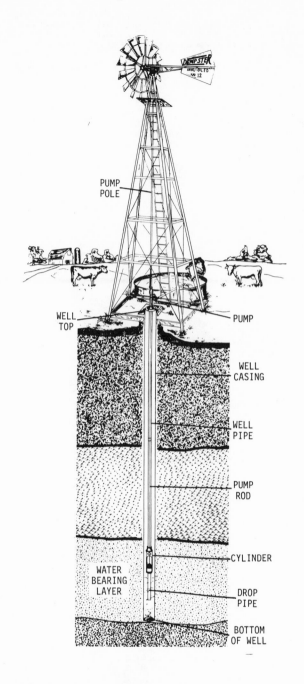

**Dempster® Industries, Inc.
Beatrice, Nebraska 68310
(402) 223-4026**

Dempster® manufactures *No. 12 Annu-Oiled Windmills* for pumping water. They are multi-blade mills in 6, 8, 10, 14, and 18 foot sizes. The blades are made of heavy gauge steel and fastened to circles to keep proper curvature and position. Machine-cut equalizing gears run in an oil bath that needs changing only once a year. Gears and other working parts are housed in a weatherproof hood made of galvanized sheet steel.

Dempster steel towers with anchor and wood pump poles are available at an additional cost. They come in 22, 28, 30, 33, 39, and 40 foot heights.

**Dunlite**
**Head Office, Manufacturing, and Export Division**
28 Orsmond St.
P.O. Box 100
Hindmarch, South Australia 5007
61 846 3832

Dunlite has manufactured a high quality, 2kw wind generator for over 30 years. The *Dunlite 2000W* has a maximum continuous output of 2000 watts at 25 mph winds. The three-bladed, galvanized steel propeller is governed by a feathering mechanism in winds up to 80 mph. The gear-driven, brushless alternator cuts in at 10 mph. The *Dunlite 2000W* includes voltage regulator and control box.

Dunlite has recently begun production of a 5kw wind generator. Incorporating the features of the *Dunlite 2000W*, the *Dunlite 5000W* has a maximum continuous output of 5000 watts in 21.3 mph wind and cuts in at 6.9 mph.

# Elektro

**Elektro G.m.b.H.**
**St. Gallerstrasse 27**
**CH-8400 Winterthur**
**Switzerland**

Since 1938, Elektro has been manufacturing a variety of wind turbines with interchangeable parts that withstand severe climatic conditions. They all run at low speeds and have a long service life, sometimes 30 to 40 years.

The vertical-axis, six-bladed turbine is ideal for areas with high windspeeds. Two types are available: *Model W50* has a maximum output of 50 watts; and *Model 250* has a maximum output of 150 watts. Both can withstand windspeeds of more than 60 mph and do not need an automatic control.

The horizontal-axis, propeller-type turbine has two or three blades and is available with maximum outputs of 600 to 10,000 watts. The 6000- and 10,000-watt models can supply electricity for an average home (excluding cooking and hot water heating, which can be done with gas). They can be used with or without a handbrake.

All Elektros have wooden blades governed by centrifugal weights and adjustable tail fins and use field or permanent magnet alternators. Models up to 6 kw are direct drive.

Elektro also manufactures wind generators for heating only and sells towers, batteries, inverters, and controls separately or in systems with their turbines. A recently published manual, *Thirty-Seven Years Experience with Elektro Windmills*, explains their products and history. ($30.50).

Canadian distributor:
Future Resources and Energy Ltd.
P.O. Box 1358
Station B
Downsview, Ontario M3H 5W3
(416) 630-8343

American distributor:
Real Gas and Electric Co.
Box F
Santa Rosa, California 95401

**Mehrkam Energy Development Co.**
179E
R.D. 2
Hamburg, Pennsylvania 19526

Mehrkam Energy Development manufactures the *Mehrkam Machine*, a four-blade, horizontal-axis wind turbine that produces high output in average windspeed. It begins charging at windspeeds of 5 mph and automatically shuts off at 40 mph or more (rotor speeds of 60 rpm or more). Its aluminum blades rotate slowly to ensure long life. It can be operated automatically or manually by means of an indoor control panel.

Three models are available with propeller diameters of 38, 40, and 75 feet that have outputs of 20,000, 45,000, and 150,000 watts respectively at 27 mph windspeed.

Turbines consist of rotor shaft and blades; 20, 45, or 150 kw, AC, three-phase alternator; indoor control panel, main bearings, power transmission equipment, electric brake, turbine housing, overspeed control, voltage regulator, failsafe control package, automatic yaw control, and instruction manual. The *Mehrkam Machine* also includes a 40- or 60-foot tubular tower with working platform and step rungs. Batteries, synchronous inverter, and automatic lubricant are extra.

Energy Development also provides wind-energy site surveys and custom systems design for battery storage, synchronous inverters, and electric-resistance heating.

*Self-supporting tower with 3.5 kw direct-drive Elektro.*

## Kedco, Inc.
**9016 Aviation Blvd.**
**Inglewood, California 90301**
**(213) 776-6636**

Kedco manufactures a family of seven wind generators based on Jack Park's three-bladed down-wind plans (see *Helion*, above). *Models 1200* (12 foot diameter) and *1600* (16 foot diameter) are both rated at 1200 watts maximum for battery-charging applications. *Models 1205* and *1605*, also for battery-charging, are rated at 1900 watts maximum.

*Models 1210 and 1610* are supplied with 2000 watt DC generators. Model *1620* is supplied with a 3000 watt DC generator of permanent magnet design for synchronous inverter operation, as well as wind furnace and other applications.

The fundamental difference between the *1200* and *1600* series is the blade diameter. The increase in diameter from 12 to 16 feet nearly doubles the energy yield.

All models have aluminum blades and the following features: automatic blade feathering, ground shut-off and re-set cables, automatic vibration-sensing shut-off, and gear drive.

The *1200/1600 Owner's Manual* costs $7.50 each. The price is refundable upon purchase of any complete Kedco wind generator.

## KMP
**Lake Pump and Parish Windmills**
**Box 441**
**Earth, Texas 79031**
**(806) 257-3411**

The *KMP Parish Windmill* is a sprocket-and-chain drive device for pumping water. Its eighteen factory-installed, aluminum blades are six, eight, or ten feet in diameter. A right-angle control vane keeps the mill out of strong winds; a variable tail vane controls speed and pump rod stroke. It is easily repaired and requires minimum upkeep.

## Lubing-Maschinenfabrik
**Ludwig Bening**
**2847 Barnstort**
**Postfach 110**
**West Germany**

Lubing manufactures about 50 different sizes of wind driven water pumps and only one type of windmill generator—a downwind, horizontal-axis machine. The Lubing mill is rated at 400 watts in a 27 mph wind.

The six-bladed Lubing propeller has three small, fixed-pitch blades which start the mill at 9 mph. The three larger variable-pitch blades produce the bulk of the power at higher wind speeds. All the blades are made of epoxy resins reinforced with fiber glass. A centrifugal governor, fitted to each of the variable-pitch blades, prevents them from exceeding the maximum speed of 600 rpm.

Output from the alternator is converted from AC to 24 volts DC at the control panel. The electronic controls regulate the charging of the batteries automatically, and when a battery voltage of 28.5 volts is reached the charging current is cut off.

The basic system includes three foot stub tower and control panel. The Lubing is also sold complete with aluminum tubular tower in three sizes. The tower is easy to bolt in place and has the added advantage of being hinged at the base, which enables the owner to raise the mill by means of the winch provided.

Candadian distributors:
Budgen and Associates
72 Broadview Ave.
Pointe Claire, Quebec
Canada
(512) 695-4073

*The six-bladed Lubing propeller.*

## North Wind Power Co., Inc.
**Box 315**
**Warren, Vermont 05674**
**(802) 496-2955**

North Wind Power sells *North Wind Eagle Generators*, rebuilt Jacobs Wind Electric Plants sold during 1931–1956 and claimed by many to be the most durable and efficient wind generators ever manufactured.

In the Jacobs system, a slow-speed DC generator featuring long-lasting carbon brushes is direct-driven by a self-feathering, three-bladed propeller 14 feet in diameter made of aircraft quality Sitka spruce. Full rated power is reached in winds under 20 mph, or 250 rpm.

The rebuilt Jacobs generators have been disassembled, cleaned, and reconditioned. The armature is baked and dipped and all brushes and bearings replaced. It is fitted with a new blade-actuated governor and a new set of matched and balanced propellers.

North Wind Power also sells complete wind energy systems. For areas where commercial power is available, they offer two packages. Each includes a 36-foot guyed tower, a 4 kw Gemini synchronous inverter, and either a 2- or 3-kw, 110 volt *North Wind Eagle Generator*.

Two systems are available for remote areas: the DC system includes a 2 kw, 32-volt *North Wind Eagle Generator*, a 358 amp-hour battery bank, a 36-foot guyed tower, solid-state controls. The AC/DC system includes a 3 kw, 32-volt *North Wind Eagle Generator*, 358 amp-hour battery bank, 36-foot guyed tower, solid-state controls, and a 1 kw AC/DC inverter.

In addition, North Wind Power sells wind instruments, including anemometer recorder systems, a wind speed compilator, and a wind data accumulator.

They also sell their own and other manufacturers' solid-state controls, inverters, battery banks, and towers; educational demonstration packages; and books and plans. They conduct site investigations and feasibility studies for wind, solar, water, and integrated energy systems. Their catalog ($2.50) gives details of all their products.

**Product Development Institute**
**4440 Secor Road**
**Toledo, Ohio 43623**
**(419) 473-1140**

Product Development Institute manufactures the *Wind Jennie*® a propeller-type wind generator with three aluminum blades and tail vane. It starts charging in 9 mph winds and reaches maximum output of 3,000 watts at 20 mph windspeed. A feathering mechanism protects blades from excess wind speeds.

The complete *Wind Jennie*® package is designed to be interfaced with the power company line. A solid-state inverter matches the *Wind Jennie's*® current to the power company's. An alternator is also included.

PDI offers towers from three manufacturers at an additional cost: Dyco tripod, iron tower with steel bracings, finished in silver polyurethane; Rohn guyed or self-supporting tripod towers with hot dip galvanized finish; and Pi-Rod solid steel towers with hot dip galvanized finish. Towers come in 40-, 60-, 80-, or 100-foot heights. All are complete with fastenings and mounting materials for the *Wind Jennie*®.

**Sencenbaugh Wind Electric**
**P.O. Box 11174**
**Palo Alto, California 94306**
**(415) 964-1593**

Sencenbaugh Wind Electric, started in 1972 as an agent for Dunlite, has now developed its own range of products as follows:

Sencenbaugh Wind Generator *Model 1000-14* is rated 1 kw at 22 mph wind. An upwind horizontal-axis machine with a three-bladed propeller 12 feet in diameter, it is constructed of machine-carved Sitka spruce with bonded copper leading edge. The propeller speed is 175 rpm at cut-in and 290 rpm at maximum output. Transmission is through a helical gear with a 3:1 ratio and is over-designed to use only 25 percent of rated capacity at full output. Gear and alternator, a three-phase low-speed type, are both sealed in a cast aluminum body. Maximum continuous output at 14 volts DC is 1,000 watts at 22-23 mph; peak output is 1,200 watts. The cut-in and charge rates are electronically controlled by a solid state speed sensor and voltage regulator pioneered by Sencenbaugh in 1973. Propeller overspeed control is provided by a foldable tail at 25-30 mph. Maximum design wind speed limit is 80 mph. Package includes control panel.

Sencenbaugh *Model 500-14* is similar to the above, except for the following: The 500-14 has an output of 500 watts at 25 mph, a peak output of 600 watts, and the propeller is only 6 feet in diameter. It is designed for use in severe climates with high average wind speeds. Thus, it has a small propeller, direct drive, and is designed to withstand a maximum wind speed of 120 mph. The propeller speed cut-in is 280 rpm, and at maximum output 1,000 rpm.

Sencenbaugh *Model 24-14* is a 24-watt wind generator designed to trickle charge 12-volt batteries on boats. The 20 inch diameter propeller direct-drives a permanent magnet DC generator. The maximum output is rated at 21 mph.

Sencenbaugh also supplies Rohn towers especially equipped with tower tops for their wind plants in 40, 50, 60, 70, and 80 foot heights.

Sencenbaugh sells inverters, batteries, meteorological instruments and Sitka spruce propeller blades in addition to its own and Dunlite windplants. They will rent their equipment for a deposit of the full list price of the item. Their catalog costs $2.

**TWR Enterprises**
**72 West Meadow Lane**
**Sandy, Utah 84070**

Tom W. Rentz runs an information and consultation service for alternate energy systems. He also custom-builds wind generators.

His simple, inexpensive *Power Tower* vertical-axis wind turbine includes aluminum turbine components, alternator, automatic regulator, controls, pulleys and belts, mounting stub, shroud covers, top support frame, power feed connector, and installation instructions. The homeowner supplies pole and support cables, batteries, and optional inverter. Three models are available:

    1 kw 12-14 VDC @ 24 mph
    3 kw 24-36 VDC @ 25 mph
    5 kw 32-36 VDC @ 26 mph

All units start charging at about 8 mph.

The *Model A* wind turbine is a very reliable, horizontal-axis turbine with few moving parts. It can be mounted on a pole or tower or suspended from a taut line between two supports. It is designed to charge a 12 volt DC battery and can also be used with an inverter. It is best used for supplemental or recreational energy. Also available in three-bladed models.

The *Wind Titan* is a horizontal-axis, propeller-type turbine with two or three blades of aluminum or spruce. A feathering device and folding rudder act as governors. It also includes alternator, safety brake, and automatic voltage regulator. It can be belt or gear driven. An inverter is optional. Three models are available:

|  | Blades | Diameter | Output |
|---|---|---|---|
| nonfeathering | 2 | 10 feet | 12 VDC (500 watts) @ 25 mph |
| feathering | 2 | 14 feet | 12-14 VDC (1200 watts) @ 25 mph |
| feathering | 3 | 18 feet | 32-36 VDC (3000 watts) @ 25 mph |

They all start charging at about 8 mph.

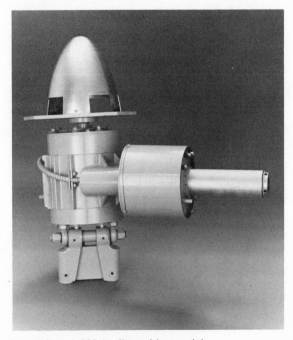

*Sencenbaugh 500-14 direct-drive model.*

**Winco/Division of Dyna Technology, Inc.**
**7850 Metro Parkway**
**Minneapolis, Minnesota 55420**
**(612) 853-8400**

The Winco *Wincharger®* is a 12 volt generator suitable
for minimum lighting in a cabin or campsite. The mill is a
two-bladed, propeller type six feet in diameter with a
patented air brake governor that operates by centrifugal
force in winds over 23 mph. It direct drives a DC
generator, starting at 7 mph. It has a maximum capacity
of 200 watts and can generate 20 kwh per month at 10
mph, 23 kwh per month at 12 mph, and 30 kwh per
month at 14 mph.

A ten foot stub tower and control panel are included.
Voltage regulator costs $75 extra.

Winco® also makes three series of electric generators:
a basic portable power series; a high performance series
with automatic idler and superior motor starting ability;
and a heavy duty, continuous power series using slow
speeds for long life and full economy.

*The Winco* Wincharger.®

## Wind Generators Compared

| Manufacturer | Make | Blades No. | Diam. | Rated Output | Volts |
|---|---|---|---|---|---|
| Aermotor | Model 702 | 18 | 6 ft. | N.A. | N.A. |
| | | 18 | 8 ft. | | |
| | | 18 | 10 ft. | | |
| | | 18 | 12 ft. | | |
| | | 18 | 14 ft. | | |
| | | 18 | 16 ft. | | |
| AeroLectric | Edmund Wind Wizard | 3 | 9 ft. | 600 watts @ 25 mph | 12 |
| Aero Power | SL1000 Wind-powered Electric System | 3 | 10 ft. | 1000 watts @ 20 mph | 12 |
| Aerowatt | 24 FP7 | 2 | 3.3 ft. | 28 watts @ 16 mph | 12/24 |
| | 150 FP7 | 2 | 6.7 ft. | 130 watts @ 16 mph | 12/24 |
| | 300 FP7 | 2 | 10.7 ft. | 350 watts @ 16 mph | 12/24 |
| | 1100 FP7 | 2 | 16.7 ft. | 1125 volt-amperes @ 16 mph | 12/24 |
| | 4100 FP7 | 2 | 30.7 ft. | 4100 volt-amperes @ 16 mph | 12/24 |
| Ampair Products | Ampair 50 | 14 | 26 inches | 50 watts | 12 |
| Chalk Wind Systems | | Multiple | 16 ft. | 700 watts @ 20 mph | |
| Dempster® Industries, Inc. | No. 12 Annu-Oiled Windmill | Multiple | 6 ft. | N.A. | N.A. |
| | | | 8 ft. | | |
| | | | 10 ft. | | |
| | | | 12 ft. | | |
| | | | 14 ft. | | |
| | | | 18 ft. | | |

**The Wind Energy Supply Company Ltd.**
**Iroko House**
**Bolney Ave.**
**Peacehaven**
**Sussex BN9 8HF**
**England**

The Wind Energy Supply Company makes *Wesco®*
*System A Electricity Generating Windmills. System A*
windmills feature three-bladed rotors operating upwind of
the tower; automatic feathering; octagonal section tower;
optional guy wire bracing system; and electrical energy
conversion options, including electric resistance heating,
water pumping, and battery charging.

Two models are available. *Model A30* has a rotor diameter of approximately 10 feet and a rated output of 1800
watts in a 22 mph wind; *Model A55* has a rotor diameter
of approximately 18 feet and a rated output of 6500 watts
in a 22 mph wind. Both cut in at 8 to 11 mph winds and
can survive winds up to 125 mph. They are gear driven.

*Wesco® generator.*

**Zephyr Wind Dynamo Company.**
See Alternators and Inverters.

| Cut in | Cut off | Price | Features |
|---|---|---|---|
| | | $ 460<br>$ 685<br>$ 1170<br>$ 1995<br>$ 3305<br>$ 4570 | For pumping water.<br>Positive oiling system.<br>Adjustable stroke.<br>Automatic regulation.<br>Towers and stub towers available. |
| 9 mph | 50 mph | $ 995 | Suitable for recreational vehicles and vacation homes.<br>Sold by Edmund Scientific Co. |
| 6 mph | | $ 2995 | Spruce blades.<br>Includes gear-driven alternator, mill, voltage regulator, controls, batteries.<br>Towers available. |
| 6 mph<br>6 mph<br>6 mph<br>6 mph<br>6 mph | 125 mph<br>125 mph<br>125 mph<br>125 mph<br>125 mph | $ 3564<br>$ 6568<br>$10,099<br>$19,689<br>$42,758 | For industrial use.<br>Direct-driven alternator in Models 24 FP7, 150 FP7, and 300 FP7.<br>Gear-driven alternator in 1100 FP7 and 4100 FP7.<br>Wood propellers in all except 4100 FP7, which uses aluminum. |
| 10–16 knots<br>(11–18 mph) | 85 knots<br>(98 mph) | About $600–$700 | For permanent installation on cruising yachts.<br>Suitable for low or average windspeeds.<br>Includes mounting tube, alternator with rectifier, and mill.<br>Mounting equipment, voltage regulator, and read-out unit cost extra. |
| 3 mph | | | For pumping water or generating electricity by belt-drive alternator.<br>Custom-built.<br>Aluminum blades attached to wire spokes. |
| | | $ 445<br>$ 675<br>$ 1150<br>$ 1980<br>$ 3135<br>$ 6435 | For pumping water.<br>Steel blades.<br>Positive oiling system. |

**Continued**

## Wind Generators Compared *(Continued)*

| Manufacturer | Make | Blades No. | Diam. | Rated Output | Volts |
|---|---|---|---|---|---|
| Dunlite | Dunlite 2000W | 3 | 13 ft. | 2000 watts @ 25 mph | 24/32/110 |
| | Dunlite 5000W | 3 | 19 ft. | 5000 watts @ mph | 110 |
| Elektro G.m.b.H. | W50 | 6 | | 50 watts | 6/12/24 |
| | W250 | 6 | | 150 watts | 12/24/36 |
| | WV 05 | 2 | | 600 watts | 12/24/36/48 |
| | WV 15G | 2 | 9'10" | 1200 watts | 12/24/36/48 |
| | WV 25G | 2 | 12 ft. | 2200 watts | 24/36/48/115 |
| | WV 35G | 3 | 14'5" | 4000 watts | 48/60/115 |
| | WVG 50G | 3 | 16'5" | 6000 watts | 60/115 |
| | WVG 120G | 3 | 22 ft. | 10,000 watts | 115 |
| Energy Development Co. | Mehrkam Machine | 4 | 38 ft. | 20,000 watts @ 27 mph | |
| | | 4 | 40 ft. | 45,000 watts @ 27 mph | |
| | | 4 | 75 ft. | 150,000 watts @ 27 mph | |
| Kedco, Inc. | 1200 | 3 | 12 ft. | 1200 watts @ 21–22 mph | 12 |
| | 1600 | 3 | 16 ft. | 1200 watts @ 16–17 mph | 12 |
| | 1205 | 3 | 12 ft. | 1900 watts @ 24–25 mph | 24 |
| | 1605 | 3 | 16 ft. | 1900 watts @ 20–21 mph | 24 |
| | 1210 | 3 | 12 ft. | 2000 watts @ 25–26 mph | Variable |
| | 1610 | 3 | 16 ft. | 2000 watts @ 21–22 mph | 180 maximum |
| | 1620 | 3 | 16 ft. | 3000 watts @ 25–26 mph | Variable 180 maximum |
| KMP | Parish Windmill | 18 | 6 ft. | N.A. | N.A. |
| | | 18 | 8 ft. | | |
| | | 18 | 10 ft. | | |
| Lubing Maschinenfabrik | | 6 | | 400 watts @ 27 mph | 24 |
| North Wind Power Co., Inc. | Eagle II | 3 | 14 ft. | 2000 watts @ 24 mph | 32 |
| | | | | 2000 watts @ 22 mph | 110 |
| | Eagle III | 3 | 14 ft. | 3000 watts @ 24 mph | 32 |
| | | | | 3000 watts @ 22 mph | 110 |
| | Commercial systems: | | | | |
| | Eagle II | 3 | 14 ft | 2000 watts @ 22 mph | 110 |
| | Eagle III | 3 | 14 ft. | 3000 watts @ 22 mph | 110 |
| | Remote systems: Eagle II | 3 | 14 ft. | 2000 watts @ 24 mph | 32 |
| | Eagle III | 3 | 14 ft. | 3000 watts @ 24 mph | 32 |
| Product Development Institute | Wind Jennie® | 3 | | 3000 watts @ 20 mph | 220 |

| Cut in | Cut off | Price | Features |
|--------|---------|-------|----------|
| 10 mph | 80 mph | About $3100 | Steel blades.<br>Includes mill, voltage regulator, control box, gear-driven alternator. |
| 6.9 mph | 80 mph | About $4370 | |
| | | $ 1494<br><br>$ 1927 | Vertical-axis.<br>Can withstand high windspeeds.<br>Towers, batteries, inverters, and controls available. |
| | 120 mph | $ 2086<br>$ 2549<br>$ 3202<br>$ 4392<br>$ 5063<br>$ 7808 | Wooden blades.<br>Includes mill, direct-driven alternator.<br>Towers, batteries, inverters, and controls available. |
| 5 mph<br>5 mph<br>5 mph | 40 mph<br>40 mph<br>40 mph | | Includes mill, 40- or 60-foot tower, voltage regulator, controls, alternator.<br>Batteries, inverter, lubricant extra. |
| 6–8 mph<br>7–9 mph | 70 mph<br>60 mph | $ 2295<br>$ 2895 | For battery-charging.<br>Aluminum blades. |
| 6–8 mph<br>7–9 mph | 70 mph<br>60 mph | $ 3345<br>$ 3945 | For battery-charging. |
| 10–12 mph<br>9–11 mph | 70 mph<br>60 mph | $ 2595<br>$ 3195 | Supplied with DC generator. |
| 10–12 mph | 60 mph | $ 4495 | Supplied with DC generator. |
| | | | For pumping water.<br>Aluminum blades.<br>Sprocket-and-chain drive. |
| 9 mph | | | Blades made of epoxy resins reinforced with fiber glass.<br>Includes controls, mill, alternator, three-foot stub tower.<br>Full-size aluminum tubular towers available. |
| 8–10 mph<br>7–10 mph<br>8–10 mph<br>8–10 mph | 27 mph<br>27 mph<br>27 mph<br>27 mph | $ 3300<br>$ 4000<br>$ 4400<br>$ 5100 | Rebuilt Jacobs wind generators.<br>Includes mill, direct-driven generator. |
| 8–10 mph<br>8–10 mph | 27 mph<br>27 mph | $ 5477<br>$ 6577 | For areas where commercial power is available.<br>Includes North Wind Eagle Generator; 36-foot, guyed tower; 4 kw Gemini Synchronous Inverter. |
| 8–10 mph | 27 mph | $ 6115 | DC system for remote areas.<br>Includes North Wind Eagle Generator; 358 amp-hour battery bank; 36-foot, guyed tower; controls. |
| 8–10 mph | 27 mph | $ 7924 | AC/DC system for remote areas.<br>Includes North Wind Eagle Generator; 358 amp-hour battery bank; 36-foot, guyed tower; controls, 1 kw inverter. |
| 9 mph | | $ 3215.80 | Aluminum blades.<br>Includes mill, alternator, controls, synchronous inverter.<br>Towers available with mounting and fastenings for Wind Jennie.® |

Continued

## Wind Generators Compared *(Continued)*

| Manufacturer | Make | Blades No. | Diam. | Rated Output | Volts |
|---|---|---|---|---|---|
| Sencenbaugh Wind Electric | 1000–14 | 3 | 12 ft. | 1000 watts @ 22–23 mph | 12/24 |
| | 500–14 | 3 | 6 ft. | 500 watts @ 25 mph | 12/24 |
| | 24–14 | 3 | 20 inches | 24 watts @ 21 mph | 12 |
| TWR Enterprises | Power Tower | | | 1 kw @ 24 mph<br>3 kw @ 25 mph<br>5 kw @ 26 mph | 12/24<br>24/32<br>32/36 |
| | Model A | Multiple | 5 ft. | | 12 |
| | Wind Titan | 2<br>2<br>3 | 10 ft.<br>14 ft.<br>18 ft. | 500 watts @ 25 mph<br>1200 watts @ 25 mph<br>3000 watts @ 25 mph | 12<br>12/14<br>32/36 |
| Winco (Dyna Technology) | Wincharger® | 2 | 6 ft. | 200 watts @ 23 mph | 12 |
| The Wind Energy Supply Co., Ltd. | Wesco® System A windmills:<br>Model A30<br>Model A55 | <br><br>3<br>3 | <br><br>10 ft.<br>18 ft. | <br><br>1800 watts @ 22 mph<br>6500 watts @ 22 mph | |

# Wind Instruments and Towers

**Dwyer Instruments, Inc.**
**P.O. Box 373**
**Junction Ind. 212 and U.S. 12**
**Michigan City, Indiana 46360**
**(219) 872-9141**
**(312) 733-7883**

Dwyer manufactures small, inexpensive wind measuring devices. The Dwyer Hand-Held Wind Meter gives an accurate direct reading in mph for both high (4–66 mph) and

low (2–10 mph) wind speeds. It comes in a clear plastic case and costs $8.95.

The *Mark II* Windspeed Indicator consists of a wall-mounted indicator panel, which indicates windspeed in 0 to 80 mph and in 1 to 12 Beaufort Scale, and a rooftop vane that acts as a sensor. The complete package also includes 50 feet of flexible, double column tubing to be connected to the rooftop vane, mounting hardware, fluid, and instructions. It costs $34.95.

**Natural Power, Inc.**
**Francestown Turnpike**
**New Boston, New Hampshire 03070**
**(603) 487-2426**

Natural Power manufactures instruments and components for wind energy systems. Their wind survey and site analysis instruments include windspeed and/or wind direction recording instruments (single-channel, $325; dual-channel, $775–$900), a wind data accumulator ($150), windspeed compilators ($825–$2160, depending on number of anemometers), and wind speed compilators with one anemometer and one wind direction head ($1500). Separate anemometer and wind direction heads for use

*Dwyer* Mark II *wind speed indicator.*

| Cut in | Cut off | Price | Features |
|---|---|---|---|
| 6–8 mph | 80 mph | $ 2950 | Includes mill, gear-driven alternator, controls. |
| 9–10 mph | 120 mph | $ 2250 | Designed for severe climates.<br>Includes mill, direct-driven alternator, controls. |
| 8–9 mph | 100 mph | $ 485 | For trickle-charging batteries on boats.<br>Deck-mounted.<br>Includes mill, generator, controls. |
| 8 mph<br>7.5 mph<br>7.5 mph | | $ 1200<br>$ 2000<br>$ 3000 | Vertical-axis.<br>Includes mill, alternator, controls. |
| | | $ 235 | Can be mounted on pole or tower or suspended on wire between two supports. |
| 8 mph<br>8 mph<br>8 mph | 65 mph<br>65 mph<br>65 mph | $ 800–$1200<br>$1400–$1800<br>$2350–$2850 | Belt- or gear-drive.<br>Includes mill, controls, alternator, voltage regulator. |
| 7 mph | | $ 625 | For light loads and vacation homes.<br>Includes mill, direct-driven generator, controls, 10-foot stub tower.<br>Voltage regulator costs extra. |
| 8–11 mph | | $4406–$9744 | For generating electricity.<br>Electrical energy conversion options include electric resistance heating, water pumping, battery charging. |

with these instruments cost $50 each. Anemometer and wind direction heads with interface electronics are $160–$240.

Natural Power also stocks a wind energy monitor by Enertech Corp. ($325) and windspeed/wind direction indicators by Maximum, Inc. for $70 to $270, depending on housing and single- or dual-channel programming.

Telescoping instrument towers by Unarco-Rohn are available in 30-, 40-, or 50-foot heights and cost $35, $45, or $55 respectively.

Their components for wind energy systems are equipped for various voltages. They include a generator control panel for a DC generator used to charge a battery pack, a dynamic loading switch used to prevent overcharging and underdraining and to choose appropriate modes of electricity supply (from turbine, storage, or alternate source), a voltage regulator, and a brushless DC alternator.

Generator Control Panel—$385–$400
Dynamic Loading Switch—$115
Voltage Regulator—$75
Alternator—$400

They also stock Gemini Synchronous Inverters by Windworks, Inc. that cost $780 to $1450.

Natural Power instruments and components can either be purchased or leased for a minimum of three months.

**Taylor Instruments**
**Sybron Corporation**
**Arden, North Carolina 28704**
**(704) 684-8111**

The Taylor Wind Speed Indicator is a precision instrument with two scales: 0 to 25 and 0 to 100 in a mahogany case. It is very accurate, especially at the lower ranges. Sold with 60 feet of lead-in wire and instructions, it costs $185.

**Unarco-Rohn**
**Division of Unarco Industries, Inc.**
**6718 West Plank Road**
**P.O. Box 2000**
**Peoria, Illinois 61656**
**(309) 697-4400**

Unarco-Rohn designs and manufactures both guyed and self-supporting towers for use with electric wind generators. Their towers are hot-dip galvanized after fabrication and come with top sections compatible with many wind generators, including Sencenbaugh, Dunlite, Elektro, Jacobs, and Zephyr.

# Alternators and Inverters

**Delatron Systems**
**553 Lively Boulevard**
**Elk Grove Village, Illinois 60007**
**(312) 593-2270**

Delatron manufactures DC-to-AC inverters. Their VC-type inverters are especially suitable for alternate energy applications, such as wind electric systems. They feature low-idle (no-load) power consumption and high in-rush current-handling capability. Their efficiency is 80 percent minimum. Models run from $2800 to $4200.

Their VS type inverters are suitable for applications where a pure sine wave is required, such as for television and telephone operation. Their efficiency is 90 percent minimum. Models cost from $3500 to $5100.

All Delatron inverters feature low DC voltage shut-down and overload shut-down. Their output voltage is 115 to 230 VAC, 60 Hz. They range in size from 3 KVA to 6 KVA. It is advised that they be used with a DC input voltage of 48 or 120 VDC.

Delatron also makes deep cycle lead acid batteries that can store from 1400 to over 2000 watts for 20 hours. They cost $115 to $150.

**Georator™ Corporation**
**P.O. Box 70**
**9016 Prince Williams St.**
**Manassas, Virginia 22110**
**(703) 368-2101**

Georator™ manufactures the *Nobrush®* permanent magnet alternator. It is available in frequencies up to 1000 Hz and in power ratings from 150 VA to 25 KVA. The rugged Series 36 alternator has stable output voltage, short circuit immunity, high overload capacity, low RF noise, and low heating. It has a maximum operating speed of 600 rpm, with many models operating within 1800 rpm. It can be mounted with shaft horizontal, vertical or at any angle.

The *Nobrush®* permanent magnet alternator is built to customer specifications with regards to the power, voltage, and frequency at a requested speed.

*Georator™ generator-alternator.*

**Natural Power, Inc.**
See Wind Instruments and Towers.

**West Wind Electronics, Inc.**
**P.O. Box 542**
**Durango, Colorado 81301**
**(303) 884-9709**

West Wind manufactures prototype inverters ($1250) that have been operating since August 1975 with no failures. The 6 kw inverters provide a square wave output of 90 to 140 volts AC. Despite the square wave voltage, no overheating problems have occurred with induction motors or transformers. It is direct-coupled (no output transformer); therefore, each AC appliance must have its own fuse in the event of inverter malfunction. It is 90 percent efficient.

Options include overvoltage and undervoltage shut-down protection ($250); an automatic load demand switch that saves 100 watts continuous ($250) and a sine wave filter for TV's, stereos, and other appliances that may not work properly on square wave voltage.

The Voltage Control Switch protects storage batteries from over or undercharging by sensing battery voltage levels and activating power switches used to control various loads.

Two models are available: *Model A* switches on large loads when batteries are charged and energy is still available from the windmill, thus preventing overspeeding ($110); *Model B* starts a back-up generator when batteries are discharged and stops it when batteries are fully or partially charged. (The backup generator must have its own starter motor and logic circuits.) *Model B* also will switch off the field current of the mill when excess energy is available, thus preventing overcharge ($85).

**Windworks, Inc.**
**Rt. 3**
**Box 329**
**Mukwonago, Wisconsin 53149**
**(414) 363-4088**

Windwork's *Gemini Synchronous Inverter* converts voltage from a DC power source, such as a wind turbine, to AC at standard line voltage and frequency. With the *Gemini,* excess AC voltage can be stored in the public utility grid. When less power is available than is required, the power company can supply it at standard rates, giving credit for excess power fed to it previously. The overall cost of the *Gemini Synchronous Inverter* is lower per kilowatt than battery/inverter systems, but satisfactory arrangements must be made with the local power company, and the homeowner must be prepared to sacrifice some of his freedom.

The *Gemini Synchronous Inverter* is available in single-phase systems with power capacities of 4 or 8 kw, an input voltage of 0–200 volts DC, and an output voltage of 120–240 volts AC. It is 95 percent efficient. The 8 kw model costs $1,450; the 4 kw model costs $780.

**Zephyr Wind Dynamo Company**
**21 Stanwood Street**
**Brunswick, Maine 04011**
**(207) 725-6534**

Zephyr Wind Dynamo Company manufactures *Very Low Speed Permanent Magnet Alternators (VLS-PM)*. These direct-drive alternators are suitable for horizontal- and vertical-axis turbines. Their chief advantage is that they do not require shaft speed increasers. They are built in a modular system that allows costly stator sections to be added or removed while the alternators are in service, providing versatility and easy maintenance. They achieve load matching without power-consuming or switching components. Almost any turbine power curve can be matched. Other features of the *VLS-PM* include heavy duty bearings, weathertight construction, and solid-state circuitry to provide overvoltage protection. The *Series 311B VLS-PM* has a rated output of 1500 watts at 450 rpm, 180 hz, two-phase. Its voltage is rated at 24 volts AC parallel-connected and 48 volts AC series-connected. Its diameter is 13.9 inches overall and it will support most turbines five meters in diameter and under. It is about 75 percent efficient.

The *Series 647 VLS-PM* is rated at 15 kw at 300 rpm, 270 hz. Buyer specifies voltage and one, two, three, or six phases. It is 27.5 inches in diameter and 82 percent efficient.

Zephyr also manufactures the *Wind Dynamo*, a three-bladed downwind machine that is still in the experimental stage, and the *Tetra-helix*, a prototype slant-axis wind machine.

# Agents

**Alaska Wind & Water Power**
**P.O. Box 6**
**Chugiak, Alaska 99567**
**(907) 688-2896**

Active agents for a complete range of wind generators and water turbines.

**Alternate Energy Systems**
**150 Sandwich Street**
**Plymouth, Massachusetts 02360**
**(617) 747-0771**

**Automatic Power**
**P.O. Box 18738**
**Houston, Texas 77023**
**(713) 228-5208**

**The Big Outdoors People**
**2201 N.E. Kennedy Street**
**Minneapolis, Minnesota 55413**
**(612) 331-5430**

Main activity is in geodesic dome housing, but also involved in alternative energy and design of wind power systems.

**Boston Wind**
**2 Maston Court**
**Charlestown, Massachusetts 02129**

Boston Wind sells new and used wind generators and accessories and offers an installation service. It also holds courses, workshops and slide-lectures and publishes a quarterly newsletter.

**Budgen & Associates**
**72 Broadview Avenue**
**Pointe Claire, P.Q. H9R 3Z4**
**Canada**

Dr. Harry Budgen is technical advisor on alternative energy to Brace Research Institute of Macdonald College, which has a Lubing, a 5 kw Elektro and a 25 ft.-diameter sail windmill on campus. Budgen & Associates supply Lubing and Dunlite wind generators and pumps and also plans for a Brace-designed wind generator with three-bladed, 32-ft. diameter propeller, developing 49.5 hp in 30 mph winds.

**Clean Energy Systems**
**RD 1, Box 366**
**Elysburg, Pennsylvania 17824**
**(717) 799-0008**

Offers mechanical engineering design assistance on wind power and other renewable energy sources.

**Earthmind**
**5246 Boyer Road**
**Mariposa, California 95338**

This group of wind power enthusiasts includes Michael Hackleman, author of two excellent books: *Wind & Windspinners* and *The Homebuilt, Wind-Generated Electricity Handbook*, (see *Bibliography*). Earthmind deals mainly with reconditioned Jacobs and Winchargers, and since it is a non-profit organization, proceeds from sales go towards establishing its research center.

**Electro Sales Co., Inc.**
**100 Fellsway West**
**Somerville, Massachusetts 02145**

Electro Sales supplies surplus inverters, motors, and controls. They are also the distributor for Carter Electric Company, which manufactures rotary converters and inverters.

**Energy Alternatives, Inc.**
**69 Amherst Road**
**Leverett, Massachusetts 01054**
**(413) 549-3644**

These agents for Dunlite, Jacobs, Elektro and Aero Power windmills also offer integrated sun, wind and wood designs.

**Enertech**
**P.O. Box 420**
**Norwich, Vermont 05055**
**(802) 649-1145**

Enertech distributes wind energy systems. Their *200 Series* features the Winco *Wincharger®*; the *500/1000 Series* utilizes Sencenbaugh wind plants *Model 500* or *Model 1000*; and the *2000 Series* uses the *Dunlite 2000*. Systems include towers, batteries, and an inverter or synchronous inverter as required.

Enertech is also the distributor for *Sparco* wind-powered water pumps. These inexpensive, propeller-type wind plants have self-feathering blades. They are easily installed and can be dismounted and drained in freezing weather. In winds of 7 mph, they will pump over 30 gallons of water per hour.

Two types are available: *Model D* is a diaphragm-type designed to draw up to 13 feet through a hose run horizontally from a nearby water source; *Model P* is a piston-type that will draw water up to 33 feet from a well, boring, bridge, or pier directly underneath.

Enertech also sells wind measuring instruments and how-to manuals, such as its own *Planning a Wind-Powered Generating System* ($2).

**Environmental Energies, Inc.**
**P.O. Box 73**
**Front Street**
**Copemish, Michigan 49625**
**(616) 378-2000**

Founded by Al O'Shea, one of the organizers of the American Wind Energy Association, EEI deals in Dunlite, Winco, rebuilt Jacobs and Elektro machines. It offers a complete installation service and stocks a line of

Creative Electronics inverters. EEI practices what it preaches: The shop is powered by an Elektro and is heated by a wood-burning stove and solar energy. Send $5 for their detailed and informative booklet on wind, solar and other energy systems.

**Future Resources & Energy Ltd.**
**167 Denison Street**
**Markham, Ontario L3R IB5**
**Canada**
**(416) 495-0720**

Fred Drucker of FRE, during his frequent visits to Elektro in Switzerland over the past three years, has developed a thorough understanding of Elektro wind generators. As a result FRE is now the sole Canadian agent for Elektro. Each machine is checked for quality control before erection. FRE specializes in wind and solar combinations.

**Independent Energy Systems**
**6043 Sterrettania Road**
**Fair View, Pennsylvania 16415**

IES offers reconditioned Jacobs. Send $2 for information on wind, solar and wood services.

**Independent Power Developers**
**Box 1467**
**Noxon, Montana 59853**
**(406) 847-2315**

IPD, agent for Dunlite machines, was recently awarded a contract by the Montana Department of Natural Resources to build and demonstrate a 15-ft diameter, three-bladed downwind machine to develop 18 kw in a 33 mph wind. The blades will be made of aluminum.

**Jopp Electrical Works**
**Princeton, Minnesota 55371**

Martin Jopp, rightly referred to as a "wind wizard," started back in 1917, when he built a few hundred Jopp Wind generators. His own home has been powered by two 3 kw Jacobs wind generators for years. Jopp now turns out new parts for old Jacobs mills at very reasonable prices. What he doesn't know about Jacobs is not worth knowing. He writes on the subject, answering letters in *Alternative Sources of Energy*.

**Prairie Sun & Wind Company**
**4408 62nd Street**
**Lubbock, Texas 79409**

Agent for Winco & Aero Power.

**Quirks**
**33 Fairweather Street**
**Bellevue Hill**
**NSW 2023, Australia**

Markets the Dunlite wind generator.

**Real Gas & Electricity Co.**
P.O. Box 193
Shingletown, California 96088
(916) 474-3456
(707) 526-3400 (Santa Rosa office)

Designs and installs systems using Dunlite and Elektro wind generators. Offers complete installation service or supervisory assistance. They also deal with solar and water power.

**Rede Corporation**
P.O. Box 212
Providence, Rhode Island 02901
(401) 861-5390

Rede is U.S. agent for DAF Darrieus wind generators.

**Sigma Engineering**
Box 5285
Lubbock, Texas 79417
(806) 762-5690

Regional distributor for DAF Darrieus rotors. See Rede Corporation above.

**Sunstructures, Inc.**
**Integrated Architectural Design**
201 E. Liberty Street, No. 6
Ann Arbor, Michigan 48104
(313) 994-5650

Specializes in integrated wind and solar systems. Also conducts workshops.

**Total Environmental Action**
Church Hill
Harrisville, New Hampshire 03450
(603) 827-3374

Offers a wide range of architectural and engineering services in the alternative energy field. Emphasis on research, design and teaching.

**Wind Energy Systems (Sunflower Power Co.)**
Route 1, Box 93-A
Oskaloosa, Kansas 66066
(913) 597-5603

WES sells second-hand wind generators—Jacobs, Wincharger, Wind King, etc.— is agent for the Gemini inverter, and designs and builds integrated energy systems. Manager Steve Blake, who has also had extensive experience in building and testing Savonius rotors at the Brace Research Institute also works with the Appropriate Technology Group at the same address.

**Windependence Electric**
P.O. Box M 1188
Ann Arbor, Michigan 48106
(313) 769-8469

Windependence sells a range of reconditioned wind generators—Allied, Winpower, Jacobs, etc.

# Additional Sources of Information

**Alternate Sources of Energy**
Route 2
Milaca, Minnesota 56353

This very fine journal with many excellent articles on wind power includes "Martin Answers" by Martin Jopp. ASE is *the* journal for the home builder of windmills. It contains lots of solid, safe and intelligent advice. They have published many plans (and by far the best) for home windmill builders. ASE No. 24 (Feb '77) is a special wind power issue. Six issues yearly are well worth the $10 cost.

**American Wind Energy Association**
Box 329
Route 3
Mukwonago, Wisconsin 53149

The AWEA is a national association that represents manufacturers, distributors, and researchers involved in the development of wind energy. Membership is $25 per year. The AWEA issues a quarterly newsletter, publishes the *Wind Technology Journal* and holds convivial and enlightening conferences.

**Brace Research Institute**
**McGill University**
Ste. Anne De Bellevue
Quebec, Canada
HOA 1CO

Brace Research Institute publishes booklets and plans concerning alternate energy systems. Their wind energy titles include:
   *How to Construct a Cheap Wind Machine for Pumping Water*, by A. Bodek. $1.25.
   *Performance Test of a Savonius Rotor*, by M.H. Simonds and A. Bodek. $2.
   *Windmill Power Pumps with Intermediate Electrical Power Transmission*, by M.A. Memarzadeh and T.H. Barton. $1.50.
   *A Simple Electric Transmission System for a Free Running Windmill*, by T.H. Barton and K. Repole. $2.
   *Notes on the Development of the Brace Airscrew Windmill as a Prime Mover*, by R.E. Chilcott. 50¢.
   *Windpower Packet*, $1.50. Details of commercially available windmills and short windpower bibliography.

Enclose payment with order. Add 25¢ if ordering only one leaflet or if paying by check. Make checks payable to the Publication Department.

**Earthmind**
**5246 Boyer Road**
**Mariposa, California 95338**

*Wind and Windspinners* by Michael Hackleman covers the electrics of wind systems and tells how to build a Savonius rotor.

**Edmund Scientific**
**1006 Edscorp Building**
**Barrington, New Jersey 08007**

The *Windy Ten Dutch Windmill Plans* are for those who want to build a Dutch Four-arm. Propeller is eight feet in diameter and can produce up to 500 watts if coupled to a generator. Suitable for the serious romantic only. $16.

**Farallones Institute**
**15290 Coleman Valley Road**
**Occidental, California 94565**

*Homemade Windmills of Nebraska* by Erwin Barbour, originally published in 1898, describes how to build "weird and wonderful" windmills for pumping and sawing.

**Flanagan's Plans, Inc.**
**Box 891**
**Cathedral Station**
**New York, New York 10025**
**(212) 222-4774**

Flanagan's Plans sells plans for the patented *Quixote Sailwing Windmill Rotor* designed at Princeton University by staff members of the Flight Concepts Laboratory. The three-bladed, horizontal-axis machine has a rating of 1 kw in a 20 mph wind and an efficiency of 75 percent. Maximum wind speed is 50 mph.

The plans include drawings, instructions, and patterns for the rotor, shaft, sails, and bearings. The Quixote is easily constructed by the amateur with locally available materials for about $550. Plans cost $25 and include license for construction.

*Testing the prototype rotor on the Flanagan's Plans "mobile tower."*

**Forrestal Campus Library**
**Princeton University**
**Princeton, New Jersey 08540**

*The Princeton Sailwing Program* by Dr. T. Sweeney is a short report on the two-bladed Sailwing developed at Princeton University. $2.

**Four Winds Press**
**50 West 44th Street**
**New York, New York 10036**

*Catch the Wind* by Landt and Lisl Dennis is a well-written general introduction to wind power. $7.95.

**Great Plains Windustries**
**Box 126**
**Lawrence, Kansas 66044**

*Windustries* is a fine regional quarterly newsletter, mainly concerned with wind power. A subscription costs $10; $15 for institutions.

# HELION Inc.

**Helion, Inc.**
**Box 445**
**Brownsville, California 95919**
**(916) 675-2478**
**(916) 692-1560**

Helion is a nonprofit research and educational organization founded by Jack Park. It offers books and plans about wind energy and other alternate energy systems.

*Simplified Wind Power Systems for Experimenters,* by Jack Park. $6. Covers site analysis, load estimation, windmill sizing and design, and systems.

*Power from the Wind,* by Palmer Putnam. $10.95. The story of the Smith-Putnam 1,250 kw wind generator.

*12/16 Construction Plans.* $10. Plans for construction of a 2,000 to 5,000 watt generator using aluminum blades 12 or 16 feet in diameter. Features belt drive transmission, overspeed governor, and your choice of generator. (See Kedco product description.)

*Small Wind Machines.* $10. Slide presentation. Includes descriptive pamphlet.

Helion also provides consulting services and conducts lectures and workshops. Call or write for arrangement of fees and schedules. When ordering publications, add $1 postage and handling to payment.

***Home Energy Digest***
**8009—34th Ave. South**
**Minneapolis, Minnesota 55420**

*The Home Energy Digest and Wood Burning Quarterly* offers practical advice and detailed information to the homeowner interested in alternative energy as a means to self-sufficiency. Articles by experts cover not only wood burning but solar energy, wind power, water power, and energy conservation techniques.

Four issues per year cost $7.95.

**Intermediate Technology Publications**
**9 King Street**
**London WC2**
**England**

*Food from Windmills* by Peter Frankael describes the windmill-building activities of the American Presbyterian Mission in Ethiopia. Contains lots of good details on how to build sail mills—mainly 11-foot-diameter and used for water pumping.

**Jack Park**
**Box 4301**
**Sylmar, California 91342**

*Simplified Wind Power Systems for Experimenters* by Jack Park contains data of interest to home builders on the aerodynamic, structural and mechanical design of wind-driven propellers. $8.

**Low Energy Systems**
**3 Larkfield Gardens**
**Dublin 6**
**Ireland**
**01-960653**

Low Energy Systems publishes booklets and offers advice for those interested in alternative energy. In the field of wind energy, they offer the following:

*Vertical Axis Sail Windmill Plans.* $4. Plans for rotor and tower, suitable for water-pumping and grain-grinding.
*Trickle Charger Windgenerator Plans.* $1.50. Suitable for operating light electrical appliances.

**The Mother Earth News**
**P.O. Box 70**
**Hendersonville, North Carolina 28739**

*Mother Earth News,* the magazine for self-sufficiency, carries occasional articles on wind power, but we could do with more. Well worth $10 for six issues a year. TMEN also reprinted Homemade Six-Volt Wind-Plants, originally published in 1939. Send $1.

**National Center for Alternative Technology**
**Machynlleth**
**Powys, Wales**
**England**

The *Do-It-Yourself Sail Windmill (Cretan) Plans* show how to build a 12-foot diameter Sail Wind Generator, 200 watt output at 15 mph, maximum 300 watts.

**The Bookstore at Natural Power, Inc.**
**New Boston, New Hampshire 03070**
**(603) 487-5512**

Natural Power sells energy-related publications from their bookstore or by mail. Wind energy titles include:

*The Generation of Electricity by Wind Power,* by E.W. Golding. $19. A classic textbook including drawings, diagrams, photographs, and bibliography.
*Helion Model 12/16 Windmill Plans.* $10. (See *Helion*).
*Electric Power from the Wind,* by Henry Clews. $2. A practical guide to individual applications.

*Power from the Wind,* by P.C. Putnam. $9.95. (See *Helion.*)
*Wind and Windspinners,* by Michael Hackleman. $7.50. Step-by-step introduction for the beginner.
*Simplified Wind Power Systems for Experimenters,* by Jack Park. $6. (See *Helion*).
*Wind Machines,* by Frank Eldridge. $4.25. An overview of the viability, history, and future of wind machines.
*The Homebuilt Wind-Generated Electricity Handbook,* by Michael Hackleman. $7.50. Covers discovery, restoration, and installation of wind electric machines manufactured in the United States in the 1930's through the 1950's.
*Windworks Poster.* $3.50. (See *Windworks*.)

When ordering, add 75¢ postage and handling. Make check payable to The Bookstore at Natural Power, Inc.

**New Alchemy Institute**
**P.O. Box 432**
**Woods Hole, Massachusetts 02543**

No. 2 of the *Journal of the New Alchemists* contains details of how to build a Sailwing rotor. $6.

**Publications**
**Eng. Research Center**
**Foothills Campus**
**Colorado State University**
**Fort Collins, Colorado 80523**

*Energy from the Wind* by Burke and Meroney is the bibliography of bibliographies on wind energy—complete and annotated. $7.50. A "First Supplement" (from 1975 to 1977) is also available for $10.

**Rain**
**2270 N. W. Irving**
**Portland, Oregon 97210**

*Rain* is a fine monthly "Journal of Appropriate Technology." The April '77 issue contained an excellent article on the 200 kw Dutch Gedser mill—a mill much praised for its low cost and suitability for local manufacture. A *Rain* subscription is $10, a single issue $1.

**Structural Clay Products Ltd.**
**230 High Street**
**Potters Bar, Herts**
**England**

*Reinforced Brickwork Windmill Tower* by A.B. Bird concentrates mainly on designing and building brickwork towers. It also contains a section on how to build a 40-foot-diameter Sail Windmill.

**TWR Enterprises**
**72 West Meadow Lane**
**Sandy, Utah 84070**

TWR Enterprises (see product description) offers one set of plans for building a wind generator for as little as $300.

*Windgenerator Plans.* $6.50. Plans for an 800/1200/1600 watt, three-bladed turbine using friction drive or gears.

Send 50¢ and a stamped self-addressed envelope for more information on publications and consulting services.

**Volunteers in Technical Assistance**
**3706 Rhode Island Ave.**
**Mt. Rainier, Maryland 20822**

VITA is a nonprofit development organization based in the United States. It supplies information and assistance by mail to people seeking help with technical problems.

Publications concerning wind energy include the following:

*Low Cost Windmill for Developing Nations,* by Helmut Bossel. VITA, 1970. $2.95. Instructions for building a windmill with five major components. Can use spare auto parts.

*Tanzanian Windmill,* by Dick Stanley, VIA/VITA, 1977. $3. Instructions for building a water-pumping windmill developed in Tanzania.

*Savonius Rotor Construction: Two Vertical-Axis Wind Machines from Oil Drums,* by Jozef A. Kozlowski. VITA, 1977. $3.25. Instructions for building two-stage rotor for pumping water and three-stage rotor for charging auto batteries.

Include payment with order. Make checks payable to VITA Publications Service.

VITA also publishes two newsletters, *VITA News* and *Vis-a-Vis,* containing information on VITA programs, notices of important events, technical abstracts, profiles of VITA volunteers, and lists of problems requiring solutions. Available upon request from VITA Communications Department. Donations accepted.

**Wind Energy Report®**
**P.O. Box 14**
**Rockville Centre, New York 11571**

*Wind Energy Report®* is an international newsletter devoted to reporting events and trends in the field of wind energy. It features articles by experts, reports on new products, reviews of publications, and news of prominent personalities in the field.

The sixteen-page newsletter is published monthly. A subscription for one year costs $75.

**Windworks, Inc.**
**Box 329**
**Rt. 3**
**Mukwonago, Wisconsin 53149**

In addition to manufacturing the *Gemini Synchronous Inverter,* Windworks provides consulting services, plans, and publications in the field of wind energy.

*Sail Windmill Plans.* $25. Plans for construction of a horizontal-axis sail windmill 25 feet in diameter. Includes instructions for building a 42-foot **octahedron** module tower developed by Windworks.

*Wind Energy Bibliography.* $3. Compilation of books, articles, and papers dealing with wind energy and related fields.

*Wind Energy Chart.* $3.25. Educational chart depicting chronology of wind power development. Text on opposite side provides introduction to the field of wind energy and includes lists of publications and references.

# 4

# Water Power

Photo by Ellen Foscue Johnson

ater generates one-eighth of America's electric power. At the same time, more than twice again this amount of potential hydropower is currently undeveloped, representing a vast resource of unexploited energy. The Federal Power Commission estimates that the United States has 470 billion kilowatt-hours per year of undeveloped water power resources—equal to an annual 276 million barrels of oil. Moreover, the FPC study concentrated on medium and large-scale sites, excluding many small streams and rivers with less than 5000 kilowatt capacity. But 5000 kw is enough power to serve the needs of several thousand families. The Army Corps of Engineers has identified 49,000 *existing* dams over twenty-five feet high. Of these, only 1400 are now used for power generation. The installation of additional generating capacity at existing dam sites could add as much as 54 million kilowatts to the nation's electric power. According to David Lilienthal, former chairperson of the Tennessee Valley Authority and the Atomic Energy Commission, "these small and medium-sized projects can be developed at lower capital costs per unit—and will produce electricity at lower production costs per unit—than we are likely to get from huge new generating stations using less permanent, less reliable, more hazardous resources."[1]

Even if you are not fortunate enough to have an old dam on the property complete with millrace and turbine house, a vigorous stream can supply your house with plenty of useful power for heating, cooling, lighting, and operating tools and appliances. Like wind power, however, hydropower is not free. A complete water power electric generation system can cost many thousands of dollars, though homebuilt or small-scale systems may cost much less. A sturdily built hydropower system will provide many years of free energy, paying for itself many times over, for as long as rivers flow.

# Traditional Waterwheels

Watermills are one of civilization's earliest inventions. The first known reference to one is in 85 BC, but they undoubtedly were in use long before

[1] David Lilienthal, "Lost Megawatts Flow Over Nation's Myriad Spillways," *Smithsonian*, March 1978.

*DELL' ARTIFICIOSE MACHINE.*

Figure 4–1. Vertical-axis watermill from *Theatrum Machinarum Novum,* by G.A. Bockler, *c.* 1662. Reprinted from John Reynolds, *Windmills and Watermills* (New York: Praeger, 1970).

then. They fulfilled one of our most basic needs—grinding grain to make flour.

## VERTICAL AND HORIZONTAL AXIS

Two basic kinds of early waterwheels can be distinguished: the *vertical axis* wheel (Figure 4–1), and the *horizontal axis* wheel (Figure 4–2). The former was probably the first to be used and has become known as the "Greek mill," though it may have originated in the Middle East and was used throughout northern Europe. It is best suited to hilly country with small fast-flowing streams.

The horizontal axis wheel became known as the "Roman mill" because it was used throughout the Roman Empire. It is suitable for larger, slower streams and requires extensive gearing to transmit the force.

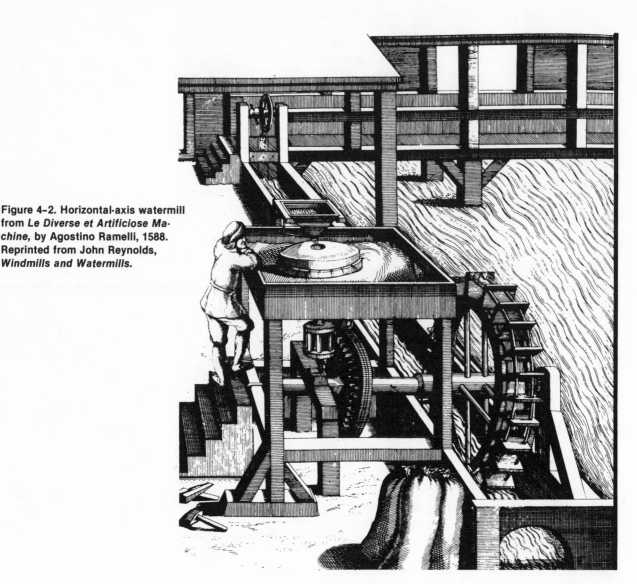

Figure 4-2. Horizontal-axis watermill from *Le Diverse et Artificiose Machine,* by Agostino Ramelli, 1588. Reprinted from John Reynolds, *Windmills and Watermills.*

## UNDERSHOT AND OVERSHOT WHEELS

The earliest horizontal axis waterwheels were *undershot,* that is, only the bottom paddles were submerged in the stream (Figure 4-3). However, during the later Roman period the more efficient *overshot* wheel was developed (Figure 4-4). The water was fed onto the top of the wheel so that both the weight of the water and the impact of the stream flow were used for turning the wheel. The overshot wheel requires a good *head* of water, that is, the supply of water falling onto the wheel must be significantly higher than the level of the water leaving the wheel (called the *tailwater*). Overshot wheels were common throughout Europe until the Industrial Revolution.

The overshot wheel has the most efficient design of any traditional waterwheel, though undershot and *breastshot* wheels (Figure 4-5) are quite useful for high rates of flow with low head. Overshot wheels even have several advantages over the more sophisticated water turbines. They require little maintenance and operate well despite fluctuations in the rate of flow of the stream. They are not affected by trash and grit that may be floating in the water (heavy objects like logs pass out over the wheel and fall clear by virtue of their own momentum). They are much easier to build than more modern turbines as they do not require machine tooling or accurate balancing.

The water must be brought to the top of an overshot wheel by a *sluice* (or *penstock*) that should be about six inches above the wheel and should have a sluice gate to regulate the flow of water. The water should fall into the buckets just as they pass the top of their circuit. The buckets should hold the water until they reach the bottom of their circuit, thus deriving the maximum benefit from the weight of the water. For optimum efficiency, with a limited amount of water, the buckets should be filled only about one-quarter full so that the water does not spill out until the last possible moment. The amount of water in the buckets is regulated by the sluice gate (Figure 4–6).

The buckets are held in place by a pair of wheels. These can be constructed from strong wood or steel. A drum type wheel is probably the easiest to construct since it avoids the problems of making spokes.

Although traditional waterwheels like these turn slowly and are best suited for pumping or grinding grain or driving machinery, it is possible to gear them up to turn the armature of a small generator to produce electricity.

Overshot wheels need at least enough head to clear the wheel (usually about eight feet) and work well with heads of up to thirty feet. The *flow* of water—that is the amount and velocity of water passing a given point in the stream—is also important. Overshot wheels work best with a flow of one to thirty cubic feet per second.

The power available in a stream depends on the head and the flow. The amount of that power an overshot wheel can capture is determined by the diameter and width of the wheel. At best, an overshot wheel can use up to 70 percent of the available power. But the wheel turns at between 6 and 20 revolutions per minute, which is much lower than the 1500 rpm required by a generator, so for producing electricity the efficiency of an overshot wheel is reduced by friction losses in the gearing and belting necessary to increase the rotational speed enough to power a generator.

Very heavy-duty gears are required to withstand the waterwheel's powerful torque. A new gearbox suitable for use with a twenty-foot wheel might cost over $6000. Many people avoid this expense by using spur or helical gears, tractor gear boxes or truck back axles for the initial step-up. After the speed is increased four to twelve times, V-belts and pulleys can be used for the secondary step-up. Secondhand gears and parts can be found in scrapyards for much less cost than new components.

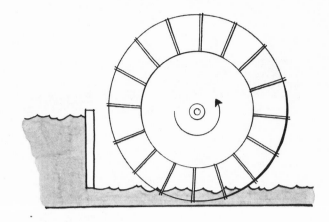

Figure 4-3. Undershot wheel.

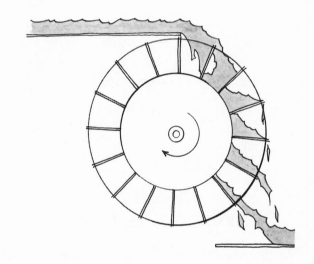

Figure 4-4. Overshot wheel.

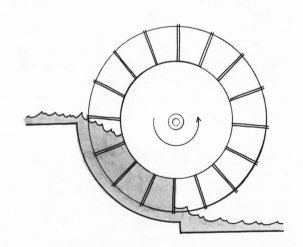

Figure 4-5. Breastshot wheel.

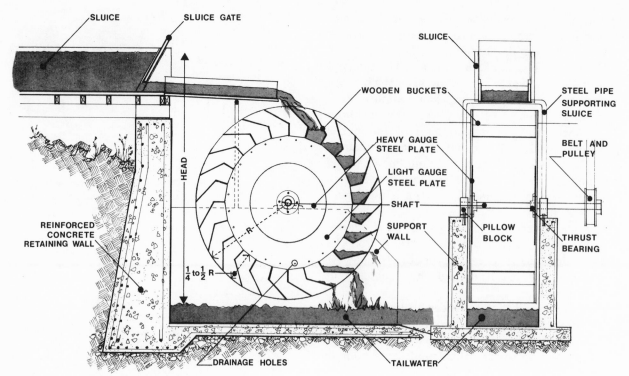

Figure 4-6. A simple overshot wheel.

# Modern Water Turbines

During the Industrial Revolution, careful study of the way water flows led to the development of turbines, which feed the incoming water through guide vanes onto the blades of the rotating wheel at a precise angle. The sophisticated design of both blades and guides causes the wheel to turn at the high speeds necessary for generating electricity. Modern turbines are so efficient that they often capture over 90 percent of the energy available in the water.

### IMPULSE TURBINES

A simple impulse turbine, such as the Pelton wheel (Figure 4-7), uses a nozzle to increase the pressure of the incoming water. The water shoots out of the nozzle, hits a divided bucket and is deflected in a double curve. It then falls into the tailwater, having given up almost all of its momentum. The impulse turbine is driven by the velocity of the water rather than by its weight.

Very little water (a low flow—at least 10 cubic feet per minute) but high speed and pressure (at least fifty feet of head) are needed to run an impulse turbine efficiently. Above these levels, variations in rate of flow and amount of head do not significantly reduce its efficiency of 80 to 90 percent.

Figure 4-7. Pelton wheel has buckets on shaft in center.

For impulse turbines, the head is measured from the level of the water supply to the *level of the nozzle* rather than of the tailwater. But this difference is small, since the nozzle and wheel should be mounted as close to the tailwater as is possible without touching it even at times of high water (Figure 4–8).

The nozzle for an impulse turbine should be carefully aimed, so that the jet of water hits each bucket perpendicularly and is evenly divided by the center ridge. A gate valve in the nozzle regulates the flow for maximum efficiency. A deflector can divert the water from the buckets if the wheel needs to be stopped suddenly. The buckets should be as smooth and evenly balanced as possible to minimize friction.

An impulse turbine is more difficult to build than a simple overshot wheel, but it is better suited for generating electricity because it rotates at higher speeds (approximately half the speed of the incoming jet of water). A certain amount of machine tooling is necessary to create an efficient impulse wheel. Because of the high pressure of the water, both the nozzle and the buckets will gradually wear down and should be made easily replaceable.

REACTION TURBINES

Reaction turbines work on the same principle as rotating lawn sprinklers. The water entering a reaction turbine is guided through fixed passages onto the moving blades of the runner wheel. The force of the incoming water makes the blades begin to rotate. As the water is deflected along the curved blades it accelerates, increasing the speed of rotation, which in turn increases the speed of acceleration.

The runner blades absorb the energy of the moving water so efficiently that they turn at a speed approximately equal to that of the incoming water.

Reaction wheels (Figure 4–9) are considerably smaller than impulse turbines, which are in turn considerably smaller than traditional waterwheels.

**Francis turbines.** In the original reaction turbine, the water entered at the center and was flung out the edges, just as in a lawn sprinkler. In 1849 J. B. Francis developed a reaction turbine with an inward flow—the water is fed in from the sides and flows out the bottom. Still used today, Francis-type turbines are adaptable to a wide range of conditions. They can operate with anywhere from 5 to 3000 feet of head, though they work best with from 70 to 1000 feet. They require more flow than impulse turbines, but not as much as propeller turbines.

**Propeller turbines.** The other main kind of reaction turbine, a propeller turbine, works like a motor boat propeller in reverse. Instead of making the blades rotate to move the water, the moving water forces the blades to rotate. The propeller type of turbine spins very fast even with low

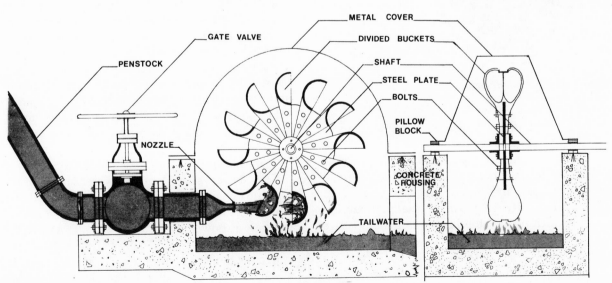

Figure 4-8. A simple Pelton wheel that can be built from sheet metal.

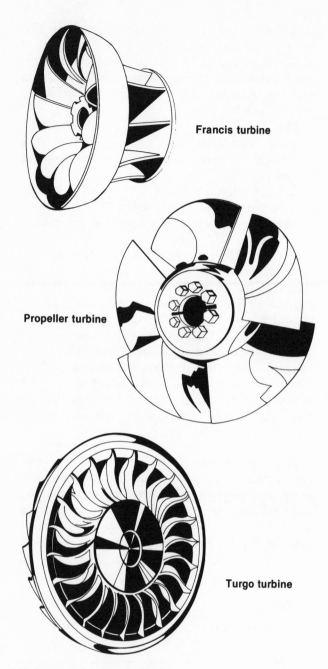

Francis turbine

Propeller turbine

Turgo turbine

Figure 4-9. Reaction turbines.

to adjust the amount of water entering the turbine so that it always operates at maximum efficiency, and in case of emergency can be gradually stopped (the flow of water cannot be shut off suddenly, because tremendous pressure builds up in the pipe leading to the turbine). Reaction turbines usually have gate valves at the bottom of the guide passages to regulate the amount of water falling onto the runner blades.

Reaction turbines are so precisely made and designed that they are very difficult to build at home (though it is possible to convert centrifugal pumps and propeller-type pumps to work as turbines). They must be carefully installed and maintained to avoid leaks and minimize friction.

Because of vapor pockets formed by deflecting water at high speeds, corrosion is a problem especially if there is grit in the water. The blades are usually made of cast steel, coated with stainless steel on the parts most subject to wear, but still they need to be resurfaced or replaced periodically to maintain their efficiency.

# Gearing and Generators

Watermills generate electricity in much the same way that windmills do. The turbine provides a rotational force that turns the armature of a generator. The generator must be carefully selected to match both the power output of the wheel and the electrical demands of the household.

Once the armature of a generator achieves its required rotational speed, it produces electricity at a constant rate. Most generators need very high rotational speeds (around 3000 rpm), but some start generating at speeds as low as 150 rpm. In other cases the output is directly proportional to the speed of the armature until its rated speed is reached, after which the output is constant (Figure 4-10).

The slower speed of the waterwheel or turbine, on one hand, the more gearing is required to run the generator, and consequently the greater the loss of power by friction. An overshot wheel might have to be geared up by a ratio of 1 to 100, whereas a modern turbine might require no gearing at all. On the other hand, the slower the wheel turns, the easier it will be to build and to repair.

heads of water (down to three feet), but it requires relatively high rates of flow.

Unlike impulse turbines, every reaction turbine is designed for maximum efficiency with a specific amount of head and rate of flow. Any variation reduces their efficiency substantially. Reaction turbines with adjustable blades can compensate for these variations but are substantially more expensive.

Reaction turbines have to be completely submerged in water. Some form of regulator is needed

Installing a slow-moving waterwheel allows the stresses of high rotational speeds to be taken up by the gears or belts, which are simpler and more easily replaced than the wheel itself.

## AC OR DC CURRENT

The comparative advantages of AC and DC current are discussed at length in the Wind Power section, along with the criteria for choosing an alternator. There are some differences, of course. Water power is much less variable than the wind; it can be relied upon for continuous service. For this reason, one can expect a steady output at the calculated level of power, except for seasonal flooding or dry spells.

## ELECTRICAL STORAGE

If water power is ample and reliable, storage may not be necessary. If storage is desired, batteries may be used, as with wind electric generation. A millpond may be constructed to hold water until droughts occur. Or a synchronous inverter may be installed to connect the system with the utility lines, using the electric company for "storage." See page 137 for details about the synchronous inverter.

## GOVERNORS

If power is to be used directly rather than stored, a governor is needed to regulate power output to match the demand. Governors for water power systems can be mechanical or electronic. *Mechanical flow* governors regulate the flow of water into the turbine, reducing power output as required. *Electronic* governors regulate the alternator output, either by reducing the electric field (as an automobile voltage regulator does) or by diverting excess power to secondary needs (such as space heating, battery charging, flywheels, and so on).

# Available Energy

The amount of power available in a stream depends on the *flow* of the stream (volume and velocity of the water) and on the *head* (the distance the water falls from the supply or intake to the water level at which the flow impacts on the generating unit, or rejoins the stream below the power plant). The flow is determined by nature, and the head by the location of the power plant.

## MEASURING THE FLOW

Before you decide on the location and type of your power plant, you will need to estimate the smallest flow that is available at a chosen site, and the largest flows you may have to cope with.

Unless ten to twenty years of records are already available for your stream, to estimate the low and high flows it is generally essential to measure actual flows at several times in the year—particularly near the close of wet and dry periods, as in the spring and fall. These figures, together with the area of the drainage basin above your location, then can be related to the flows of another—usually larger—stream in your general area, on which a long record *is* available. For this purpose, unless you are yourself a hydrologist and have access to such records, it will be advisable to take your own measurements to your county or state office of engineering and ask their personnel to determine this relation and supply you with probable minimum and maximum flows for your stream and location. You should get acquainted with them anyway, because you may soon have to get a permit for the stream structure you will need to install, and may require advice on permissible designs for any necessary dam and spillway.

The flow rate of a very small stream can be

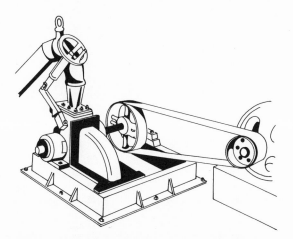

Figure 4-10. An Ossberger Universal 5 hp turbine. Penstock is on the left, the belting and generator on the right.

measured directly by diverting the entire stream into a container of known volume and measuring the time required to fill the vessel. If, for example, a 55-gallon drum is filled in thirty seconds, then the stream has a flow of 110 gallons per minute. Several trials should be performed during wet and dry spells to obtain an average figure—and the likely maximum and minimum flows.

The easiest way to measure the flow of a larger stream is to toss in a floating object and measure the time it takes to travel a given distance. Do this several times and average the results for greater accuracy. Since water flows faster at the surface than at the bottom, multiply this result by 5/6 to obtain the average speed for the whole stream. Then calculate the cross section of the stream by measuring the width and the average depth (take several readings at approximately equal intervals). Multiply the average cross-sectional area (in square feet) times the average speed (feet per minute) to obtain the rate of flow (cubic feet per minute).

A second method is to construct a "channel sill" or *contracted weir*. This is a temporary barrier (see Figure 4–11) containing a rectangular opening that narrows or "contracts" the stream so that its cross-sectional area is not more than four-tenths of the normal stream cross-section. As shown in the illustration, the edges of the opening (B) should be beveled toward downstream; and

the water flowing through it should fall free into the stream on the lower side.

To measure the depth of water flowing over the weir, drive a stake in the stream bed three or more feet upstream from the weir, to a depth such that a mark on the stake is exactly level with the bottom of notch B. Measure the depth (D) in inches of water over the mark, and read the volume of flow in cubic feet per minute per inch of notch width from Table 4–12. Multiply this volume by the notch width in inches to obtain the total stream flow in cubic feet per minute.

For very large flow volumes (which may even inundate your stable channel section or sill) you can approximate estimates of the peak flows by use of the *Manning formula*. Data required are a detailed cross-section of the channel at or near your selected location and including the elevation of the highest flow (sometimes mapped after the storm, with peak heights obtained from silt marks or entrapped grass or brush) and a careful estimate of the natural "roughness" of the channel to obtain a reasonable value for the channel-roughness coefficient $n$. Tables of $n$ and details of the measurement and calculation procedures are given in any handbook of hydraulics.

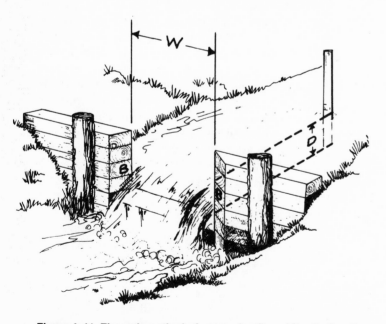

Figure 4–11. The weir method of measuring flow. After finding the depth over the notch (D), read the cubic feet of flow per minute on Table 4–12.

**Table 4–12. Measuring the Flow Using the Weir Method.**

| Inches Depth on Stake D | Cfm per inch of Weir Notch Width W |
|---|---|
| 1 Inch | .40 |
| 2 | 1.14 |
| 3 | 2.09 |
| 4 | 3.22 |
| 5 | 4.50 |
| 6 | 5.90 |
| 7 | 7.44 |
| 8 | 9.10 |
| 9 | 10.86 |
| 10 | 12.71 |
| 11 | 14.67 |
| 12 | 16.73 |
| 13 | 18.87 |
| 14 | 21.09 |
| 15 | 23.38 |
| 16 | 25.76 |
| 17 | 28.20 |
| 18 | 30.70 |
| 19 | 33.29 |
| 20 | 35.94 |
| 21 | 38.65 |
| 22 | 41.43 |
| 23 | 44.28 |
| 24 | 47.18 |

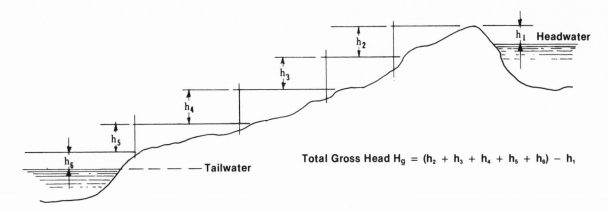

Figure 4–13. How to measure the head of water with a carpenter's level. Make several successive measurements and add them together to find the overall head.

Total Gross Head $H_g = (h_2 + h_3 + h_4 + h_5 + h_6) - h_1$

## MEASURING THE AVAILABLE HEAD

Together with the expected minimum rate of flow in cubic feet per minute, the potential electric power depends also on the available head. For example, a 1000-watt Hoppes hydroelectric unit requires a minimum of 180 cfm flow with about nine feet of head, or a little over 60 cfm with twenty-five feet of head.

To maximize the available head, locate the water intake for the power plant at the head of a steep reach of steam or a waterfall, and the power plant location itself as much lower than this level as possible. Then measure the vertical distance between these two elevations. This measurement can be made most easily by running a series of levels with a simple surveyor's level or even a Locke hand level and calibrated rod or one or more angles and distances with a surveyor's transit or an Abney hand level, and a measuring tape (see Figure 4–13). If you don't

have and can't borrow one, either of these simple hand levels can be obtained from an engineering supply firm or from a mail-order supply store such as Brookstone Company in Peterborough, New Hampshire.

Once you have measured the *gross available head*, you must reduce it somewhat to allow for various losses. For one thing, the wheel must run free of the tail water, so a few inches are lost. More important, friction in the pipelines will result in an effective loss of head. Table 4–14 gives head losses for PVC pipe. Steel, iron and concrete pipe all cause very high head losses, and all are more expensive than PVC. Deduct these figures to determine the *net head* available to drive the wheel or turbine.

## CHOOSING A WATER POWER PLANT

Please notice that any water power plant requires a specified minimum flow and head to

Table 4–14. Head Loss for Plastic Pipe.

| Pipe Size | FLOW CFM | | | | | | | | | | | | | | | | | |
|---|---|---|---|---|---|---|---|---|---|---|---|---|---|---|---|---|---|---|
| | 3 | 6 | 12 | 18 | 24 | 30 | 36 | 42 | 48 | 54 | 60 | 66 | 72 | 78 | 84 | 90 | 120 | 150 |
| | (Head Loss per 1,000 ft. of Pipe) | | | | | | | | | | | | | | | | | |
| 2″ | 18 | 63 | 230 | | | | | | | | | | | | | | | |
| 2½″ | 6 | 21 | 75 | 161 | 274 | | | | | | | | | | | | | |
| 3″ | 2 | 9 | 30 | 64 | 110 | 166 | 234 | 312 | | | | | | | | | | |
| 4″ | ½ | 2 | 7 | 15 | 26 | 40 | 56 | 74 | 95 | 118 | 144 | 172 | 201 | 230 | 268 | 305 | | |
| 6″ | 0 | ¼ | 1 | 2 | 4 | 5 | 7 | 10 | 13 | 16 | 19 | 23 | 27 | 30 | 36 | 40 | 69 | 105 |
| 8″ | 0 | 0 | ¼ | ¼ | ½ | 1¼ | 1¾ | 2⅓ | 3 | 3¾ | 4½ | 5⅓ | 6⅓ | 7⅓ | 8½ | 9½ | 16 | 25 |

(Steel pipe in fair condition will have about twice the head loss shown above.)

produce electric power. As mentioned earlier, an overshot wheel requires at least eight feet of head and 60 to 1800 cfm of flow. Even the smallest (500-watt capacity) Hoppes hydroelectric unit requires eight feet of head and 96 cfm of flow, or twelve feet of head and about 60 cfm of flow. And a 10,000-watt plant requires 960 cfm at twelve feet of head, or 480 cfm at twenty-five feet of head (see Leffel Company Bulletin No. H-49). These statistics indicate the smallest stream and rate of fall that are practical.

If the stream has a large flow and a low head, the best turbine choice is a reaction-type because it is driven by the water's mass rather than by its velocity. If the stream has a high head but a low rate of flow, the best choice is an impulse turbine like the Pelton, which uses the water's velocity rather than its mass.

The available power from a stream may be calculated with the following formula:

$$T = \frac{Q \times h \times E}{708}$$

where $T$ = the output in kilowatts,
$Q$ = the rate of flow, in cubic feet per minute,
$h$ = the net head, in feet,
$E$ = the overall efficiency of the system.

The system's overall efficiency may be estimated to lie between 45 percent (for an overshot waterwheel) and 62 percent (for a turbine). If you multiply the electrical output $T$ by the number of hours in a month, you have the estimated monthly power capacity of the system. Remember, though, that reduced flow rates will reduce the efficiency of power generation.

# Dams

Invariably your power plant will require damming the stream for one or more of these reasons: (1) to provide maximum head for the plant; (2) to divert a portion of the stream or all of the stream through the plant; (3) to protect the plant by making floodwaters bypass it; and (4) to store water in a pond so as to conserve the supply during times when the plant demands less than is in the stream, and then to supply water to the plant during times when it demands more flow than is in the stream. If the pond is large enough such storage is of much benefit during periods of very low flow.[2]

## LEGAL REQUIREMENTS

Before entering seriously into plans for the investment of capital in a dam and power plant, you should by all means know what are the governmental requirements for such structures on or affecting a stream.

First and most basic is the common-law doctrine of riparian rights in the East, under which stream-dwellers and users downstream from your plant have the right to stream volume and "regimen" (behavior pattern) substantially undisturbed by your activities. You may need to look into any effects you may have on your downstream neighbors; although, in the case of a comparatively small power plant, such effects are probably negligible.

More important are any state requirements for permits. In Vermont, for example, any impoundment that stores more than 500,000 cubic feet must have a permit from a state agency. If you contemplate selling any electric power, the permit will have to be granted by the state Public Service Board; if the impoundment is for agricultural purposes, you will deal with the Vermont Natural Resource Conservation Districts. And if, as is most probably your case, you or any organization plans to develop electric power purely for your own uses and without sale or profit, the permits will be granted by the State Water Resources Board.

In any event, do check with your state government. Aside from permits, the appropriate agency will doubtless give you advice and perhaps technical assistance with your project. For example, its engineers doubtless will have, as in Vermont, statistics and analyses that will aid you in estimating the most probable minimum and maximum stream discharges at your proposed power-plant site and advice on possible impoundments.

## CHOOSING A SITE

Dam sites are chosen primarily to maximize the available head, but ease of construction and effects on the landscape and natural ecosystems should also be considered. A dam is easier to construct if it is placed in a natural cut where the stream is quite narrow. Flooding the area behind the dam destroys some part of a natural ecosystem, but the

2. See also Pamphlet "A" of James Leffel and Company, Springfield, Ohio.

pond created may improve the overall ecosystem by encouraging a greater variety of plant and animal life than would a fast-running stream. Creating the pond may also change the water table nearby, and the dam may affect the course of the water much farther downstream than you expect.

## CONSTRUCTION AND MATERIAL

The main difficulty involved in constructing a dam is preventing the water from seeping through or under it. Usually the dam is built around some sort of piling driven into the earth or bedrock below to prevent erosion from underneath. The stream bed should be cleared of all vegetation and loose material so that a firm seal can be achieved between the dam and its foundation. The land above the dam that will be submerged should also be cleared of vegetation to avoid polluting the water.

Dams may be built of earth, timbers, masonry, or concrete (Figure 4–15).

In an *earth* dam, the earth is built up in compacted layers around a central, impervious core that extends across the stream and into the foundation. The upstream, submerged side should be protected against waterlogging and wave action by a layer of clay, stone rip-rap, or even "gunite" sprayed concrete. Some ideas on earth-dam design and construction are given in Agriculture Handbook No. 387, "Ponds for Water Supply and Recreation," by the Soil Conservation Service, though this publication is primarily oriented toward farm ponds. Also see "Build a Pond," Bulletin A-19, from Garden Way Publishing.

*Timber* dams are usually built of frames of heavy logs or timbers, filled with stones, logs and gravel or earth, and faced with protective planking. Sheet-piling of planking is sunk into the foundation material at the front and usually at the back of the dam to minimize seepage; and of course all of the wood materials should be treated against rot. For stability, the longitudinal width and height of timber dams should be similar to those of masonry and concrete dams.

*Gravity* dams built of concrete or masonry—stones, concrete blocks, or other stone-like material cemented with mortar—rely on their mass for stability, so that in general they should be only about ⅔ as high as they are wide. (More precisely, the overturn moment should fall within the middle third of the dam's cross-section.) And of course, the base of the dam must be sealed by a cutoff wall extending into the foundation material. If the foundation and abutments of the dam site are strong—such as solid bedrock—

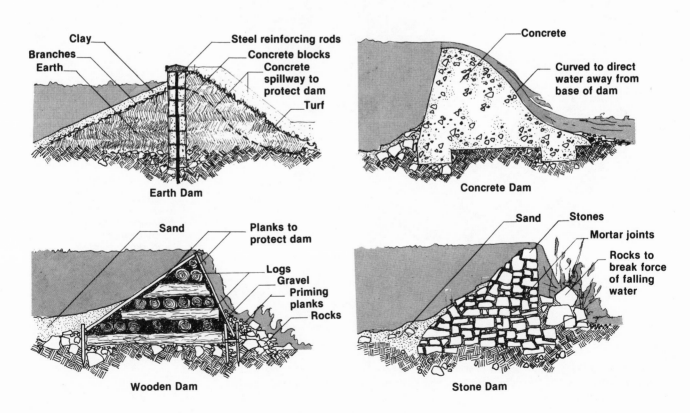

Clay
Branches
Earth
Steel reinforcing rods
Concrete blocks
Concrete spillway to protect dam
Turf

**Earth Dam**

Concrete
Curved to direct water away from base of dam

**Concrete Dam**

Sand
Planks to protect dam
Logs
Gravel
Priming planks
Rocks

**Wooden Dam**

Sand
Stones
Mortar joints
Rocks to break force of falling water

**Stone Dam**

material may be saved by employing a concrete arch or gravity-arch design; this, however, requires skilled engineering design and would be limited to comparatively elaborate water power systems.

PROTECTING THE DAM

Whatever dam type you choose, it is exceedingly important to protect it and the rest of the hydropower equipment from damage or destruction by excessive flows. In the case of small dams and comparatively small maximum discharges, it may be permissible to design the whole structure as a spillway and to divert the water required for the power plant out of the stream and back into it below the plant. Thus excess water may be allowed to spill over the crests of small wood, masonry or concrete dams if measures are provided to break the force of the overflowing water or divert it away from the base of the dam. Large rocks placed at the downstream toe of the dam

will do, as will a channel design to insure a substantial depth of tail water submerging the toe during high discharges.

All earth dams, however, and any dams that are exposed to excessively high floods, require a solid spillway large enough to accommodate the greatest discharge expected. In addition, all earth dams with separate earth spillways should be provided with "trickle tubes" or other measures to prevent small, sustained excess flows from saturating the protective vegetation on the spillway. Earth spillways and trickle tubes for earth dams in comparatively gentle topography are well discussed in the Soil Conservation Service's Agriculture Handbook No. 387.

THE MILLRACE

If the mill is not to be at the site of the dam, a millrace will be necessary to carry the water from the dam to the mill. The millrace can be either an open channel or an enclosed pipe. Often

1. Stream
2. Dam with spillway
3. Intake to millrace
4. Millrace
5. Intake to turbine penstock
6. Trashrack
7. Overflow of millrace
8. Penstock
9. Turbine inlet valve
10. Water turbine
11. Electric generator
12. Trailrace

Figure 4-16. Bringing the supply of water to the turbine is a major part of creating a water power system. The dam, penstock, and sluice all have to be designed to withstand flooding.

both are used, the open channel conducting the water almost horizontally to the pipe, which carries the water at a steeper angle down to the mill. For traditional waterwheels, however, the use of just an open channel is preferable. But the pressure building up in the pipe increases the efficiency of modern turbines (Figure 4–16).

The millrace should have a sluice gate to regulate the flow of water. A trashrack covering the inlet will prevent debris from clogging the machinery (more important for turbines than for traditional waterwheels). The trashrack must be kept clean.

To reduce friction losses, the millrace should be as straight and smooth and short as possible. It should be well supported along its entire length as it will have to carry a great weight of water. If a pipe is used, it must be large enough not to impede the flow of water.

If an open channel is used, it can be made of earth or gravel only if low water velocities are expected (less than about five feet per second, and with side walls sloped to an angle less than 30 degrees. Wood, concrete, or masonry channels can tolerate higher velocities and, if necessary, they can slope downwards more steeply, but always remember to retain as much head as possible for power generation.

# Economics

There is obviously no point even considering building a water power plant unless a stream is available that has an adequate flow and head of water. Nor is it worth considering unless a lot of time and money can be devoted to the project. The construction of dams, sluices and waterwheels is complicated and exacting work, and however worthwhile doing it yourself seems, it may well be less frustrating and more efficient to pay the extra money for earth-moving equipment or for a modern water turbine.

The number of manufacturers of small-scale turbines has dwindled to a few well-established companies dedicated to producing, installing and servicing equipment that really will last a lifetime. But naturally such products are expensive. A ½ kw Leffel turbine, for example, costs about $4300, a 2 kw model, $4850 and a 10 kw model, $7300. Obviously the smaller units will

take longer to pay for themselves. Investing in a water turbine may be expensive, but it is almost certain to give dependable service for many years.

With waterwheels there is no alternative to doing it yourself, which means a lot of research as well as a knowledge of machinery and of welding techniques. If an old mill is available, a waterwheel will be considerably cheaper and easier to install. Many old waterwheels (and mills) were abandoned as steam engines took over their work. Their junked parts are well worth hunting for. Nowadays most homebuilt watermill generators are made from junked parts installed in old millraces. Depending on the condition and price of the parts, building a waterwheel may be a relatively inexpensive way to produce electricity.

Since the cost of a water power installation is largely dependent on individual site conditions, it is not possible to generalize about the economics of hydropower. Manufacturers will be glad to help you plan a system to suit your needs and to determine the costs and output of the projected system. Since water power systems are usually complicated and expensive, it is best to seek the advice of a professional early in the project. To estimate the limit of your investment, though, remember that one kilowatt of power capacity equals 8760 kilowatt-hours per year, amounting to a $700 per year saving (assuming a cost of 8¢ per kilowatt-hour). So a 1-kw system costing $3500 will pay for itself in about five years; $7000 spent on a 2-kw system will also break even in five years (or less, if electric rates rise). To give you a rough idea, here are some representative actual system costs.

**Case 1: Overshot Waterwheel:** 16 foot net head, 900 cfm flow

| 16-foot-diameter | |
|---|---|
| fiber glass waterwheel | $2960. |
| Tractor gear box | 80. |
| V-belts, pulleys, used generator | 400. |
| Sluice gate, intake flume, | |
| wheel support, discharge pit, | |
| powerhouse | 2000. |
| | $5440. |

Assuming an average output of 5 kw, this system produces $3504 worth of electricity per year, paying for itself in about one and a half years. The tractor gear box may wear out in a year or two.

**Case 2: Impulse Turbine:** 95 foot net head, 22 cfm flow

| IPD Mini-Pelton DC generator, batteries & 3 kw inverter | $3300. |
| 400 feet of 4 inch diameter class B PVC pipe | 1000. |
| | $4300. |

At 8¢ per kwh, this system breaks even in four years.

**Case 3: Impulse Turbine:** 183 feet net head, 62 cfm flow

| Pelton wheel generator, 9½ inch diameter, 9 kw output, with electronic load governor and switch gear | $2640. |
| 2200 feet of 8 inch diameter class B PVC pipe (laid by owner) | 2640. |
| Equipment rental, rock blasting, inlet, powerhouse, etc. | 2145. |
| | $7425. |

Assuming an average output of 5 kilowatts, this installation will pay for itself in about two years.

USED EQUIPMENT

Great savings are possible if used hydropower wheels, turbines or generators are available. But take care: each item is designed to serve a specific head and flow rate. An old 10 kw Francis turbine designed for a net head of thirty feet will not produce 10 kw if the available head is only thirteen feet—a fact you may discover many laborious weeks later. If possible, write to the original manufacturer, giving the turbine serial number and original location, and ask for details on its suitability. The manufacturer may charge for this service, but it will be worth it.

# Watermills and Housing

Modern hydroelectric turbines have very little visual impact on the landscape. They are generally contained in small weatherproof shelters, located at some distance from the house. Remote controls or automatic governing devices can be installed that regulate the water entering the turbine according to the need for electricity.

A traditional waterwheel is a much larger, noisier and more cumbersome object. Before building a wheel alongside the house, it would be wise to consider what noise levels would be acceptable in the living room. A waterwheel makes at least as much noise as a small waterfall. Old watermills were carefully constructed with no metal parts touching—the noise of pieces of metal banging, grinding and squeaking against each other doubtless have proved too much for the poor miller and his family.

Another major consideration to take into account before rushing headlong into the construction of a watermill is the extraordinary power the mill will have to contend with in times of flood. At such times, any water power plant needs to be well protected, or else hours of hard work are likely to be washed away as the spillway overflows, the dam collapses, and the waterwheel careens downstream. The potential outburst of a gentle little stream must *not* be underestimated.

Water has many uses besides generating power, and building a watermill automatically creates possibilities for improving a homestead. The pond behind a small dam can become a swimming pool and fishing hole. The water stored there can be used for irrigation. Water can become an integral part of the house, too. In hot, dry climates the water could be channelled through or around the house for cooling. The still surface of a pond to the south of the house could be used to increase the efficiency of wall-mounted solar collectors—the water reflecting solar energy back onto the house.

Water is an exciting element for the home landscape designer and a very powerful one. Understanding the way water flows and the functions it serves is necessary before interfering with the natural course of a stream.

# References

Baumeister, Theodore, ed. *Mark's Standard Handbook for Mechanical Engineers*. New York: McGraw-Hill, 1967. See section on hydraulic turbines.

Daniels, A.M. "Power for the Farm from Small Streams." U.S. Department of Agriculture, 1925. Available from the Superintendent of Documents, U.S. Government Printing Office, Washington, D.C. 20402.

*Energy Primer*. Menlo Park: Portola Institute, 1974. Send $4.50 to the Portola Institute, 558 Santa Cruz Avenue, Menlo Park, California 94025.

Hamm, Hans W. "Low-Cost Development of Small Water Power Sites." Includes plans for a 12-inch Banki-Mitchell turbine. Send $2.25 to VITA, 3706 Rhode Island Avenue, Mt. Rainier, Maryland 20802. Plans for 1 kw river generator cost $1.

*Handbook of Homemade Power*. By the staff of the *Mother Earth News*. New York: Bantam, 1974. Includes reprint of the classic five-part series, "How to Build Your Own Water Power Plant," by C.D. Bassett, originally from *Popular Science*, 1947.

"How to Build a Farm Pond." U.S. Department of Agriculture. Send 50¢ to the Superintendent of Documents, U.S. Government Printing Office, Washington, D.C. 20402. Ask for Leaflet Number 259.

"Hydraulic Power." James Leffel and Company, Springfield, Ohio. Ask for Bulletin Number H-49. Also see Leffel's Pamphlet "A".

Leckie, Jim; Masters, Gil; Whitehouse, Harry; and Young, Lily. *Other Homes and Garbage*. San Francisco: Sierra Club Books, 1975. $9.95. Includes a brief section on water power, emphasizing the engineering calculations of flow, power output, and gear design.

McGuigan, Dermot. *Harnessing Water Power for Home Energy*. Charlotte, VT: Garden Way Publishing, 1978. $4.95. Very complete, readable and up-to-date guide to buying and installing a hydropower system.

Paton, T.A.L. *Power from Water*. London, 1961.

"Ponds for Water Supply and Recreation." U.S. Department of Agriculture, Soil Conservation Service, 1971. Send 70¢ to the Superintendent of Documents, U.S. Government Printing Office, Washington, D.C. 20402. Ask for Agricultural Bulletin Number 387.

Reynolds, John. *Windmills and Watermills*. New York: Praeger Publishing Co., 1970. A good historical study.

Warren, George. "Farm Water Power." U.S. Department of Agriculture, 1931. Available from the Superintendent of Documents, U.S. Government Printing Office, Washington, D.C. 20402.

Crowley, C.A. "Power from Small Streams." *Popular Mechanics*, September 1940 (Part 1) and October 1940 (Part 2).

Lilienthal, David. "Lost Megawatts Flow Over Nation's Myriad Spillways." *Smithsonian*, March 1978.

Oakes, Thomas. "Water Power." *Mother Earth News*. November 1973. Reprinted in *The Mother Earth News Handbook of Homemade Power*, 1974.

"Water Power for Your Home." *Popular Science*, May 1977.

# Water Power Catalog

The following pages list companies and products in the field of water power generation. Naturally, this is not a complete catalog—there are many excellent products that could not be represented here. More detailed studies of water power doubtless will lead you to additional manufacturers.

All information contained in the catalog section was supplied by the various manufacturers or taken from *Harnessing Water Power for Home Energy,* by Dermot McGuigan. We have summarized what is available; we have not judged its quality. Our goal is to help you, the reader, locate information or products to evaluate for yourself the suitability of water power.

Within the catalog section are product comparison charts that we have created. Keep in mind that prices are constantly changing. If you want more information about any product or manufacturer, we ask that you write directly to the company, *not* to Garden Way Publishing.

# Waterwheel Manufacturers

**Campbell Water Wheel Company**
**420 South 42nd Street,**
**Philadelphia, Pennsylvania 19104**

This company was founded in 1925 by John Blake Campbell, the oldest manufacturer of waterwheels and the last of the old waterwheel craftsmen. In the past 60 years, he has been manufacturing, installing and renovating water- wheels. Overshot waterwheels are his specialty and these are manufactured to order. Turbines can be installed but are not manufactured by Campbell.

**Westward Mouldings Limited,**
**Greenhill Works**
**Delaware Road**
**Gunnislake, Cornwall, England**

Westward Mouldings Ltd. manufactures a range of fiber glass waterwheels as follows:

| | | | |
|---|---|---|---|
| Wheel diameter | 8 feet | 16 feet | 20 feet |
| Number of buckets | 16 | 32 | 40 |
| Bucket capacity | 3.6 cu. ft. | 4.8 cu. ft. | 7.2 cu. ft. |
| Max. advised rpm | 15 | 10 | 6/8 |
| Max. output (approx.) | 3.6 kw | 11 kw | 25 kw |
| Price | $1,200 | $3,200 | $4,800 |
| Price of home-assembly kit (suitable for importing) | | $2,400 | $3,600 |

The maximum output in kilowatts shown above is based on a 65% waterwheel efficiency with the buckets filled to 70% of capacity; the figures exclude the increase in power which may result from the installation of an apron on the lower quarter of the wheel. The output relates to shaft power only, from which should be deducted generator and gear losses.

The calculations are based on the following equation:

$$\text{Output (kw)} = \frac{D \times B \times B.no \times rpm \times 0.65}{708}$$

where
- $D$ = wheel diameter from bucket centers
- $B$ = working bucket capacity (0.7 of total capacity, approximately)
- $B.no$ = number of buckets
- $rpm$ = revolutions per minute
- $0.65$ = efficiency factor
- $708$ = kw conversion factor

*Example:* A 16 ft. wheel with buckets filled to 70% capa- city, 3.36 cu. ft., revolves at 8 rpm. Therefore its output is as follows:

$$\text{Output} = \frac{14 \times 3.36 \times 32 \times 8 \times 0.65}{708}$$
$$= 11 \text{ kw shaft power}$$

# Cross-Flow Turbine Manufacturers

**Balaju, Yantra Shala (P) Ltd.,**
**Balaju,**
**Katmandu, Nepal**

BYS manufactures a range of nine small cross-flow tur- bines. In Nepal these turbines are used for mechanical purposes. If you are interested, write to them, enclosing a dollar or two, and ask for details.

**Bell Hydroelectric**
**3 Leatherstocking Street,**
**Cooperstown, New York 13326**
**(607) 547-5260**

Bell Hydroelectric manufactures a complete range of cross-flow turbines, a very exciting addition to the now complete range of water turbines manufactured in America.

Bell Hydroelectric manufactures its turbines individually and to order, hence prices are not readily available. But as an indication of cost, a large installation capable of generating 35 kw would be around $20,000. Bell cross-flow turbines may be used on a wide variety of heads from 5 to 350 feet, with outputs from 2 kw upwards. It is generally found that the cross-flow is most cost- effective when used on the medium-head range, i.e. from 15 to 50 or 100 ft. Propeller turbines are cheaper on very low heads and Pelton wheels on the very high heads.

James Bell, the hydroelectric engineer who started the company, will be glad to send details of his turbines ($2.00) and at the same time will give a cost estimate for any particular site if given details of head, flow and power required.

**Ossberger-Turbinenfabrik
D-8832 Weissenburg
Bayern
Germany**

Ossberger manufactures the *Mitchell-Ossberger Cross-Flow Turbine* for operation with small and medium water supplies. A number of models can handle heads from 3 to 660 feet, with the highest output per unit being 1000 hp. They have an overall efficiency of 80 percent.

The *Ossberger Turbine* features a small and a large guide vane. The small vane handles restricted water supplies; the large vane handles medium flows. Both sections together handle full flows. In this way, the Ossberger can run at optimum efficiency in fluctuating water supplies.

The Ossberger *Universal types A* and *B* are suitable for small waters with low heads and slow flow speeds. Their output ranges lie between 2.1 and 12 hp. They directly drive generators or transmissions by means of belt pulleys. They are manually regulated by means of a handwheel on the turbine. The handwheel also can be placed in another location and fitted with ropes and pulleys to allow for remote control.

The *Hydro-Light* is a manually controlled, small hydraulic power generating plant also for use with low-head water supplies with slow flow speeds. It consists

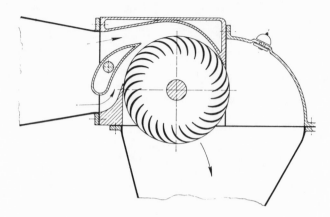

*Flow pattern in Ossberger cross-flow turbines.*

of an *Ossberger Draft Tube Turbine,* with an efficiency of 80 percent, mounted on a rigid bed frame. The three-phase generator, including flywheel, is driven by a belt-and-pulley arrangement. It includes a control panel. Like the *Universal types A* and *B,* it can be remote controlled by cable drive.

# Cross-Flow Turbines Compared

| Manufacturer | Make | Head | Flow | Output | Price | Features |
|---|---|---|---|---|---|---|
| Bell Hydro-electric | Bell Cross-Flow Turbine | 5 ft. to 350 ft. | | 2 kw and up | | |
| Ossberger Turbinen-fabrik | Mitchell-Ossberger Cross-Flow Turbine | 3 ft. to 660 ft. | | 1 kw to 1000 kw | | Part-gate construction for more efficiency with low water flow rates. Includes turbine, frame, connecting piping, draft-tube, gearing, automatic mechanical governor, flywheel, generator, switch board. |
| | Universal A | 13 ft. 20 ft. 26 ft. 33 ft. | 104 cfm 127 cfm 148 cfm 170 cfm | 1.5 kw 2.8 kw 4.5 kw 6.3 kw | $4400 for all models | Suitable for low heads with slow flow speeds. Direct-driven generator not included. Manual control by handwheel can be altered for remote control by cable drive. |
| | Universal B | 33 ft. 66 ft. 99 ft. | 47 cfm 66 cfm 80 cfm | 1.7 kw 5 kw 9 kw | Same as above | Same as above. |
| | Hydro-Light | 12 ft. to 29 ft. | 60 cfm to 170cfm | 5 kw maximum | $8000 | Suitable for low heads with slow flow speeds. Includes Ossberger Draft-Tube Turbine, beltdrive generator, flywheel, control panel. Can be remote controlled by cable drive. |

# Pelton Wheel Manufacturers

**Alaska Wind and Water Power**
**P.O. Box G**
**Chugiak, Alaska 99567**
**(907) 688-2896**

Francis Soltis of Alaska Wind and Water Power worked closely with Bill Kitching of Small Hydroelectric Systems & Equipment in the development of their Pelton wheel systems. As an engineer, he has been involved in small water power for almost a decade. His Alaskan company markets and installs the complete range of turbines manufactured at the SHSE foundry. Send $3 for brochure.

For an engineering fee of $25 and a complete "Data Sheet" from the brochure, he will calculate the most efficient and economical turbine for the site. The cost of the brochure and engineering fee is refundable upon purchase of any of their Pelton wheels, casings, complete systems, or components.

**Elektro G.m.b.H.,**
**St. Gallerstrase 27**
**Winterthur, Switzerland**

Elektro has been manufacturing turbines and wind generators for the past 30 years. Apart from their range of Peltons they also manufacture a small Francis turbine. Their four Pelton wheels range in cost from $1,100 for 300 watts to $12,000 for up to 24 kw, which is more expensive than US-made turbines. Elektro has a simple way of improving the output of small Pelton wheels during times when the flow is low. It is to build a small reservoir capable of containing the normal volume of water that would flow in 15 to 30 minutes—i.e., for a flow of 3 cfm the reservoir would contain 45 to 90 cubic feet. When water supply is very low then the Pelton wheel efficiency drops considerably. To prevent this, a ball-valve closes the pipeline allowing the reservoir to fill. When it re-opens, the Pelton drives at full efficiency until the reservoir is emptied and then the cycle begins again. This means that instead of a continuous output of, say, 25 watts (600 watt hours per day), output can be increased to eight hours at 300 watts (2400 watt hours per day). Though Elektro is considering export of Pelton turbines in the future, *these Elektro wheels are not currently available in the United States.*

**Independent Power Developers, Inc.**
**Box 1467**
**Noxon, Montana 59853**
**(406) 847-2315**

IPD manufactures water power systems for both high- and low-head applications. These systems include turbine, generator, batteries, inverter, and all inter-system electrical hookups. They can be installed and maintained by the home-owner and require limited site preparation.

The DC generator provided is a 32-volt, 70-amp, brushless type. The battery bank consists of six batteries per 3 kw of peak system output. They will withstand repeated discharging and recharging with an output efficiency of 75 percent and an expected life of 15 years.

The inverter provides a maximum of 3 kw of power at 95 percent efficiency. It includes solid-state construction, input and output metering, and overload protection. Low idle current allows the system to remain on at all times, eliminating the need for load sensing equipment to turn the system on and off.

The high head turbine is a 4-inch Pelton-type impulse turbine capable of 80 percent efficiency. It produces a maximum of 3 hp at 3500 rpm. Water is fed to the cast aluminum, epoxy-coated wheel through a stainless steel nozzle.

The low-head turbine is a Nagler, fixed propeller-type capable of 80 percent efficiency. It produces over 6 hp under optimum conditions. The propeller and stainless steel power shaft are weather resistant. Both turbines are housed in rust-resistant aluminum and have standard hookups.

Both systems are available in one of four classes:

| Peaking Output | Continuous Output | Monthly Power Output |
|---|---|---|
| 3 kw | 280 watts | 200 kw/hour |
| 6 kw | 700 watts | 500 kw/hour |
| 9 kw | 1700 watts | 1200 kw/hour |
| 12 kw | 8500 watts | 6000 kw/hour |

IPD also sells a voltage tester, transformer, power sentry, transfer switch, backup generator, inlet filter, and trashracks.

**Jyoti Ltd.** See Francis and Propeller Turbine Manufacturers.

**Pumps, Pipe and Power**
**Kingston Village**
**Austin, Nevada 89310**
**(702) 964-2483**

PPP supplies Pelton wheels with outputs from 15 kw upwards. They use Woodward governors for speed control. PPP practice what they preach and generate their own power with a Pelton wheel operating under 450 feet of head.

**Small Hydroelectric Systems**
**& Equipment**
**P.O. Box 124**
**Custer, Washington 98240**
**(206) 366-7203**

SHSE manufactures a complete range of Pelton wheels. They also sell the basic drawings and parts for their home construction.

| Pelton Wheel Castings | Aluminum Alloy | Bronze |
|---|---|---|
| 4½-inch casting | — | $250 |
| 9-inch casting | — | $300 |
| 18-inch casting mounted on a 2-inch shaft | — | Price on request |

The prices shown above do not include the housing, bearings, or nozzle. *(Continued)*

187

| Ready-to-run Turbines in Housing | Aluminum Alloy | Bronze |
|---|---|---|
| 4½-inch wheel, *Water-Lite* with 4 nozzles and alternator mounting plate | $500 | $650 |
| 9-inch wheel with 1-inch shaft and bearings | $750 | — |
| 9-inch wheel with 1 3/16-inch shaft and bearings | — | $1,250 |
| Two 9-inch wheels with 1 3/16-inch shaft and bearings | $1,000 | — |
| Two 9-inch wheels with 1 7/16-inch shaft and bearings | — | $1,500 |
| Complete 15-kw Pelton wheel hydroelectric plant with Lima brushless alternator and Woodward governor | | from $6,000 |

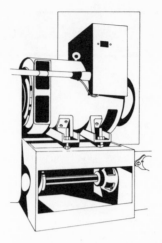

*Pelton wheel with attached alternator.*

SHSE also stocks a comprehensive range of DC and AC generators, batteries and inverters suitable for use with the miniature *Water-Lite* unit, designed to produce up to 2 or 3 kilowatts. The *Water-Lite* unit has four jets, one or all of which can operate at any given time. It will produce power on low or high heads, and the number of jets can be varied to suit seasonal changes in water flow.

SHSE wheels are marketed and installed by Alaska Wind and Water Power (see previous page).

## Pelton Impulse Wheels Compared

| Manufacturer | Make | Wheel Size | Head | Flow | Output | Price | Features |
|---|---|---|---|---|---|---|---|
| Elektro G.m.b.H. | | | | | 300 watts / 24 kw | $1100 / $12,000 | Reservoir built up by ball-valve in pipeline to provide normal amount of water needed for full efficiency when water flow is low. For local sale only. |
| Independent Power Developers, Inc. | High-Head System | 4 inches | | | 3 kw | $3159 | Includes wheel, inverter, battery bank, DC generator. Also available in 6, 9, and 12 kw. |
| Jyoti Ltd. | Micro-Hydel Turbine Set | | 197 ft. to 425 ft. | 66 cfm to 150 cfm | 25 kw | $7500 to $12,000 | Includes Pelton or Turgo impulse wheel, mechanical governor, flywheel, generator, and control panel. |
| Small Hydroelectric Systems and Equipment | Water-Lite | 4½ inches | | | 2 or 3 kw | $500 (aluminum) $650 (bronze) | For high or low heads. Four jets can be adjusted for seasonal changes in water flow. Includes wheel with 4 jets and alternator mounting plate. |
| | Hydroelectric plants | 9 inches 18 inches | | | 15 kw | From $6000 | For A.C. power generation. Includes wheel, Lima brushless alternator, and Woodward governor. |
| | Wheels | 9 inches | | | | $750 | Aluminum. One-inch shaft and bearings. |
| | | 9 inches | | | | $1250 | Bronze. 1 3/16-inch shaft and bearings. |
| | | Two 9 inches | | | | $1000 | Aluminum. 1 3/16-inch shaft and bearings. |
| | | Two 9 inches | | | | $1500 | Bronze. 1 7/16-inch shaft and bearings. |

# Francis and Propeller Turbine Manufacturers

**Barber Hydraulic Turbines Ltd.**
**Barber Point**
**P.O. Box 340**
**Port Colborne, Ontario, Canada L3K 5W1**

Barber has been manufacturing turbines since 1867, and currently it is developing a *Mini-Hydel* unit in the test laboratory. The unit will be a semi-standard packaged set using propeller (for low heads) and Francis (high heads) runners. Base output is intended to be about 20 kw. Prices were not available on going to press.

An affiliated company, Canada Frontier Water and Power Limited, conducts feasibility studies, site visits, design of small dams and power plants, project management, etc.

**Canyon Industries,**
**5346 Mosquito Lake Road**
**Deming, Washington 98244**

Canyon Industries is one of the few small turbine manufacturers in the world that uses hydropower for its own energy needs (another is Land and Leisure Services). After two years of tests Canyon now produces the *Hydromite*. On a head of 15 to 34 ft. and with a flow of 30 to 40 cfm, it will produce 150 to 700 watts, if coupled to a suitable generator. A continuous 500 watt output will give 12 kw hours a day, not a lot but quite enough to meet the needs of a cottage for lighting and small electrical appliances. But its main virtue is that it operates on a low head, whereas all other standard small output mini-turbines require a head of at least 50 ft. The unit, which weighs just 6½ lbs., costs $395, excluding the generator. Canyon hopes to have a unit complete with generator suitable for battery charging available soon. The runner is basically a propeller, with guide vanes to increase its efficiency. Further details are available from Canyon Industries. Send $1.00.

**Elektro G.m.b.H.**
**St. Gallerstrasse 27**
**Winterthur, Switzerland**

Elektro manufactures a small Francis turbine set. On a head of 25 to 64 ft. and with a flow of 32 to 64 cfm, it will produce between 0.5 and 2 kw. The unit, which comes with a draft-tube and alternator but no governor, costs between S.Fr. 8000 and 10,000 ($5100 and $6400 approximately).

**G & A Associates**
**223 Katonah Avenue**
**Katonah, New York 10536**
**(914) 232-8165**

Back in 1972 Ken Grover started G & A, which specializes in small water power. Grover's interest in the subject began on the farm where he was born, which was without electricity until he rigged a waterwheel on a nearby stream to turn a pair of truck generators, an inexpensive system that provided power for 20 years. With a degree in mechanical engineering behind him, Grover continued his interest in water power. He has now invented, manufactured and installed a new radial flow turbine. While it is a Francis turbine, this new design incorporates some important cost-saving differences that could make it attractive as a runner for use in many situations.

As well as the radial inflow, G & A also manufactures Kaplan turbines. Both are suitable for use on very low to medium heads. The average output of such turbines installed to date is 3 to 25 kw, but they may be scaled up to any size. Power generated is usually used for heating, battery and inverter systems, or combinations of both. Send a dollar to G & A for further details.

**Gilbert Gilkes and Gordon Ltd.,**
**Kendal, Westmorland**
**England**

Gilkes was founded in 1856 and they are the oldest manufacturers of water turbines in the world. They have kept a record of every turbine manufactured by them and can tell just what head and flow each was designed to operate under. In fact, they still have the original design for their turbine No. 1, a 4-kw Thomson Vortex, built in 1856, which operated for over a century. May the same be said 100 years hence of their new *Hydec* range (see p. 190).

They also manufacture a complete range of Francis and Pelton turbines to order. Unfortunately they tend to be very expensive per installed kilowatt as compared to the *Hydec*. They are also developing an electronic load governor.

**Independent Power Developers, Inc.**
See Pelton Wheel Manufacturers.

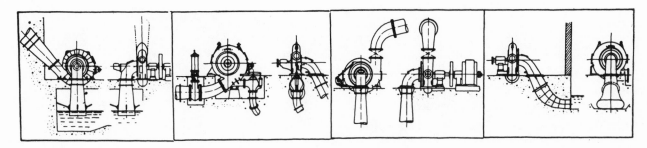

## The James Leffel & Company
## Springfield, Ohio 45501

Leffel has been manufacturing water turbines since 1862. Their products include custom-built turbines in a wide range of capacities and types. They also supply runners, turbine casings, shafts, bearings, and turbine maintenance parts for rebuilding.

Their *Hoppes Hydro-Electric Unit* is the only self-contained one of its kind made in the U.S.A. The *Hoppes*, on a head of 13 to 25 feet, can produce between 0.5 and 10 kw. It is driven by a fixed-pitch propeller turbine made of bronze. The turbine shaft is made of heat-treated alloy steel. The generator sits above the turbine and is directly connected to it. A mechanical governor regulates the propeller speed by controlling the flow of water through the unit. The electrical equipment and governor are protected by a steel plate housing. The switch panel has a main line switch, voltmeter, fused cutout, and rheostat.

Write for their Pamphlet "A" and Bulletin H-49 for more information.

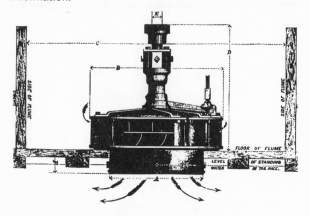

*An 1870-vintage Leffel hydraulic turbine.*

## Jyoti Ltd.,
## R.C. Dutt Road
## Baroda—390 005, India

Jyoti manufactures a range of three *Micro-Hydel* turbine sets as follows:

| Output kw | Head Feet | Flow cfm | Cost |
|---|---|---|---|
| 3–5 | 10–40 | 156–435 | $5,500–8,000 |
| 10 | 20–40 | 281–543 | $6,000–7,000 |
| 25 | 197–425 | 66–150 | $7,500–12,000 |

All figures are approximations only. The standard unit includes mechanical governor (with flywheel), generator and control panel. Francis and propeller runners are used on the low-head sets, Pelton and Turgo impulse wheels on the high-head version. Jyoti also manufactures a range of turbines with outputs from 25 to 1000 kw.

| K.M.W. Fack, S681 01, Kristinehamn, Sweden | and | A.B. Bofors-Nohab, Fack, S 461 01, Trollhattan, Sweden |
|---|---|---|

Both these companies supply fixed- and adjustable-bladed propeller turbines with outputs from 100 kw upwards.

## Land and Leisure (Services) Ltd.,
## Priory Lane
## St. Thomas, Launceston
## Cornwall, England

Land and Leisure is run by brothers Rupert and James Armstrong Evans, who carry on the hydro-power tradition from their father and grandfather. In fact the house where they were raised, and where they now have their workshop, is served by an old metal water-wheel and a first-class Francis turbine.

Land and Leisure supplies new propeller turbines and Pelton wheels, either as complete units or just the runner alone. They are currently working on a number of installations mainly using twin sets of fixed-blade propeller turbines. On the twin-propeller installations, propellers of two different sizes are used. The large propeller will function at full efficiency on 70 percent of peak flow and the smaller one on 30 percent. When the flow is at its full peak both turbines are opened up. They find this method works out cheaper than a variable pitch Kaplan turbine. Land and Leisure was first in the water power field to develop and install electronic load governors.

### THE HYDEC TURBINE SET

This is a recent and welcome addition to the group of turbines available today. Within its range on medium to high heads it is competitively priced against the Francis and Pelton turbines. Its design and construction is simple, as is the installation and maintenance of the unit. The efficiency of the Hydec is about 80 percent, which is average for most small turbines. The runner is the Gilkes Turgo Impulse Wheel. The wheel and its casing are both made of cast iron. The shaft is steel and the governor is an oil spring-loaded type which operates a stainless steel jet deflector. The inlet valve is a manually operated butterfly valve. Its output range is from 5 kw under heads as low as 40 ft. up to 150 kw under a head of 350 ft.

| | Cost | |
|---|---|---|
| Mean Diameter of Runner | Single Jet | Twin Jet |
| 7.5 in. | $7,840 | $9,300 |
| 10.5 in. | $9,760 | $11,500 |
| 13.0 in. | $11,200 | $13.000 |
| 16.5 in. | $12,500 | $14,700 |

These prices include the wheel, complete with casing, governor, inlet valve and inlet pipe. Suitable governors and control panels can be supplied at additional cost. But, to quote an example, a 16.5-in. twin jet unit developing 25 kw on a net head of 40 ft. was recently sold, complete with generator and switch panel, for $19,200.

The Hydec is available from Gilbert Gilkes and Gordon Ltd. (see description on p. 189).

## Francis and Propeller Turbines Compared

| Manufacturer | Make | Head | Flow | Output | Price | Features |
|---|---|---|---|---|---|---|
| Canyon Industries | Hydromite | 15 ft. to 34 ft. | 30 cfm to 40 cfm | 150 watts 700 watts | $395 | Suitable for lighting and operating small electrical equipment in cottage. Includes propeller turbine with guide vanes. |
| Elektro G.m.b.H. | | 25 ft. to 64 ft. | 32 cfm to 64 cfm | 0.5 kw to 2 kw | $3200 to $4000 | Includes Francis turbine, draft-tube, alternator. For local sale only. Not available in U.S. |
| Independent Power Developers, Inc. | Low-Head System | 5 ft. to 50 ft. | | 3 kw | $3700 | Includes Nagler, fixed-pitch propeller turbine; inverter; battery bank; DC generator. Also available in 6, 9, and 12 kw. |
| James Leffel Company | Hoppes Hydro-Electric Unit | 13 ft. to 25 ft. | 70 cfm to 980 cfm | 0.5 kw to 10 kw | | Self-contained unit. Includes fixed-pitch, propeller turbine; direct-drive generator; mechanical governor; switch panel. |
| Jyoti Ltd. | Micro-Hydel Turbine Set | 10 ft. to 40 ft. | 156 cfm to 435 cfm | 3 kw to 5 kw | $5500 to $8000 | Includes Francis or propeller turbine; mechanical governor, flywheel, generator, and control panel. |
| | | 20 ft. to 40 ft. | 281 cfm to 543 cfm | 10 kw | $3600 to $7000 | Same as above. |

# Small Water Power Directory

The following list gives the names of those who have a special interest in the manufacture and installation of small water power plants. No doubt there are many small engineering firms spread throughout the world which have, in the past, made small turbines and would, if asked, be willing to manufacture to order. It is worthwhile asking in your locality if there is anyone who owns a turbine and finding out who the manufacturer was.

**AMERICA**

**Barber Hydraulic Turbines, Ltd.**
**Barber Point**
**P.O. Box 340**
**Port Colborne**
**Ontario, Canada L3k 5W1**
See Francis and Propeller Turbine Manufacturers.

**Campbell Water Wheel Company**
**420 South 42nd Street**
**Philadelphia, Pennsylvania 19104**
See Waterwheel section.

**Canyon Industries**
**5346 Mosquito Lake Road**
**Deming, Washington 98244**
See Francis and Propeller Turbine Manufacturers

**Cumberland General Store**
**Route 3, Box 479**
**Crossville, Tennessee 38555**
Markets the Leffel Hoppes unit.

**G & A Associates**
**223 Katonah Avenue**
**Katonah, New York 10536**
See Francis and Propeller Turbine Manufacturers.

**F.W.E. Stapenhorst, Inc.**
**285 Labrosse Avenue**
**Pointe Claire**
**Quebec H9R 1A3, Canada**
North American representative for Ossberger turbines.

**Guy Immega,**
**Lasqueti Island,**
**British Columbia, Canada**
Willing to act as a consultant on small hydropower systems in his area. Has written for a number of books and journals on the subject.

**Independent Energy Systems, Inc.,**
P.O. Box 1265
**Blowing Rock,**
**North Carolina 28605**
Apart from installing turbines manu-
factured by Leffel and Independent
Power Developers, I.E.S. is engaged
in development work on its own
complete system and on a small
impulse turbine.

**Independent Power Developers,**
**Box 1467**
**Noxon, Montana 59853**
For product range, see Pelton and
Propeller Manufacturers.

**The James Leffel & Company**
**Springfield, Ohio 45501**
For product range, see Francis and
Propeller Turbine Manufacturers.

**Niagara Water Wheels Ltd.,**
**Box 326, Bridge Station**
**Niagara Falls, New York 14305**
Handle small-to-medium-sized turbines. They offer design, manufacturing and installation services
using new and rebuilt turbines.

**Small Hydroelectric Systems and**
**Equipment**
**P.O. Box 124**
**Custer, Washington 98240**
For product range see Pelton Wheel
section.

EUROPE

**A.B. Bofors-Nohab**
**Fack, S46101**
**Trollhattan, Sweden**
*See* Francis and Propeller Turbine
Manufacturers.

**Vincent Allen Associates**
**291 High Street**
**Epping, Essex, England**
Consulting engineers with an interest
in small water power.

**P.W. Agnew**
**Department of Mechanical**
**Engineering**
**The University**
**Glasglow, Scotland**
Will advise on equipment in Scotland.
Developing a small propeller
turbine.

**Dress and Company**
**4760 Werl/West**
**Postfach 43, West Germany**
No longer manufacturing standard
sets.

**C. Dumont and Cie.**
**Pont de Ste. Uze 26240**
**St. Vallier**
**Drome, France**
Manufactures small Francis, Pelton
and Kaplan turbines together with
all associated equipment.

**Elektro GmbH,**
**St. Gallerstrasse 27**
**Winterthur, Switzerland**
For product range, see Pelton Wheel
and Francis sections.

**Escher Wyss Limited**
**Zurich, Switzerland CH-8023**
Have just started production of
*Mini-Straflo* turbines. With out-
puts starting at 400 kw, it is not
exactly mini.

**Gilbert Gilkes and Gordon Limited**
**Kendal, Westmorland, England**
See Hydec panel and mfg.
description.

**Intermediate Technology**
**Development Group Limited,**
**9 King Street,**
**London WC2E8HN**
Mainly involved in the development of
low-head propeller turbines and high-
head Pelton wheels in the 5 to 50 kw
capacity.

**K.M.W.**
**Fack S681 01**
**Kristinehamn, Sweden**
See Francis and Propeller
Turbine Manufacturers.

**Land and Leisure (Services) Limited**
**Priory Lane,**
**St. Thomas, Launceston**
**Cornwall, England.**
See Francis and propeller
Manufacturers.

**Officine Buehler**
**Taverne,**
**Canton Ticino, Switzerland**
Reported to manufacture a wide
range of turbines.

**Ossberger Turbinenfabrik,**
**8832 Weissenburg**
**Bayern, Germany.**
See Cross-Flow Manufacturers.

**Westward Mouldings Ltd.,**
**Greenhill Works**
**Delaware Road**
**Gunnislake**
**Cornwall, England**
See Waterwheel section.

OTHER COUNTRIES

**Balaju Yantra Shala (P) Limited,**
**Balaju, Katmandu, Nepal**
See Cross-Flow section.

**Barata Metalworks and Engineering**
**P.T.**
**J.L. Ngagel 109,**
**Surabaya, Indonesia**
Manufactures Francis and Cross-Flow
turbines with outputs ranging from
18 kw upwards.

**Jyoti Limited,**
**R.C. Dutt Road**
**Baroda 390 005,**
**India**
See Francis and Propeller Turbine
Manufacturers.

**Low Impact Technology**
**(Australia)**
**34 Martin Street**
**South Melbourne,**
**Victoria, Australia**
Alain Gerrard, who started L.I.T.,
powers his home with a water
turbine. Can supply and install a
whole range of natural energy
equipment.

**Speedright Equipment Limited,**
**P.O. Box 169**
**Levin, New Zealand**
Manufactures a small turbine set
for battery charging.

**Tientsin Electro-Driving Research**
**Institute**
**Tientsin, China**
Trial-producing a range of small
turbines, 0.6 to 12 kw capacity.

# Additional Sources of Information

*Alternative Sources of Energy*
Route 2
Box 90-A
Milaca, Minnesota 56353

Number 14 of this journal contains a reprint of "Water Power: Hydraulic Engineering, 1899," a good article, full of facts and figures for the construction of waterwheels. $1.50.

**The Central Office of the World Energy Conference**
**201 Grand Buildings**
**Trafalgar Square**
**London WC1**
**England**

Volume 2 of *Transactions of World Power Conference*, published in 1924, consists of 814 pages on water power. Mostly big plants but some small ones included.

**The Electrical Research Association**
**Cleeve Road**
**Leatherhead**
**Surrey**
**England**

*Electric Power Plant International* is published yearly by this association. It includes the names and addresses of all alternator and inverter manufacturers in the world, together with details of their range. Very expensive; try your local or college library.

**National Center for Alternative Technology**
**Machynlleth**
**Powys, Wales**

They have recently installed a 10-foot diameter wooden waterwheel. The plans are available for $1.

**School of Engineering**
**Oregon State University**
**219 Covell Hall**
**Corvallis, Oregon 97331**

Bulletin Series No. 25. 1949, "The Banki Water Turbine," contains a translation from the German paper by Donat Banki, "Neue Wasser-turbine" (Budapest, 1917). It also includes tests on a cross-flow runner, which at low efficiency (65 percent) produced 2 kw at 280 rpm using 133 cfm on a 16-foot head. The theory of the Banki is well covered, and instructions for the construction of the above runner are included. Good value for 50 cents.

**The Society for the Protection of Ancient Buildings**
**55 Great Ormond Street**
**London WC1**
**England**

The society has published a series of booklets on European watermills.

**Volunteers in Technical Assistance**
**VITA Executive Offices**
**3706 Rhode Island Ave.**
**Mt. Rainier, Maryland 20822**
**(301) 277-7000**

VITA is a private, nonprofit development organization based in the United States. It supplies information and assistance by mail to people seeking help with technical problems.

VITA Publications offers the following manuals on the subject of water power:

*Low-Cost Development of Small Water Power Sites,* by Hans Hamm. VITA, 1967. $2.95. Provides information for determining potential of water source, choosing a turbine, constructing dams and Michell-Banki turbines. Includes manufacturers' addresses.

*Design Manual for Water Wheels.* VITA, 1975. $4.50. Instructions for constructing an overshot wheel for grinding grain and pumping water.

*Technical Bulletin #1. 1 kw River Generator.* $1. Instructions for constructing a 1-kw generator unit with 80 percent efficiency. Operates at 6 ft./sec.

Include payment with order. Make checks payable to VITA Publications Service.

VITA also publishes two newsletters, *VITA News* and *Vis-a-Vis.* They contain updates on VITA programs, notices of important events, technical abstracts, profiles of VITA volunteers, and lists of problems requiring solutions. Available upon request from VITA Communications Department. Donations accepted.

**Water Wheel Designs for Handicrafters**
**Paul W. Dillow**
**2742 Victoria Drive**
**Alpine, California 92001**

Paul Dillow sells plans for the construction of water wheels for $10 each. Three sets of plans are available:

| Wheel diameter | 4 feet | 6 feet | 8 feet |
|---|---|---|---|
| Bucket width | 23 inches | 23 inches | 33 inches |
| Bucket depth | 6 inches | 8 inches | 8 inches |
| Maximum rpm | 30 | 20 | 15 |
| Required flow | 190 cfm | 330 cfm | 420 cfm |
| Maximum shaft power | 0.8 kw | 1.8 kw | 3.5 kw |

## BOOKS

Anderson, F., *Electricity for the Farm.* New York: Macmillan Co., 1915. Subtitled "Light, Heat and Power by Inexpensive Methods from the Water-Wheel or Farm Engine." Good for those who want to use a water wheel with a DC generator.

Ball, R.S. *Natural Sources of Power.* London: Constable, 1908. Wind and water power, but mainly water.

Bradbury. *Hydraulic Systems and Maintenance.* UK: Iliffe, 1972.

Doland, James J. *Hydro Power Engineering.* New York: Roland Press, 1954. A textbook for civil engineers.

Fairbairn, Sir William. *Treatise on Mills and Millwork.* London: Longmans, 1861, 1878. The complete work on watermills. Available through some library services.

Harris and Rice. *Power Development of Small Streams.* Orange, Mass.: Rodney Hunt Machine Company, 1920.

Mosonyi, E. *Water Power Development.* Budapest: Hungarian Academy of Sciences, 1960. Volume 1: Low-Head Water Plants. Volume 2: High-Head Water Plants. Includes an interesting section on midget power plants.

Schwenk, T. *Sensitive Chaos.* R. Steiner Press, 1965. An excellent photographic and written study of water and wind as living, flowing elements.

*Small-Scale Power Generation.* United Nations, 1967. Wind and water power.

Spannhake, William. *Centrifugal Pumps, Turbines, and Propellers.* Mass.: MIT Press, 1934. Highly technical.

Syson, L. *English Watermills.* London: Batsford, 1965.

Taylor, W.T. *Practical Water Power Engineering.* New York: Van Nostrand, 1925. London: Crosby Lockwood, 1925. Deals with rainfall and run-off, measurement of flow. Good on reservoirs, site selection and canals. Sixty pages of electric power transmission. Small-to-medium installations.

*Water Power Engineering.* London: R. Hammond, 1958. Megawatt plants.

*Water Turbine Plant.* J.O. Boving, Raithby, Lawrence and Company, 1910. Lots of good drawings and technical information on Pelton and Francis turbines.

Wilson, P.M. *Water Turbines.* London: Her Majesty's Stationary Office, 1974. Very good introductory booklet.

# 5

# Wood Heat

For centuries the burning of wood was our only source of heat. Early fireplaces were large, dirty, smoky, and highly inefficient (Figure 5-1), but during the seventeenth and eighteenth centuries a variety of improvements began to emerge in different countries. America contributed to this advancement (through the work of such early pioneers as Benjamin Franklin) in the design and popularization of more efficient ways of burning wood. In the United States during the years 1850–1900, the wood-burning cast iron stove was the major source of domestic heating. It was used primarily for cooking and hot water supply until it was supplanted by coal-burners—and eventually by gas and oil. With the advent of the "energy crisis," the old dies for cast iron stoves have been brought back into use. Stove manufacturers are once again looking for more convenient and efficient ways of heating with wood. The fireplace, which never really died out because it was always either useful, or a luxury the average homeowner wanted, is now available with modifications that make it a more efficient source of auxiliary heat.

Figure 5-1. Early fireplaces were often smoky and always inefficient.

# Fireplaces

For those who want to heat entirely with wood, the choice should be between stoves and furnaces. A conventional fireplace is just too inefficient; about 90 percent of the heat usually goes up the chimney. And it is surprisingly easy to build a fireplace that actually increases the heat loss of the house by drawing all the warm air out of the room and up the chimney. When heating was done entirely with fireplaces, a house of moderate size often consumed four times as much wood as does a house using modern wood-burning stoves.

For those who must see the flames dancing in an open fireplace, however, there are several ways to improve its efficiency. In 1800, Count Rumford discovered that the heat radiated from a conventional fireplace could be increased by making it shallower (reducing the distance from the front to the back), and by sloping the rear wall forwards. He also discovered that smoking could be reduced by inserting a chimney shelf at the bottom (or *throat*) of the chimney. This *smoke shelf* reduces the size of the entrance to the flue, increasing the speed of the air moving upwards and preventing the downdrafts that cause a fireplace to smoke. Rumford recommended a four-inch

throat. Modern standards recommend eight inches, but most modern fireplaces have the added sophistication of a damper to regulate the size of the opening.

Other efforts to save more of the heat from a fireplace usually involve changing the heat distribution system. A conventional fireplace *radiates* heat to the walls, furniture, objects (and people) in the room (Figure 5-2). It does not warm the air in the room, except insofar as the warmed surfaces heat the air next to them. However, with a source of radiant heat it is possible to be comfortable despite low air temperatures (for example, outside on a cold but sunny winter day).

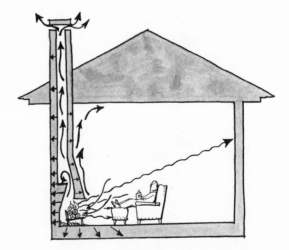

Figure 5-2. Heat transfer from a conventional fireplace.

Most of the heat *radiated* by a fire is absorbed by the walls of the fireplace and *conducted* through them. If the walls are made of masonry, they will store the heat and gradually release it to the rest of the house (this is why the early New Englanders put the chimney in the middle of the house). Most of the air that is directly heated by the embers rises up the chimney, so in this way the heat is *convected* out of the room.

Several methods have been invented that use convection to distribute the heat from the fireplace more efficiently. Specially designed grates made of hollow pipes are heated by both radiation and conduction from the burning embers (Figure 5-3). Air blown through the pipes and back into the room absorbs a lot of heat that would otherwise be lost. Sometimes these units can be uncomfortably efficient—a blast of hot air is not as pleasant as radiant warmth. And unless the unit includes a fan to boost convection, its heat-extracting capacity may be negligible.

The "Franklin"-type fireplace with closing doors is a compromise between the beauty of an open fire and the efficiency of an enclosed stove. Closing the doors considerably reduces the amount of warm air drawn out of the room and up the chimney as well as increases the efficiency of combustion.

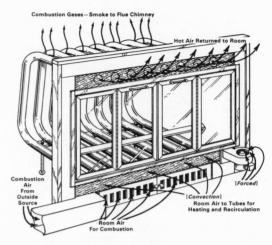

Figure 5-4. A combination fireplace grate and glass door is still more efficient, using outside air for combustion and returning warm air to room.

The first "Franklin stove" took in air from a draft beneath the floor (Figure 5-5). Some of the air was used for combustion, the rest passed around the firebox and flue and back into the room. This ingenious arrangement allowed for the distribution of heat within the room by convection. Modern versions of the Franklin stove (Figure 5-6) do not use this warm air circulating system, and even with their doors closed they do

Figure 5-3. Tubular fireplace grate heats room by convection. For best performance, get a fan-type grate.

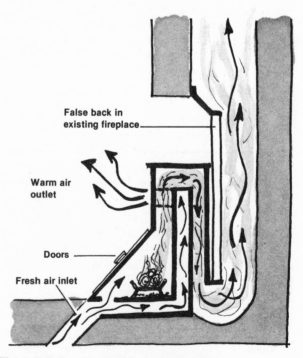

Figure 5-5. Ben Franklin's original 1742 "Pennsylvania stove." Modern "Franklin stoves" are much less efficient.

not give nearly as much heat as either airtight stoves or old-fashioned Franklin stoves. Modern warm air *circulating fireplaces* are available that pass air around the back and sides of the fireplace to pick up extra heat (Figure 5–7). The air can then be directed out into the room or to the upper floors of the building.

A fireplace will also heat much more efficiently if it uses primary combustion air ducted in directly from outside, rather than using heated room air. Some prefab fireplaces, such as the Martin *Octatherm*, include duct connections for outside combustion air intake. New construction can incorporate combustion air ducts into the fireplace design. In an existing fireplace, it may be possible to bring combustion air in through the ashpit or cleanout in the hearth. If you do adapt your fireplace in this way, allow for a total intake duct area equal to the chimney flue, so the fire will not be choked for oxygen. And close the fireplace opening with glass doors, so that room air cannot enter the fireplace (Figure 5–4). A warm-air circulating fireplace with combustion-air intake ducts and glass doors is a very efficient source of heat, and a far cry from the marginal energy value of a conventional fireplace.

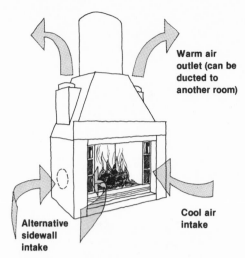

Warm air outlet (can be ducted to another room)

Cool air intake

Alternative sidewall intake

Figure 5–7. A *Heatilator*-type warm air circulating fireplace.

# Wood-Burning Stoves

The major improvement in wood-burners since the fireplace era has been the gradual reduction in the draft so that no more air goes into the stove and up the chimney than necessary for efficient combustion. Modern "airtight" stoves hold a fire longer and require less attention than others.

The high efficiencies of airtight stoves are achieved by providing air in correct amounts where and when it is needed—for example, "primary" air at the base of the fire to burn the coals, and secondary air above the wood to burn the gases that give rise to the long flame characteristic of wood fires (Figure 5–8).

The modern wood stove routinely holds a fire for twelve hours and can be kept going all winter long. This is a great advantage over older stoves, not solely for reasons of comfort, but also because constant kindling of fires is a big nuisance. Long refueling times also mean that those with nine-to-five jobs can heat their homes with wood. Airtight stoves burn the wood so completely that ashes need be removed only once a week or so. This, too, is quite an advantage over inefficient wood-burners and coal stoves. All in all, the modern wood stove may be cited as an example of genuine technological progress, at least by comparison with its predecessor, the fireplace.

The convenience of modern airtights comes at a price, however—formation of very flammable

Figure 5–6. A modern Franklin-type stove.

**Figure 5–8. Typical airtight cast iron stove. Noncombustible hearth extends 12 inches outward on sides, 18 inches at front.**

*creosote* in the chimney (Figure 5–9). Chimney fires occurred regularly in the nineteenth century, and are occurring frequently again today as more people heat with modern wood-burning stoves. The modern stoves are even more dangerous than the old ones in this respect, partly because of the way they are used. At bedtime they are customarily packed full of fuel and the draft is turned down. The fire cools to the point where combustion is incomplete, and many unburned gases enter the chimney, which also cools to some extent under these conditions. If cool enough, the unburned gases and water condense to form an acid solution that runs back down the flue until the water reevaporates, leaving solid creosote behind. If your chimney is not in good repair and the cresote in it ignites, there is some chance that the resulting fire could spread to the rest of the house. If it is of an approved safety design and without cracks, you have less to worry about. But before installing a stove, you must be sure you have a sound chimney.[1]

In the nineteenth century, cast iron stoves were made in great numbers in this country.

Almost every town of any size had a foundry. With changing technology, American stoves today are often constructed economically of sheet steel, though the renewal of interest in wood heat has also brought back American cast iron stoves in very recent years.

### STEEL STOVES

When you look at a steel stove, two important considerations are the thickness of the metal and the quality of the welds. The thicker the steel, the longer it will take to rust out.[2] If the thickness is

---

1. For information on woodburning safety, see *Using Coal and Wood Stoves Safely* (Boston: National Fire Protection Association, 470 Atlantic Avenue, Boston, Mass.). Also see Mary Twitchell, *Wood Energy* (Charlotte, Vt.: Garden Way Publishing, 1978. $7.95) and Jay Shelton, *Wood Heat Safety* (Garden Way Publishing, 1979. $8.95).

2. Thickness of steel is measured in "gauge" numbers. Fifteen gauge corresponds to about 1/16 inch; 11 gauge equals about 1/8 inch. Steel should be at least 3/16 inch thick (6 gauge) if it is in direct contact with fire.

less than about 1/16 inch, the steel will probably bend and bow when heated unless reinforced. This is not serious unless it interferes with airtightness. In some stoves the sheet metal is protected from the heat of the firebox by cast iron or firebrick linings. (These also promote a higher temperature in the firebox and in theory should help ensure complete combustion.) Good welds show no porosity and are slightly convex, neither very flat nor with lumps higher than either of the parent metals (Figure 5–10).

Most steel stoves have cast iron doors that cannot be welded to the steel and so are bolted on with furnace cement as a sealer. The furnace cement tends to break apart and fall out. When this happens control over the draft, and therefore over the fire, is lost. Once a year, it is wise to inspect the seals and apply more furnace cement where necessary. When the asbestos gasket around the loading door becomes worn, it too will have to be replaced to ensure a tight fit.

American steel stoves with automatically controlled dampers are sometimes said to work on the *wood distillation* principle, that is, a load of fuel goes through a pattern of drying, burning the combustible gases, and burning the charcoal. The firebox temperature tends to rise through each stage, but the draft is reduced automatically, to keep heat production more or less even.

Figure 5–10. A modern steel stove, this a *Tempwood* (see catalog).

Figure 5–9. Creosote buildup like this can ignite, with the resulting chimney fire endangering the house itself. Airtight stoves and their chimneys must be cleaned frequently.

CAST IRON STOVES

Cast iron box stoves are more expensive and usually preferred over steel stoves because of their heavier construction, which gives them longer lives and better heat-retaining capabilities. While slower to heat up, cast iron stoves radiate heat more evenly. Modern cast iron stoves, whether imported or American made, are highly sophisticated, with internal baffles, excellent draft control, and good airtightness when shut down.

Cast iron stoves need no automatic draft control because they operate on a very different principle from steel stoves. In cast iron stoves an even temperature is maintained by inclusion of a baffle in the upper part of the firebox. This forces the draft into an S-shaped pattern, so that the logs burn from front to back like a cigarette (Figure 5–11). The fire remains qualitatively the same throughout a fuel cycle; thus heat production is constant.

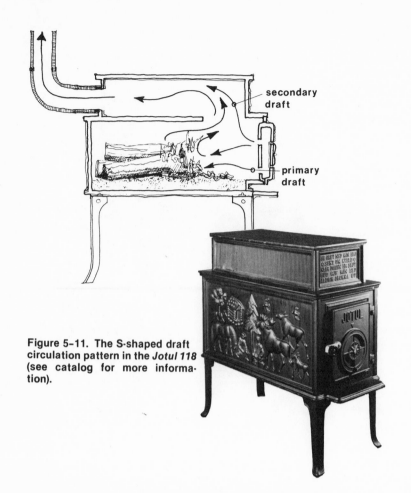

Figure 5-11. The S-shaped draft circulation pattern in the *Jotul 118* (see catalog for more information).

Figure 5-12. Typical vertical-firebox Scandinavian stove with ceramic tile exterior.

In Austria, Eastern Europe and Scandinavia there has been a long tradition of building fireplaces where the flue is extended up and down inside a large heat retaining box that forms the exterior of the stove. These models—made of ceramic tile, soapstone, or firebrick (Figure 5-12), provide a low temperature source of background heat. They heat the air in the room by direct contact—as well as by radiating heat to surfaces within the room.

Like conventional fireplaces, airtight woodburning stoves give off most of their heat by *radiation.* To do this effectively, the metal housing must get very hot. Partly for this reason, a safety clearance of 36 inches is recommended between the stove and any combustible (less if sheet metal shields are used). A guard rail is also a good idea if you have small children who could fall against the hot surface.

To avoid fire danger, the ideal location for a very hot stove is in the center of a room. Such placement also takes full advantage of heat radiated from the stove, though it may not be desirable in a retrofit installation.

WOOD HEAT CIRCULATORS

Like warm-air circulating fireplaces, there are also wood burning stoves that heat the air of the room by convection. These *wood circulators* are equipped with a metal jacket surrounding the firebox (Figure 5-13). Air passes between the two metal surfaces, is heated, and rises out into the room. Often a small electric fan is used to pull the warm air down through the cabinet and out at floor level for better distribution throughout the room.

# Wood Furnaces

One of the cheapest (but least glamorous) ways of heating a large house completely with wood is to use a wood furnace. Like an oil furnace, it takes up a lot of room and is most conveniently located in the basement of a house along with the wood required to feed it. A wood furnace is similar to a very large circulator-type stove. It has a firebox that operates on the same complete combustion principles as an efficient stove, so that wood and most residue is reduced to a minimum amount of ash. Unlike a stove, a modern wood furnace can easily be converted to burn oil. Some will switch automatically so that you have a choice of fuel and can leave the furnace to run on oil for lengthy periods (Figure 5–14). When fueled with wood it will require attention about twice a day.

To distribute the heat from a furnace, air is drawn around the firebox and circulated through ducts in the house just as in a conventional forced air heating system. Some furnaces can be used with hot water distribution systems, in which case the firebox is surrounded by water that is then piped into baseboard radiators or radiant floor systems. Suppliers of wood furnaces also offer automatic humidifiers (with forced air systems) and auxiliary equipment for heating the household water supply. An investment in a wood furnace is equivalent to buying a complete house-heating system, so it is advisable to talk to owners as well as manufacturers before making a purchase.

Figure 5–14. A Longwood *Dualfuel* combination furnace (wood and oil or gas) burns large wood chunks. Note flue gas heat reclaimer at top.

# Chimneys

Stoves and chimney should be thought of together, as a unit. Poor draft and back-puffing sometimes are blamed on the stove when the fault lies with the chimney. The lifting force on chimney gases depends on how hot they are and how high the chimney is. The higher the chimney, the better the draft. A chimney is too high only when it is in danger of being toppled by the wind or when exhaust gases are chilled at the top.

Generally, the choice is between a brick (or masonry) chimney and a prefabricated stainless steel chimney, such as *Metalbestos*. The metal chimney has the advantage of being easier to install, particularly in an existing structure. If there is any problem with smoking, it is easy enough to climb on the roof and add another section of chimney. Also, if fired only occasionally, the metal chimney heats up quickly and draws well almost immediately.

The brick or masonry chimney, though, with a flue liner and good thick walls, acts as heat reservoir in the center of the house; once warm, it provides a good draft even when the fire is low. The warm chimney helps reduce creosote build-up and back-puffing. Its disadvantage is that the masonry takes a long time to warm up, and may develop heavy creosote deposits when first used in the fall.

Another point in favor of a brick chimney is that it becomes an air conditioner in the warm

Figure 5–13. Wood-burning "circulator." Air is warmed between the firebox and outer jacket and rises into the room.

season. In winter, with a fire in the stove, gases in the chimney are hotter than the air outside, and an updraft occurs. On hot summer days, the air in the chimney is cooled below the temperature of the outside air, and a downdraft occurs. To take full advantage of this effect, disconnect the stove in the summer. This is a good idea in any case to be sure that no rust-inducing moisture enters through the chimney.

Whatever the type of chimney, an installation in the *center* of the warm house rather than up an outside wall will help greatly in reducing creosote build-up (Figure 5-15). Chimney gases will remain hotter and exit the chimney without condensing, except at the very top section above the roof. Another good idea along the same line is to keep the chimney as straight as possible from the stove, avoiding bends or elbows that slow the smoke and encourage creosote.

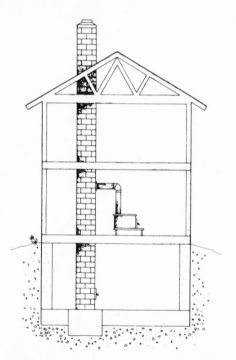

Figure 5-15. The center of a house is the best location for a wood stove.

One installation to avoid with an airtight stove is a prefabricated chimney above the roof and a plain stovepipe from the roof down to the stove. With a low fire, the ordinary stovepipe cools and becomes lined with creosote. Chimney fires are very likely with this setup, and they are especially dangerous here because the thin stovepipe weakens and corrodes over a couple of seasons.

Because of the creosote problem, a modern airtight stove should be connected to the chimney with only a short length of stovepipe.

Stovepipes stretching horizontally as far as fifty feet were common in churches in the last century, but with a good hot fire only once a week in an inefficient box stove, there was little chance of depositing tar in the pipe. The long pipe provided a way of getting heat out into the nave after it was swept prematurely out of the firebox by a high draft.

# Wood as a Source of Energy

Fossil fuels, wind, water and wood could all be considered as solar energy sources. Unlike coal and oil, however, wood is a renewable source. Moreover, in countries where there is a plentiful wood supply, generally it is true that the supply has remained constant. The statistics will probably remain so, insofar as human beings take responsibility for caring for their natural resources.

As a solar collector the tree is unique. No labor-hours nor any fuels are needed to build it. It is also unique as an energy storage device, since the energy can, with some precautions, be retrieved and used centuries after being captured. If one's definition of efficiency is broad enough, therefore, it may be said that the tree is more efficient at capturing and storing solar energy than anything we can make. In addition, the trees are simply beautiful things to have around us.

This does not mean that human-made solar energy traps are useless, but it should be clear that they belong where vegetation does not grow—roof tops and deserts, for example.

IS THERE ENOUGH WOOD?

There is presently an abundance of wood available in the United States, despite many stories in our press to the contrary. It *is* a fact however, that there are serious shortages of certain species, particularly the big trees of high quality. The amount of standing wood in this country, however, is enormous and increasing, despite soaring consumption of paper and plywood.

There are two major reasons for the comeback of wood—first, the reversion of millions of acres of former cropland in the East to forest, and second, a reduction in the per capita consumption of wood. When the settlers first arrived they cut timber faster than one would imagine, considering the tools they had to work with. Much of this wood was burned in the field, and potash and perlash from the ashes were sold in England and other countries of Northern Europe for cash used to buy farm tools. As the Midwest of the United States and highly mechanized agriculture took over, small eastern farms were abandoned, a trend that continues in some places. The deserted farms eventually become forest once again, but without human intervention the time to reach full production of commercial forest products can be over a century.

Also, *less* wood is demanded from American forests than before—largely because of the decline in the use of wood as a fuel. Interestingly, in the early days of the United States there was literally wood to burn, and as late as 1860 the average American family was consuming 17.5 cords annually for heat and cooking. Until the mid-1860's, steamboats and railroads were wood-powered. Only in the latter part of the nineteenth century did coal begin to take over. In 1900, 45 percent of the energy used in the United States still came from wood. Since then wood has been almost totally displaced as a domestic source of energy, while the harvest of other wood—"industrial wood"—has stayed fairly constant in spite of rising population. Wood and charcoal have been supplanted by other materials in thousands of applications—buildings, vehicles, furniture, iron-making, and the chemical industry.

In the United States about 500 million acres are classified as commercial forest land (not counting some 100 million acres in interior Alaska) on which the average potential growth rate of harvestable wood is near one cord per acre per year. Ideally, this means a total growth of 500 million cords in the United States each year, *if* each of those 500 million acres were well stocked with vigorous trees. Of course, they are not, especially on former farmland in the East. Realistically, then, assume an annual growth of 350 million cords of these 500 million acres, of which about 150 million cords are currently used for lumber, veneer, paper, and minor products. That leaves, then, a total of 200 million cords that could be converted to fuel without depleting the forests at all. Five cords will heat the average

American house for one year; 200 million cords will heat 40 million houses—or approximately two-thirds the total number of dwelling units in the United States.

There may actually be more potential fuelwood than this, since trees in backyards, along roadsides, in fence rows, and those on the 250 million acres of so-called nonproductive forest land are not included in the estimate. Of course, much of this wood is in remote areas and simply unavailable for all practical purposes, and much is owned by people who intend to allow it to lie fallow. The calculation does, however, help one begin to visualize the magnitude of this vast renewable resource. Bear in mind, though, the pessimistic facts of waste, and a growth of population that does not keep pace with the conservation of our natural resources.

The figures just given suggest how much woodlot is needed to supply a wood-energized house indefinitely. Five cords of hardwood per winter should be adequate for heating and cooking in a six-room house. There are well-built houses in the coldest parts of the country that get by on less. With an annual production of, say, 7/10 cord per acre, seven acres of woodlot would be the minimum size needed for the average house. But if the total annual growth were taken for fuel each year, this would mean burning some trees suitable for lumber, wasting time cutting up some very small wood, and robbing other wildlife. To be realistic, then, more than seven acres of woodlot are required to support a hypothetical average house totally heated by burning wood—perhaps twice that many. If the cutting were done with an eye to increasing lumber production, the harvest of fuelwood would then decline in time, and more acreage would be needed to supply five cords to the house. Of course these figures must be adjusted for local conditions. They do, at least, provide an initial estimate of the size of woodlot needed.

## CUTTING FUELWOOD

Cutting fuelwood in the East, where three out of every four hardwood trees are classed as *cull* or low grade, can substantially increase the growth rate of timber suitable for lumber and veneer. The principle here is simple: If the crooked, twisted, diseased, and economically unimportant trees are removed, then straight, healthy and commercially important trees left standing grow faster.

Removing cull trees creates openings in the forest canopy into which the crowns of crop trees expand, intercept more light, and produce more wood each year. Comparison with weeding the garden is apt.

Incidentally, the slash left from the thinning operation provides cover for small game. The young trees that grow up in the open spaces make good browse for deer.

A key point regarding the products of the combustion of wood is that these would be liberated in the forest by decay anyway and burning cull wood does not, therefore, lead to a net increase in environmental pollution.[3]

*Decay* is slow oxidation under the influence of microorganisms and fungi; *combustion* is fast oxidation. Complete oxidation of wood is the reverse of photosynthesis, the major products being carbon dioxide, water and energy as heat instead of light. These are the products, whether the oxidation occurs on the forest floor or in the firebox of a stove. Thus burning of wood does not lead to a net increase of atmospheric carbon dioxide, in contrast to coal and oil, since the carbon dioxide would be liberated in the forest by decay anyway.

However, burning of wood often is incomplete. In home and industrial wood-burners a wide variety of other substances, ranging from the common to the exotic, are produced in addition to carbon dioxide and water. But the point here again is the great similarity between these so-called *intermediate* products of combustion and those liberated in the forest by decay. Many of the intermediate products are volatile, and, when they are formed in decaying wood, escape into the forest air where they undergo chemical reactions with one another under the influence of sunlight. The result is the haze characteristic of forests on hot, still summer days—haze so pronounced in the Smoky Mountains that they take their name from it.

Of course, no one should draw the conclusion that it is harmless to breathe smoke from a wood fire.

There are other environmental effects of burning wood that have no direct connection with air pollution. The forest itself is affected. We can cut trees the way it was done all too often in the past,

depleting the soil of minerals, causing erosion and destroying wildlife. Or we can do it intelligently.

## CHOICE OF FUELWOOD

The densest wood makes the best fuel. In Table 5-16 species are arranged according to density with the densest at the top of each column. All the woods in the left column make excellent fuel; those in the middle are not bad, and those on the right will do. There are people in very cold parts of the world who stay warm and happy with nothing but spruce to burn. But no one with experience chooses spruce over oak if one has a choice. Inspection of the table shows that the woods used for pulp and construction are, by and large, in the right-hand column. In spite of technical advances in the use of hardwood for pulp, softwood is still preferred, and carpenters like to work with the softer woods. In the left-hand column only the oaks, black birch, black walnut and sugar maple are in much demand for lumber and veneer; thus there is a fortuitous natural division that should go a long way toward preventing cutthroat competition between cutters of fuelwood and of industrial or commercial wood.

**Table 5-16. Densities of Various North American Woods.**

| High | Medium | Low |
|---|---|---|
| Live oaks | Holly | Black spruce |
| Shagbark hickory | Pond pine | Hemlocks |
| Black locust | Nut pines | Catalpa |
| Dogwood | Loblolly pine | Red alder |
| Slash pine | Tamarack | Tulip poplar |
| Hop Hornbeam | Shortleaf pine | Red fir |
| Persimmon | Western larch | Sitka spruce |
| Shadbush | Junipers | White spruce |
| Apple | Paper birch | Black willow |
| White Oak | Red maple | Large tooth aspen |
| Honey locust | Cherry | Butternut |
| Black birch | American elm | Ponderosa pine |
| Yew | Black gum | Noble fir |
| Blue beech | Sycamore | Redwood |
| Red oak | Gray birch | Quaking Aspen |
| Rock elm | Douglas fir | Sugar pine |
| Sugar maple | Pitch pine | White pine |
| American beech | Sassafras | Balsam fir |
| Yellow birch | Magnolia | Black willow |
| Longleaf pine | Red cedar | Cottonwood |
| White ash | Norway pine | Basswood |
| Oregon ash | Bald cypress | Western red cedar |
| Black walnut | Chestnut | Balsam poplar |

---

3. J. A. Hall, *Forest Fuels: Prescribed Fire and Air Quality* (Portland, Oregon: Pacific Northwest Forest and Experiment Station, USDA, 1972).

The order in Table 5-16 is only approximate, since density varies within each species. There are cases of a beech being more dense than sugar maple, and an elm more dense then cherry, but you will not find a cherry denser than hickory.

# Economics of Wood Heating

There are considerations other than price that affect choice of fuel, such as guaranteed availability, ease of handling, and cost of heaters. But it is useful to be able to compare the prices Btu for Btu. See the results in Tables 5-17 and 5-18.

The figures were established as follows: The densities are averages of data found in various technical sources. Any actual density measurement could easily differ from the ones in Table 5-17 by 15 percent. In fact, close inspection will show minor disagreements between the tables.

The energy released on burning a pound of bone-dry wood completely is called its *fuel value*—about 8600 Btu. Air-dried wood is nearly 20 percent water by weight (relative to dry wood), and the heat liberated on burning a pound of air-dried wood is therefore less—about 7100 Btu. (The heats of combustion of bituminous coal and No. 2 heating oil are 13,500 and 19,000 Btu per

**Table 5-17. Fuel Values of Some Common Woods.**

| | Average Density (Pounds per Cord) | Fuel Value (Million Btu) | Break Even Price per Cord* |
|---|---|---|---|
| Shagbark hickory | 4400 | 31.2 | $170 |
| White oak | 4400 | 31.2 | 170 |
| Sugar maple | 4100 | 29.1 | 160 |
| American beech | 4000 | 28.4 | 156 |
| Red oak | 3900 | 27.6 | 150 |
| Yellow birch | 3800 | 27.0 | 148 |
| White ash | 3700 | 26.3 | 146 |
| American elm | 3400 | 24.1 | 132 |
| Red maple | 3400 | 24.1 | 132 |
| Paper birch | 3400 | 24.1 | 132 |
| Black cherry | 3300 | 23.4 | 128 |
| Douglas fir | 2900 | 21.5 | 118 |
| Eastern white pine | 2200 | 15.8 | 86 |

*Assumed efficiencies: wood stove, 50%; oil furnace, 65%.*
* Based on equivalent amount of oil at $1.00 per gallon.

**Table 5-18. Comparison of Heating Costs.**

| Fuel | Unit Price | Cost of 1 Million Btu | Heater Efficiency | Cost of 1 Million Useful Btu |
|---|---|---|---|---|
| Electricity | 8¢ per kwh | $23.44 | 100% | $23.44 |
| Oil | 1.00 per gallon | $ 6.34 | 65% | $ 9.60 |
| White Oak | $100 per cord | $ 3.20 | 50% | $6.40 |
| White Ash | $100 per cord | $ 3.04 | 50% | $6.08 |

pound respectively.) The third column is obtained from the second by multiplying by 7100 for the hardwoods and 7400 for Douglas fir and 7200 for white pine to take into account the resins in the latter two. Thus, the figures in the third column represent maximum heating effect from a cord of wood and must be modified by an efficiency factor to estimate the amount of heat actually transferred to the house. The best wood stoves are about 50 percent efficient under household conditions, hence, *all the figures in the third column should, realistically, be halved to find actual heating effect.*[4]

Oil furnaces are about 65 percent efficient under household conditions.[5] Since the fuel value of one gallon of heating oil is 140,000 Btu, the heating effect from one gallon is 91,000 Btu. At $1.00 per gallon, that amounts to $9.60 per million useful Btu. At the same price, the 14.2 million useful Btu from a cord of American beech would cost about $136. Thus beech at anything less than $136 a cord is cheaper than oil at $1.00 a gallon. All the figures in the fourth column have been calculated similarly. Should the price of oil change, new figures for that column can be calculated by simple proportions. For example, if oil were $1.20 a gallon, then you could pay up to $163 (136 × 1.20/1.00) for a cord of beech and still save money.

For comparison, electric heat at 8¢ per kilowatt-hour is equal to $23.44 per million Btu of heat (1 kw-hr = 3413 Btu). That's almost three times as expensive as beech at $136 per cord.

4. Data on wood stove efficiencies is meager. The Char-Wood Heater, a stove designed by Prof. Lauren E. Seeley of Yale, achieved efficiencies near 65 percent under carefully controlled conditions in experiments during World War II.

5. Standard tables used by engineers to estimate oil furnace efficiencies from stack temperature and carbon dioxide measurements range in efficiency from 40 to 90 percent. See C. M. Summers, "The Conversion of Energy," *Scientific American*, September 1971.

# Wood Heat and House Design

Before installing a wood-burning stove in an existing house, you must decide whether the house is best suited to a warm air circulator or a radiant-type stove. *Radiant* stoves will heat the fabric of the building, so they are well adapted to houses where walls and partitions are made of materials that will absorb and retain heat (such as brick or stone). They are not well suited to buildings with poor insulation or large unprotected window areas, where the heat absorbed by the walls is easily lost to the outside. *Circulator* stoves are best suited to houses where the walls provide good insulation but not necessarily thermal storage (such as conventional timber frame houses). Since they heat the air inside the house they are least suitable for drafty buildings where the hot air can easily escape through the fabric of the building. Whichever stove is used, of course, it is worth retaining as much of the heat it produces for as long as possible—and that means taking all the usual precautions such as insulating walls, covering windows at night, and preventing the escape of warm air.

Whether you have a furnace in the basement or stoves on the ground floor, the chimney should be placed in the middle of the house and not on an outside wall. This helps keep the chimney drawing well and also means that heat lost from the chimney helps warm the house. To put the chimney in the middle takes up valuable space, but where the winter is severe there is no doubt that the central part of the house is the most efficient place. Colonial houses in the South may have had chimneys at either end, but settlers in

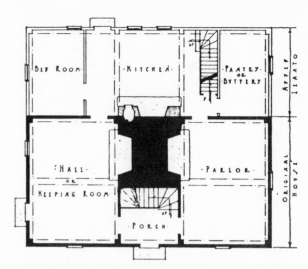

Figure 5-19. Floor plan of a typical early New England house. The masonry fireplace in the center was the only source of heat.

New England soon learned to put them in the middle (Figure 5-19).

It is also important to check building codes regarding the placement of fireplaces and flues. The standard clearance required between stovepipes and combustible surfaces is generally 36 inches, but this can be reduced by adding various layers of fireproof and insulating materials.

If there are several flues they should be close together in one chimney to help keep one another warm. In this way the flue connected to the parlor stove will draw well right away, and you will not

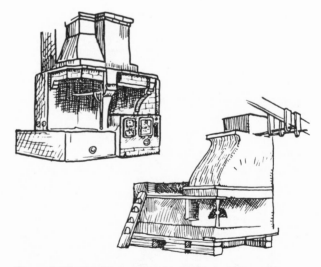

Figure 5-20. Traditional Finnish fireplaces often incorporated several fireplaces, ovens, and even seats and beds within the large mass of heat-retaining masonry.

208

have to put up with smoke every time you wish to use it (Figure 5-20).

A central masonry chimney will take the chill off upstairs bedrooms, so that they can be used for sleeping without any other heat. Stainless steel asbestos chimneys are not nearly as effective at warming the upstairs because they are too well insulated.

Stoves installed on the second floor are apt to be smoky because of short flue length. It is generally preferable to heat the upstairs by the chimney and by warm air from downstairs coming through registers or openings in the floor.

A stairwell in the center of the house, or openings in the ceiling near the fireplace or stove will allow the hot air to rise. Slits in the floor near the outer wall of the house allow the colder air to fall down and it can then be directed towards the source of heat (Figure 5-21). This simple principle, developed by Wendell Thomas, has the great advantage of eliminating drafts from windows and doors to the outside. It could be adapted to many different house designs and result in more comfortable conditions being achieved using less heat.

Any house is a constantly changing thermal

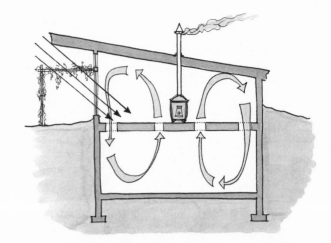

Figure 5-21. Wendell Thomas's house in western North Carolina. Registers in the floor encourage air movement around the stove, thus creating warm air convection currents within the room. Cold air from windows, door, and outside walls falls down into the basement, providing a draft-free area.

environment, the air is always moving, and the temperature of the building fabric is continually changing. Understanding how heat moves around your house and how it eventually escapes can provide you with valuable insights into energy conservation.

# References

Allen, Peter H. *Firewood for Heat*. Society for the Protection of New Hampshire Forests, 5 South State Street, Concord, N.H. 03301.

Curtis, Christopher and Post, Donald. *Be Your Own Chimney Sweep*. Charlotte, Vt.: Garden Way Publishing, 1979. $4.95. An illustrated guidebook for cleaning stoves, chimneys and fireplaces.

Curtis, Will and Curtis, Jane. *Antique Wood Stoves*. Ashville, Maine: Cobblesmith, 1974.

Gay, Larry. *Heating With Wood*. Charlotte, Vt.: Garden Way Publishing, 1974. $4.95. A brief, well-written, classic introduction to heating with wood.

Gillespie, G. Curtis. *Rumford Fireplaces*. New York: Comstock, 1906.

Hall, J.A. *Forest Fuels: Prescribed Fire and Air Quality*. Portland, Ore.: USDA Pacific Northwest Forest and Experiment Station, 1972.

Havens, David. *The Woodburners Handbook*. Portland, Maine: Media House, 1973.

Orton, Vrest. *The Forgotten Art of Building a Good Fireplace*. Dublin, N.H.: Yankee, Inc., 1969.

Putnam, J. Pickering. *The Open Fireplace*. Boston: Osgood & Company, 1882. A delightfully written, charmingly illustrated, and surprisingly up-to-date treatise on fireplace efficiency.

Shelton, Jay. *Wood Heat Safety*. Charlotte, Vt.: Garden Way Publishing, 1979. $8.95. A thorough technical guide to materials, installation, and safety clearances for wood-burning stoves and chimneys.

Shelton, Jay and Shapiro, Andrew. *The Woodburners Encyclopedia*. Waitsfield, Vt.: Vermont Crossroads Press, 1976. $6.95. An excellent comprehensive handbook to wood as a fuel. Fuelwood efficiencies, stove and furnace types, much product information.

Thomas, Wendell. "The Self-Heating, Self-Cooling House." *Mother Earth News*, reprint #39.

Twitchell, Mary. *Wood Energy.* Charlotte, Vt.: Garden Way Publishing, 1978. $7.95. A basic coverage of wood heat. Stove installation, fuelwood values, cutting firewood, comparisons of all major stoves on the market.

Summers, C.M. "The Conversion of Energy." *Scientific American,* September, 1971.

USDA. *The Outlook for Timber in the United States.* Forest Resource Report No. 20, United States Forest Service, Dept. of Agriculture, 1973.

*Using Coal and Wood Stoves Safely.* National Fire Protection Association, 470 Atlantic Avenue, Boston, Massachusetts.

Wassil, Michael. "Stovepipe Power." *Mother Earth News,* No. 24.

Wright, Lawrence. *Home Fires Burning: The History of Domestic Heating and Cooking.* London: Hillary, 1964.

# Wood Heat Catalog

The following pages list wood stove distributors and manufacturers that are currently active in this fast-changing field. Naturally this is not a complete catalog—there are many excellent products not represented here, and more are coming on the market all the time.

All information contained in the catalog sections was supplied by the manufacturers or organizations listed; we have summarized what is available from each. Our goal is to help you, the reader, locate equipment and information that will help you buy wood-burning equipment wisely.

Within the catalog section are product comparison charts. In reading these charts, keep in mind that prices are constantly changing; no book can be up to date. If you need more information about a specific product or company, we ask that you write directly to the company, *not* to Garden Way Publishing.

# Small Stoves

## The American Way
190 Range Road
Wilton, Connecticut
(203) 853-3100

Five models of cast iron stoves are replicas of early American stoves. Although none is completely airtight, all are made of heavy-duty cast iron and all joints are sealed with furnace cement. Doors are hand-set. All stoves are shipped assembled and carry a 5-year warranty on parts and labor.

The *Washington* parlor stove has front- and side-loading doors with slide draft controls. The front door has a window with mica backing, or you can remove the door and replace it with the spark screen provided. There is a polished chrome trim foot rail and the chrome crown top swings off to reveal two 8-inch cooking lids. Burns wood or coal, weighs 232 pounds and accepts 6-inch stove pipe.

The *Jefferson* model is an upright cylinder with two polished chrome spin-draft controls, chrome trim, removable shaker grate, ash removal door, and cooking lid under the swing-off cover. Weighs 207 pounds and uses a 6-inch stove pipe.

The *Betsy Ross* is a 139-pound baffled box stove that comes with grate, damper and large ash apron. It has curved side panels, cooking lid and wide-splayed legs. Takes a 26-inch log and uses 6-inch stove pipe.

The 85-pound *Knickerbocker Dandy* is a wood- and coal-burning potbelly stove that loads from the front or top. It has an 8-inch removable cooking lid, two draft controls, hinged feed door, ash removal door and shaker grate. Takes a 6-inch stove pipe. This model also comes in a smaller 60-pound version.

The *Franklin* model comes in two sizes: the 352-pound, 31-inch high model or the 434-pound and 31-inch high one. It has an interior baffle, large ash apron and hinged doors. It comes with a grate, fire screen, grill boot with a damper and a bean pot.

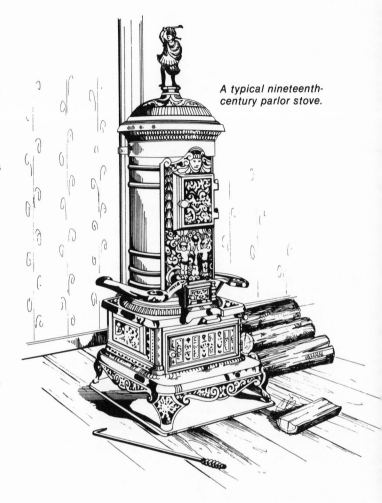

*A typical nineteenth-century parlor stove.*

## Atlanta Stove Works, Inc.
P.O. Box 5254
Atlanta, Georgia 30307

The Atlanta Stove Works, Inc. is one of the nation's oldest and most experienced manufacturers of wood and coal burning heaters. They offer six airtight woodburning models with additional or modified units for burning coal, or cooking. (Fireplaces are reviewed in another section.)

*Model 240*, the top-of-the-line wood heater, has a welded steel firebox with cast iron liner, an automatic, front-mounted thermostat control, cast iron flue collar, gasket-lined cast iron fire and ash doors, and a double bottom. The firebox is contained in a brown cabinet with bonderized finish that resists scratching and easily wipes clean. Louvers on top direct the flow of warm air into the room and a lower front grill draws intake air from cold floors. Optional manual or thermostat controlled electric blowers are available.

Atlanta's basic box stove is *Model 27* which takes a 24-inch log. It has a heavy, corrugated cast iron firebox, outside rod construction and flat swing top. Two 8-inch covers for cooking and a good-sized ash apron are standard.

The *Woodsman (Model 24)* is the next step up in a box stove for size and heating capacity. It has a cast iron firebox with side baffles and a top heat exchanger. A flip-open damper between the firebox and heat exchanger allows quick starts. The door has three spin draft controls and the sculptured scenes on front and sides make this stove a rustic beauty. Using the 6-inch accessory legs, the *Woodsman* is low enough to be vented up your present fireplace chimney. The *Huntsman (Model 241)* has a welded steel body with firebrick lining and cast iron door with three spin-draft controls. An upper heat chamber contains a 12-inch interior flue to retain warmth longer.

*Model 2502* was patented by Atlanta in 1945. It is an upright cylinder shape and consists of a large blue steel jacket around a firebox lined with heavy gauge steel. Top, bottom and door are cast iron. Fuel can be loaded from the top or front and it has a three-level thermostat and manual draft control. Comes with an all-purpose tool for adjusting controls or removing the ash door housing while the heater is hot.

## Birmingham Stove and Range Co.
## P.O. Box 2647
## Birmingham, Alabama 35202
## (205) 322-0371

The Birmingham Company makes several Franklin stove models ranging in size from 248 pounds to about 400 pounds. Each is made of cast iron, can be vented from the back or top, and includes a cast iron basket grate that will burn wood or coal. A damper in the flue vent helps to control the fire when the doors are shut. *Model 126* has glass paneled doors. Separately sold accessories include brass balls, fire screen, heat shield interior firebox, swing-out grill and the ever-popular bean pot.

The *Nordic* is an airtight cast iron box stove with heat exchanger on top. The interior baffle can be bypassed by a damper controlled from outside. The tongue-in-groove joints are furnace cement sealed. The stove has three spin draft controls on the door and a small ash apron. It weighs about 240 pounds and has a rear flue vent. Decorative scenes in relief are on the side panels.

The *Ponderosa* is a welded ¼-inch and ¹⁹⁄₆₄-inch steel stove lined with firebrick. It has a cast iron door with three spin draft controls and an ash apron. A heat exchanger on top is half the length of the stove and works by means of an interior stove pipe. This 360-pound stove will take a 24-inch log and has a rear flue vent.

The *Knight model 124* is a steel wood burner with automatic thermostat in an enamelled cabinet with top directional louvers. The gasketed fire and ash doors are made of cast iron, as are the firebox liner, grate and flue collar.

*Knight Model 524* burns wood or coal because it has a reversible grate and ceramic firebrick lining. It weighs about 250 pounds. An optional blower kit is available for both *Knight* models.

Manufactured since 1935, the *Majik 122-A* is a proven automatic airtight wood heater. It is an upright blue steel cylinder with cast iron top, bottom, doors and reversible collar. The bottom is lined with firebrick. Fuel can be loaded from the front or the top and the removable ash door makes ash cleaning easier. A special key operates all the controls: draft register, top and ash door. It weighs about 150 pounds and takes a 6-inch flue pipe.

*The Banner* is a small cast iron, flat-topped "laundry" stove. It has a sliding draft control, fuel and ash doors and two cooking lids on top. It weighs 85 pounds and is vented at the top rear.

*The Boss* is a traditional cast iron potbelly weighing 75 pounds. It has sliding draft control across the bottom, front-hinged fuel door and a removable cooking lid on top.

Last, the *Model 27* box heater is a cast iron box stove with swing top, ash apron and splayed legs; it weighs 115 pounds. It has no draft controls.

## Bow and Arrow Stove Co.
## 14 Arrow Street
## Cambridge, Massachusetts 02138
## (617) 492-1411

The *Chappee 8008* is a small stove of French design that can easily be installed in front of a fireplace. It has a brown porcelain cast iron shell, steel firebox, window on the front door and a cooking top beneath the louvered top. Its heating capacity is about 4,200 cubic feet; its shipping weight is 141 pounds.

The *Chappee 8033* burns coal or wood because it has a fire brick lining. It has the same overall appearance and features of the smaller model but it weighs 225 pounds (s.w.) and has a heating capacity of 5,600 cubic feet.

Le Petit Godin.

An elegant little French stove, *le Petit Godin (No. 3720)* has belied its efficiency for over 100 years. The body is constructed of black steel lined with firebrick. The top, firedoor and base are enameled cast iron in a choice of colors: cedar green, sand, brown and black. The gasketed firedoor has a decorative mica window and a spinsheel damper; a secondary air channel is above the door. The stove can be loaded through the top or front, which has a swing-down grate. The rotating cast iron ash grate is operated from the outside and the ash pan is removable. A deep-dish, cast iron, lift-off ash apron is under the door. The stove comes in two sizes; an all-purpose tool is supplied.

*Trolla* are Norwegian-made airtight stoves of cast iron. The design of the "100" series features internal top baffle, spin draft control on the door, cook plate on top, and sides embossed with outdoor scenes from Peer Gynt by Norwegian sculptor Oscar Lynum.

*No. 102,* the smallest stove, is equipped with a cast iron burn plate (bottom lining) for extra safety and takes a 12-inch log. It weighs 76 pounds.

The *105* comes with firebrick lining on the sides and bottom, takes a 17-inch log and weighs 178 pounds. It can be fitted with a decorative top plate at extra cost.

The *107* is the largest size box stove and is equipped with extra-thick cast iron linings. It takes a 23-inch log, weighs 253 pounds. Long legs are available on all three models at extra cost.

Trolla *No. 530* is a cast iron wood or coal burning heater with an attractive two tone enamel finish designed to fit into the decor of the modern home. The fire box has a heavy duty cast iron grate and fire brick lining to promote a hotter, longer burning fire. An automatic thermostate regulates an even temperature by controlling the damper to allow more or less oxygen into the fire box. The fire box measures 8 inches wide by 8 inches deep by 14 inches high. The front legs are pre-drilled, with screws in position, to make levelling an easy matter. Requires a 5-inch smoke pipe.

## Cawley/LeMay™ Stove Company, Inc.
## 27 North Washington Street
## Boyertown, Pennsylvania 19512
## (215) 367-2643

After using and experimenting with various wood stoves of all types, American industrial designers C. Robert Cawley Jr. and Robert C. LeMay, Jr. developed the Cawley/LeMay *Models 400* and *600*. They are large, cast iron, airtight woodstoves with draft controls on the front of the loading doors. You can reverse the interior side baffles to create smaller fireboxes—a more efficient alternative than using smaller draft settings during some seasons. An ignition grid in front of the top baffle plate acts as a thermal reservoir, stablizing the temperature of the remaining volatile gases and creating a turbulence to mix thoroughly these gases with oxygen, thus aiding secondary combustion.

Two features you'll appreciate during installation are the rotating cast iron flue fitting and adjustable leveling feet.

The stove has a glass panel in the door and scenes of native wildlife created by Martha H. Cawley on the sides. The top has two cooking lids and an unusual raised and rounded edge. Ashes that may spill while the door is open are caught by a sweep shelf and easily removed. Model 600 weighs 385 pounds.

*Cawley/LeMay Model 400.*

## Damsite Dynamite Stove Company
## RD 3
## Montpelier, Vermont 05602
## (802) 223-7139

This company makes a line of stoves in several sizes, a fireplace stove, a wood furnace, a kitchen cook stove hot water heaters and a complete wood-fired sauna package. Each one is individually hand-crafted from heavy 10-gauge steel plate and ¼-inch boiler plate. They come with secondary air inlets and secondary combustion chambers where exhaust gases are burned that would otherwise escape up the chimney and take logs up to 24 inches long. You may be interested in the hollow, tubular legs that draw cool air from floor level, heat it as it rises past the firebox and send jets of hot air out the top.

## Enterprise Sales
## R.F.D. #2
## Apple Creek, Ohio 44606

Two small but beautiful box stoves from Enterprise—*Nos. 18* and *25*—are made of cast iron throughout. Ornate designs are embossed on the curved side plates and front door. The stove top containing two cooking lids in *No. 25*, one in *No. 18*, also swings to one side to allow you to cook by placing pot directly over fire. Both stoves have draft regulators, a large ash apron and are supported by three legs—two in front, one in back. *Model 18* weighs only 63 pounds, takes a 5-inch stove pipe and 15″ lengths of wood. *Model 25* weighs 115 pounds and takes a 6-inch stove pipe. *Model No. 18* can be packed in two cartons and mailed.

## Free Flow Stove Works
## South Strafford, Vermont 05070
## (802) 765-4022

You've seen square stoves and you've seen round stoves, but you probably haven't seen a stove like this one. A group of curved steel tubes forms the main structure of the Free Flow Stove. These tubes are welded together to form a circular ribcage. The spaces between the tubes are covered with steel plates, welded onto the tubes to form the cylindrical firebox. This is done in such a way that most of the tube is inside the firebox. The air in the tubes is heated and flows out the top, setting up a convection current. A baffle plate inside the firebox produces an efficient front-to-back burn.

The face plate has a large circular door hinged with a center pressure point, over-center cam lock and fitted with an asbestos gasket. A butterfly valve draft control admits air for combustion. Flue vent is in the back plate. The Free Flow comes in three sizes: the *Circulator*, the *Wonder* and the *Furnace*, and can be connected to an existing forced air system.

*The Free Flow Circulator.*

## General Engineering and Manufacturing Corp.
### 133 S. Snowden St.
### Andrews, Indiana 46702

Earth Stove makes six different size stoves, each available in traditional or contemporary design. The "traditional" models are decorated with metal trim and gold-plated knobs. The "contemporary" models are identical stoves without the trim.

All models are steel plate with firebrick lining and have large removable front doors so you can see the fire (firescreen is included). The design provides preheating for both primary and secondary air drafts; you regulate air intake by thermostatic control.

The *900 series* stoves are small—so small they are approved for use in mobile homes. They have outer heat shields for protected radiant warmth with close clearances. Water coils are available on the *100, 300,* and *600* series; you can buy a blower kit for the *900* series.

## J and J Enterprises
### 4065 W. 11th Ave.
### Eugene, Oregon 97402

*Frontier* stoves are handcrafted from ¼-inch steel and lined with firebrick. The handfitted double doors are constructed of ⁵⁄₁₆-inch steel and reinforced for a strong effective seal. An attractive nickel plated safety screen is provided and is easy to clean. The stove is of the two level design, resulting in two cooking temperatures. Each size comes with top or rear exhaust. Chrome balls for the legs and warming plates are available as options.

Twin spin draft controls are located on the doors and a 5-inch ash apron is standard. An 8-inch flue pipe is recommended.

## Kristia Associates
### Box 1118
### Portland, Maine 04104

When the oil crisis inspired a return to wood burning, *Jøtul* became a household word. This Norwegian company founded in 1853 has long been a leader in solid fuel technology and offers a wide range of models for most tastes and purposes.

Their three versions of the airtight cast iron box stove the *Jøtul 118,* the *Jøtul 602* and the *Jøtul 606* have side and top baffles in the firebox to produce an efficient "cigar-type" burn.

The *602* designed in 1940, has bas-relief art work on the ridged sides. A decorative top is optional.

The Jøtul 507, *designed for burning coke or coal, also burns wood or peat. Heavy cast iron with green enamel finish—a real beauty.*

The *118* is essentially the same stove with a different bas-relief art on the sides and a heat exchanger chamber on top. Both stoves come in black or green enamel.

The *606* is the same box stove with a huge exchanger arch of traditional design on top. It comes in black setherm finish. You can vent the *606* and the *118* from the back or either side and the 602 from the top or back. None of these stoves has an ash apron worth mentioning.

Several stove/fireplace combinations are offered, among them the *Jøtul #1,* the *Jøtul #4* and the *Jøtul #6.* The first two have a firebrick-lined firebox and airtight, balanced door that slides under the stove when not in use. Screens are included. The third model is more of a fireplace. It has doors that slide horizontally, but even when closed its top efficiency was tested at 68 percent. Several other fireplace systems are available.

## Locke Stove Company
### 114 West 11th Street
### Kansas City, Missouri 64105

*Warm-Ever* wood heaters are firebrick-lined barrel stoves with cast iron feed doors and legs. The *W-15* is lined with eight sections of firebrick, weighs 106 pounds and takes a 15-inch log. The *W-24* is lined with 12 sections of firebrick, weighs 142 pounds and takes a 24-inch log. Both stoves have sliding draft control on the door frame and a secondary draft opening at the flue outlet. Locke also sells a kit for making your own barrel stove.

## Martin Industries
### King Products Division
### P.O. Box 128
### Florence, Alabama 35603

Several cast iron wood heaters in authentic, old-time-looking shapes are made by King Products. The *Cannon Heater,* a pot-bellied stove comes in 27-inch and 31-inch heights. Both have ash doors and pans and cast iron shaker grates. They are small stoves weighing in at 58 and 91 pounds.

The *Fatso Laundry Heater* is a similar stove but with a flat 17- by 21-inch cook top across its "belly." It weighs 23 pounds.

Next in heating capacity is the cast iron box stove with its bulging, one-piece side panels, swing top and large ash apron. It has no draft control. This stove comes in three sizes: 102, 123 and 132 pounds. Flue connection is on top.

Last in this category is the *Merit Heater,* a parlor-type stove that will burn coal or wood. It has a sliding damper, large firebox with cast liners and reversible collar flue. It is 32 inches high and weighs 130 pounds.

Two upright cylinder-shaped wood heaters, made with cast iron swing tops, bottoms and doors are less traditional in appearance. The *Wood King Model 2601* has cast linings and an ash door. *Model 6601* has a bimetallic thermostat for automatic constant heat. This model has a steel liner. Circulating blower is available as an option on the *6601.* Both stoves have 25-inch fireboxes, stand 35 inches high and weigh about 145 pounds.

Finally the top-of-the-line *King Automatic Wood Circulator 8801-B* is a steel, firebrick-lined heater with cast iron grates, ash and feed doors, door frames and flue collar encased in a contemporary cabinet with lifetime porcelain enamel finish. The louvered cabinet top lifts off for emergency cooking. The firebox takes a 24-inch log and the stove weighs 215 pounds. It comes with a thermostat that regulates a constant temperature; optional equipment include a counterflow blower, barometric damper and draft equalizer.

### The Merry Music Box
20 McKown St.
Boothbay Harbor, Maine 04538
(207) 633–2210 or 882–7163

Three models of woodburning heaters are available from the Austrian Styria Company, through Merry Music Box: the *Excelsior*, the *Reliable* and the massive *Imperial*. All three are built from design concepts directly adapted from the kacheloefen (tile stove) and are available with porcelain finish enamel. They are massive, upright stoves that stand on short cast iron legs. The lower half of the stove is taken up by the firebox, lined with firebrick on four sides and bottom. A fuel door and an ash emptying door lead to this chamber, both with locking knobs.

A steel baffle separates the firebox from the next chamber, the heat circulation tunnel, whose purpose is to disburse heat directly into the room. You may humidify the surroundings by placing a pan of water in this compartment through the front opening door.

Another steel baffle above the heat circulation tunnel directs the heat flow forward to the upper compartments of the heat accumulation chamber. This consists of two heat-absorbing compartments divided by a firebrick wall. The flue connection pipe—6 inches on most models—has an extra-thick steel damper. The distance from the floor to the bottom of the flue connection pipe is as follows: *Excelsior*, 31½ inches; *Reliable*, 35¼ inches; *Imperial*, 40 inches.

### Monarch Stoves
### Division of Malleable Iron Range Company
### Beaver Dam, Wisconsin 53916

An attractive, Franklin fireplace made by Monarch, *Model FR26C*, can be vented either top or rear. It is all cast iron and comes with boot and damper as standard equipment. The bi-fold doors can be closed for fast starts when the draft slides are open or for overnight banking with the draft checked. The stove measures 32 inches high, 39 inches wide and weighs about 312 pounds.

The contemporary style wood or coal fireplace heater, *Model HR24B* comes in red, orange, black or white. The firebox is heavy gauge steel, porcelain enameled inside and out and equipped with cast iron grates. You can slide open the twin cast iron doors and the fire screen that remains in place will allow you to feel the warmth of an open fire. The entire door mechanism is hinged at the bottom and swings down to leave a 20 x 10 inch opening. Beneath the firebox is a full size ash drawer that pulls out for easy cleaning. A draft regulator is located at the rear of the unit. Matching colored enameled stove pipe is available, with or without a damper, in 24-inch sections. Also optional are heat tempered glass doors.

The Lange 6203BR, *a ceramic tile vertical parlor stove.*

### Scandinavian Stoves, Inc.
### Box 72 Route 12-A
### Alstead, New Hampshire 13602

Lange stoves are airtight, cast iron stoves made in Denmark. *Model 6303A* has curved side plates for strength and a hand milled door with two draft regulators, one above the other. You open both for a quick start, but use only the upper regulator to govern the fire. A 5-inch flue pipe connects to the top.

*Model 6303B* is identical except that the flue outlet is in the rear. Each as a decorative cast iron cooking plate and comes with permanent, baked-on enamel finish in black, green, blue or red.

*Model 6303* has all the same features plus a baffled heat chamber on top of the firebox and a cast iron liner on the bottom. These increase the stove's radiating capacity as well as its heat-holding mass. It comes only in black or blue.

The next step up in heating capacity is *Model 6302A*. While similar to *Model 6303A* in materials and construction, it is larger and has a complex baffle system. Air leaves the firebox through two small openings at the rear, moves forward through two channels in an upper chamber toward the front of the stove, then doubles back through a central channel to the stove pipe outlet. The same stove with a heating chamber containing an oven and cooking plates is *Model 6302K*. As in *Model 6303*, this chamber squeezes more heat from a given amount of fuel.

The largest wood stove made by Lange is *Model 6203BR*, a parlor stove patterned after European tile stoves. A horizontal baffle system, great mass and comparatively large radiating surface combine to produce alot of heat in a relatively small, good-looking package.

---

### WOOD STOVE SAFETY

**Wood stove sales have boomed as thousands of people each year turn to wood heat. At the same time, the number of chimney fires has risen dramatically, with resulting loss of life and property.**

**If you install a wood-burning stove or fireplace, make sure it is safe. For details on stove installation and removing creosote buildup, see *Wood Heat Safety* by Jay Shelton ($8.95) and *Be Your Own Chimney Sweep* by Chris Curtis and Don Post ($4.95). Both are available from Garden Way Publishing, Dept 171X, Charlotte, Vermont 05445.**

## Self-Sufficiency Products
## One Appletree Square
## Minneapolis, Minnesota 55420

Self-Sufficiency Products sells three Gibraltar stoves, identical except in size, of welded ³⁄₁₆- and ¼-inch steel plate construction and firebrick lining. They have a single large door with a "Racon" window and two draft controls side by side. There is a small, "emergency" cooking surface. Trim bar and decorator draft control knobs are optional.

The smallest stove *(Gilbraltar II)* weighs 240 pounds, accepts a 20-inch log and a 6-inch flue pipe (top only); the medium size *(Gibraltar III)* weighs 272 pounds, takes a 24-inch log and has a 6-inch rear flue connection; the large stove *(Gibraltar IV)* weighs 320 pounds, handles a 28-inch log and the same 6-inch rear flue connection.

## Shenandoah Manufacturing
##    Company, Inc.
## P.O. Box 839
## Harrisonburg, Virginia 22801

All Shenandoah wood heaters are made of heavy gauge steel with airtight, firebrick-lined fireboxes. They are called *heaters* because a sensitive, bi-metal thermostat will automatically regulate the flow of air over the coals and keep room temperatures at the desired setting. All models also have a "shaker grate" and ash pan for convenient removal of ashes. Some can be adapted for coal heat.

The *R-76* and *R-76L* are identical except that the *R-76* has a cabinet made of baked-on black porcelain for added safety. A 61-watt two-speed blower is also optional. Smoke outlet is in the rear.

The *R-75* model is smaller and has an upright cylinder shape of sturdy construction. It has the same airtight design, firebrick lining, thermostat and ash removal tray as the larger heaters. The *R-65*, the same stove only smaller, is capable of a 12-hour burn.

## Southport Stoves
## 248 Tolland Street
## East Hartford, Connecticut 06108
## (203) 289-6079

Southport imports stoves made by Morsø, a Danish company founded in 1853, that makes a wide range of high-quality, airtight, cast iron stoves. All of them have baffle systems, precise draft control, precision-made and fitted doors, and enamel finish.

*Model 2B*, their smallest box stove, has curved stove plates for greater resistance to heat fatigue. An air-circulator box on the inside of the door prevents sparks from popping out the draft control, prewarms the air coming into the firebox for more efficient burning, and directs the primary air to the base of the fire. An opening at the top of the air circulator provides a secondary source of air. Accessories included with this and other stoves are stove poker, two pieces of stove pipe, a 90° elbow and a wall thimble. Short legs are optional for masonry fireplace hookup, but flue connection is only from the top.

*Model 2BO* is the same as model *2B* and *2BO* but with a heat exchanger arch on top. Both the *2B* and *2BO* burn approximately 8 to 12 hours.

*Model 1B* is a larger stove than *Model 2B*, available in matte black or glossy gray enamel finish. Unlike *Model 2B*, however, the *1B* has fitted side linings for a hottor burning firebox and greater radiating capacity. It holds enough wood to burn 12 to 16 hours.

*Model 1BO* is the same stove with a beautiful, graceful heat exchanger arch on top. The inward curves of the arch chambers create an air flow upward through the grillwork and out the grilled plates on top. The flue connection is from the center of the arch. Like the *1B*, it will hold a 12- to 16-hour fire or live coals overnight.

*Model 6B*, modern and rectangular in design, has vertical flutings to add 25 percent to the radiating surface. You put the wood in the stove by lifting the top lid, eliminating the need for a front hearth. An ash scoop is provided with each stove. The draft control on the front has a similar air-circulator box as *Model 2B*. An angled horizontal baffle system produces efficient burning. Available in dull black enamel only.

Mørso also makes a free-standing fireplace (*Model 1122*) and a stove-fireplace combination (*Model 1125*). The fireplace has an inward, upwards slant of front and sides and a pattern of triangular indentations to convect air around the unit. Tall legs permit air to circulate beneath. The firebox is lined with firebrick. A baffle system increases heat transfer. A perforated screen is provided that can decrease the air intake by 50 percent. (Screen should always be in place when wood is burning.) The fireplace is back-vented and takes a 5½-inch smoke pipe. Comes in dull black, glossy green, white, red and blue.

The combination stove-fireplace has the same design as the *1122*, only it is larger. Two swing-out doors lift off so you can see the fire and a screen (which stores underneath the stove when not in use) is supplied. The super large firebox is firebrick lined. Draft control is in the door handle. With the doors closed and the handle turned to the left, the doors are locked and sealed airtight. Air intake is through the handle itself. As the handle is turned toward the right, the doors move outward ever so slightly to allow an even flow of air into the firebox along the top and bottom. Venting of the smoke (either top or back) is through a collar containing its own spring-loaded damper. Dull black, glossy green, white, red or blue.

## Thulman Eastern Corporation
## Ellicott City, Maryland 21043

Thulman is the U.S. distributor for Waterford Iron-founders, Ltd., an Irish firm that manufactures the *Reginald 101* and *102*. Both *Reginald* stoves are little gems of compact, energy-efficient design. They are made of cast iron with furrowed side striations to collect and radiate heat. Both have three inner baffles to produce front-to-back burning and adjustable firedoor draft controls that pre-heat primary and secondary air.

The *101* has a cast iron hotplate and top or rear flue connection. It comes as a compact kit you can assemble in an hour, saving yourself around $80. Two drawbacks are the short firebox (maximum 16-inch log) and the small (practically nonexistent) ash apron (but you can purchase one as an accessory). The *101* can hold a fire all night if the firebox is really full but you'll probably knock the top baffle off the first time or two trying to get it that way.

The *102* has four flue pipe openings and removable ash tray beneath the door; it will easily hold a fire all night. It has a heat exchanger mounted atop the firebox, increasing total heat radiation area by 36 percent, and will accept a maximum 24-inch log.

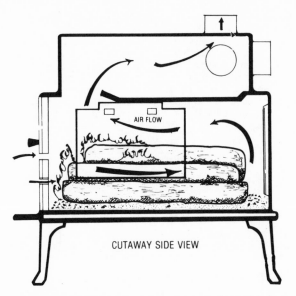

CUTAWAY SIDE VIEW

The Reginald 102. *The fire burns front to back; heat exchanger sits on top.*

## Timberline Stove, Ltd.
## 110 East 1st St.
## East Syracuse, New York 13057

Firebrick-lined fireboxes, airtight, ¼-inch steel construction and cast iron doors with triple seals are Timberline stoves' strongest features. There are three box stove models, the *T-18, T-24* and *T-33*, and two fireplace/stoves, the *T-SF* and the *T-LF*.

The fireplaces, large and medium stoves have twin screw-mounted double-seal draft controls; the smaller stove has one. A top baffle improves combustion efficiency. The box stoves have two cooking surfaces of two different temperatures.

The fireplace models have heavy cast iron doors that interlock for good air control and come with safety spark screens with positive lock. Flue connectors are made to order at rear, sides, or top.

## Victorian Woodstoves
## 1601 Park Ave. So.
## Minneapolis, Minnesota 55404

*Ulefos* box stoves are of the ornate, European type, come in four sizes and are solid cast iron throughout. They have a special bottom lining for extra safety and the doors and doorframes are precision ground for perfect seals. Internal baffle plates and a single draft control on the front door produce a "cigar-type" burn. Each size has a cooking surface on top and sides embossed with decorative scenes. Stove pipe can be connected to top, sides or back. Decorator top covers are available on *Models 864, 868* and *865*.

The largest model, *No. 172*, has a double arch heat exchanger, stands 68 inches high and weighs 374 pounds.

*Model 868* stands 24½ inches high, weighs 115 pounds and is recommended for a room of about 2500 cubic feet.

*Model 864* stands 26 inches high, weighs 143 pounds, and is recommended for a room of about 3500 cubic feet. Both stoves take a 12-inch log.

*Model 865* jumps to weight of 253 pounds, stands 31 inches high and can heat about 7000 cubic feet. It takes a 23-inch log.

## Washington Stove Works
## P.O. Box 687
## Everett, Washington 98201

Just about any type of wood burning heater—from box stove to pot belly, free-standing fireplace to zero-clearance installed fireplace is available from the Washington Stove Works. Many are shipped completely assembled. Almost all are made of cast iron.

The *Cannonball Olympic #213* is 41 inches high, 13 inches deep, takes a 6-inch flue pipe from the top and weighs 124 pounds. The *Cannonball Olympic #117* is 47 inches high, 17 inches deep, takes a 7-inch flue pipe from the top and weighs 220 pounds. The *Cannonball Martin S-50* is 30¾ inches high, 14 inches deep, takes a 6-inch flue pipe from the top and weighs 86 pounds. All three models have cook surfaces.

The *Basic Parlor Stove* is 31¼ inches high, 25½ inches wide and 22½ inches long. It weighs 180 pounds and takes a 6-inch flue pipe. The stove has front, top and side loading doors.

The *Arctic* series includes two basic box stoves. The *Arctic #1-25* is 23¼ inches high, 14½ inches wide and 33 inches long. It weighs 110 pounds and takes a 6-inch stovepipe. The *Arctic #30* is slightly larger—26½ inches high, 16½ inches wide and 37¼ inches long. It weighs 140 pounds and takes a 6-inch smokepipe.

The *Olympic Franklins* are the traditional-looking fireplace stove with bi-fold doors; the number indicates the length of the log that will fit the firebox. *Franklin #18* is 25½ inches high, 20½ inches wide and 30 inches long. It takes a 7-inch flue pipe and weighs 175 pounds.

*Franklin #22* is 29½ inches high, 23 inches wide and 33¾ inches long. It takes an 8-inch stove pipe and weighs 225 pounds. *Franklin #26* is 31¼ inches high, 25 inches wide and 26 inches long. It takes an 8-inch flue and weighs 310 pounds. *Franklin #30* is 32½ inches high, 26½ inches wide and 42½ inches long. It takes a 10-inch flue pipe and weighs 375 pounds.

All the Franklin stoves have available as options spark screens, bean pot, barbecue grill, brass rail, brass balls and log holders.

The *Olympic Crest* is a more contemporary styled Franklin that features a thermostatic draft, baffles and a heat shield. It is 32½ inches high, 36 inches wide and 24½ inches long. It takes an 8-inch flue pipe and weighs about 355 pounds. A spark screen is optional.

*Norwesters #40* and *#38* are circulating heaters, meaning that they allow air to pass between the exterior cabinet and the radiant heater (firebox). Both models have thermostatic draft control. The fireboxes have cast iron linings and measure 12 by 24 inches. The exterior cabinets are brown enamel. A factory installed blower is optional on *Model #38*.

**Yankee Woodstoves**
**Cross Street**
**Bennington, New Hampshire 03442**

All Yankee woodstoves are barrel stoves completely assembled using 18-gauge steel drums manufactured exclusively for this firm. Each has internal baffles, a cast iron door and 5-inch flue collar, reinforced door opening, heavy steel legs, draft air deflector and adjustable door catch.

The smallest stove, *Model 15*, is an upright cylinder available with top or back flue, uses 3 firebricks plus dry, coarse masonry sand, and handles 12-inch logs.

Also an upright cylinder, *Model 18* is available with a top or back flue, uses four firebricks and takes a 1½ foot log.

Horizontal *Model 28* is available with top flue only. It uses 6 firebricks and takes 24-inch logs. It is the most efficient model because it has the longest flame path. A variation, *Model 28/CR* has a door in the baffle that can be opened for quick starts, then closed for a more efficient burn.

## Small Stoves Compared

| Manufacturer | Stove | Wood Length | Flue Size | Flue Location | Materials | Price |
|---|---|---|---|---|---|---|
| The American Way | Betsy Ross (AW-4) | 26″ | 6″ | | Cast iron | $149 |
| | Knickerbocker Dandy (AW-5) | | 6″ | | Cast iron | $139 |
| Atlanta Stove Works, Inc. | Box Heater Model #27 | 24″ | 6″ | Top | Cast iron | $173 |
| | Model #2502 | 20″ | 6″ | Top | Steel with cast iron top, bottom and door | $242 |
| Birmingham Stove and Range Co. | Banner No. 19 | 10″ | | Top | Cast iron | $120 |
| | Boss No. 60 | 10″ | | Top | Cast iron | $120 |
| Bow and Arrow Stove Co. | Chappee 8008 | 16″ | 5″ | Back | Cast iron | $269 |
| | Petit Godin #3720 | 16″-18″ | 4″ | Back | Steel and cast iron, firebrick | $310 |
| | Trolla No. 102 | 12″ | 4″ | Top/back | Cast iron | |
| | Trolla No. 105 | 17″ | 5″ | Top/back | Cast iron | |
| Cawley/LeMay Stove Co., Inc. | Model 400 | 16″ | 5″ | Back | Cast iron | $475 |
| Damsite Dynamite Stove Company | Dynamite Box Stove | 24″ | 6″ | Top | 10 ga. steel | $135 |
| | Greenwood Dynamite Stove | 24″ | 6″ | Back | 10 ga. steel | |
| | Double Dynamite Stove | 24″ | 6″ | Back | 10 ga. steel | |
| Enterprise Sales | Enterprise Box Stove No. 25 | | 6″ | Top | Cast iron | $160 |
| | Enterprise Box Stove No. 18 | 15″ | 6″ | Top | Cast iron | $110 |
| Free Flow Stove Works | Circulator | 20″ | 6″ | Back | ¼″ steel firebrick | $480 |

## Small Stoves Compared *(Continued)*

| Manufacturer | Stove | Wood Length | Flue Size | Flue Location | Materials | Price |
|---|---|---|---|---|---|---|
| General Engineering and Manufacturing Corp. | Earth Stove Model 101 | 24" | 8" | Top | 10 and 12 ga. steel, firebrick | |
| J and J Enterprises | Frontier S-26-6 | 20" | 8" | Top/back | ¼" steel, firebrick | $475 |
| Kristia Associates | Jøtul No. 602 | 16" | 5" | Top/back | Cast iron | $300 |
| Locke Stove Company | W-15 | 15" | | | Steel, firebrick | |
| Martin Industries | Merit Heater No. 520 | | 6" | Back | Cast iron front | |
| | Box Heater #624 | 23" | 6" | Top | | |
| | Box Heater #628 | 26" | 6" | Top | | |
| | Box Heater #632 | 30" | 6" | Top | | |
| The Merry Music Box | Styria- "Excelsior" | | | Back | Steel, firebrick, cast iron | $945 |
| Monarch Ranges and Heaters | Model FR26C | 27" | 8" | Top/back | Cast iron | |
| | Model HR24B | 24" | 7" | Top | Steel, cast iron doors | |
| Scandinavian Stoves, Inc. | Lange #6303A | | 5" | Top | Cast iron | $295 |
| | Lange #6303B | | 5" | Back | Cast iron | |
| Self Sufficiency Products | Gibraltar II | 20" | 6" | Top | ³⁄₁₆" and ¼" steel | $339 |
| | Gibraltar III | 24" | 6" | Back | ³⁄₁₆" and ¼" steel | $379 |
| Shenandoah Mfg. Co., Inc. | Model R-77 | 26" | | Top | Steel, firebrick | $252 |
| Southport Stoves | Morsø #2B | 20" | 4¾" | Top | Cast iron | $325 |
| | Morsø #6B | 16"-18" | 4¾" | Top | Cast iron | $490 |
| | Morsø 1122 | 20" | 5½" | Back | Cast iron | $495 |
| Thulman Eastern Corp. | Reginald 101 | 16" | 5" | Top/back | Cast iron | $234 |
| Timberline Stoves | Timberline T-18 | 18" | | Top/ sides/ back | ¼" steel | |
| Victorian Woodstoves | Ulefo No. 868 | 12" | 5" | | Cast iron | $250 |
| | Ulefo No. 864 | 12" | 5" | | Cast iron | $275 |
| Washington Stove Works | Cannonball Olympic #213 | | 6" | Top | Cast iron | $380 |

## Small Stoves Compared *(Continued)*

| Manufacturer | Stove | Wood Length | Flue Size | Flue Location | Materials | Price |
|---|---|---|---|---|---|---|
| Washington Stove Works | Cannonball Olympic #117 | | 7″ | Top | Cast iron | $570 |
| | Cannonball Martin #S-50 | | 6″ | Top | Cast iron | |
| | Basic Parlor Stove | | 6″ | | Cast iron | $345 |
| | Arctic #1-25 | | 6″ | Top | Cast iron | |
| | Arctic #30 | | 6″ | Top | Cast iron | |
| | Olympic Franklin #18 | 18″ | 7″ | Top | Cast iron | $263 |
| | Olympic Franklin #22 | 22″ | 8″ | Top | Cast iron | $300 |
| Yankee Wood Stoves | Model 15 | 12″ | 5″ | | 18 ga. steel drum, cast iron | $ 57 |
| | Model 18 | 18″ | 5″ | | 18 ga. steel drum, cast iron | $ 60 |

# Medium Stoves

**All Nighter Stove Works, Inc.**
**80 Commerce Street**
**Glastonbury, Connecticut 06033**
**(203) 633-3640 or 633-3649**

By now you've probably heard of primary and secondary air inlets. Well, the All Nighter Stove people have patented an "exclusive triple air system door." The cast iron, asbestos double-seal door has two side-by-side spin draft controls to regulate the amount of air entering the firebox. An inner-door air baffle distributes air near the bottom for primary burn, in the middle for secondary burn and at the top. This last air travels across the top of the stove creating a barrier to stop escaping unburned volatile gases, forcing them back down into the flames to reburn, which, according to the All Nighter people, produces maximum efficiency.

The rest of the stove is constructed of ¼-inch and 5/16-inch boiler plate steel and firebrick lined. Although it has no baffle, it has a two-level top. Electric blower, hot water extraction cylinder and door screen are optional.

The stove comes in four sizes, ranging from the 452-pound *Big Mo'* that accepts a 30-inch log, through the *Mid Mo'* (390 pounds) and *Little Mo'* (295 pounds), down to the *Tiny Mo'* 189 pounds, 16-inch logs. (*Giant Mo'* and *Jumbo Mo'* coming soon!)

**The American Way.** *Washington Parlor Stove AW-1; Jefferson Delux AW-4;* see description under Small Stoves.

**Ashley Wood Heaters**
**1604 17th Ave. S.W.**
**Sheffield, Alabama 35660**
**(205) 767-0330**

Ashley stoves come in three sizes and two styles. The *Imperial C-60* and the *C-62* are console models with a baked enamel finish cabinet, gold accent trim and gold mesh grill for greater heat radiation. The louvered top lifts off for emergency cooking. The economy line, *Model 25-HF* has a heavy-gauge, blued steel outer shell, and cast iron legs, top, flue collar, door frame and doors.

All Ashley heaters work in the same manner regardless of style. A thermostatic damper controlled by a sensitive bimetallic coil regulates the amount of combustion air needed to maintain the comfort level you select. A downdraft system preheats primary air and discharges it above the firebox grates at two locations. The firebox has cast iron liners, grates, flue collar, feed and ash doors and door frames. A patented secondary air intake responds automatically to temperature changes and admits air above the fire zone, burning off volatile gases.

The *C-60* heats four or five average rooms, takes logs up to two feet long and holds 100 pounds or 4.5 cubic feet of wood. The *25-HF* has a 23½ inch firebox and a capacity of 5.5 cubic feet of wood. The *C-62* takes logs up to 18 inches long and has a capacity of 3.2 cubic feet of wood. A circulating blower is optionally available for all models.

**Atlanta Stove Works, Inc.** *Model #24, Woodsman; Model #241, Huntsman;* see descriptions under Small Stoves.

**Birmingham Stove and Range Co.** *Nordic, Majik 122-A;* see description under Small Stoves.

**Bow and Arrow Stove Co.** *Petit Godin #3721, Trolla 107;* see description under Small Stoves.

**Cawley/LeMay Stove Co., Inc.** *Model 600;* see description under Small Stoves.

**Fire-View Distributors**
**P.O. Box 370**
**Rogue River, Oregon 97537**
**(503) 582-3351**

The *Fire-View* is a cylindrical stove constructed of 12-gauge American steel and used on the horizontal. This shape is less susceptible to warp because it has fewer stress points to expand and contract. The end is made of 3/16-inch steel. A tempered-glass viewing window is cut into the side of the stove. A top vent allows a constant flow of air over the glass to keep it cool and free from soot buildup, but the manufacturer has also allowed for it to be removed (for cleaning) and replaced with a collapsible steel door located behind the glass. You can also use this steel door when you bank the fire for the night.

The firebox is lined with firebrick and is loaded through a gasketed door on the right end of the cylinder. (Left-end doors are available on request.) Combustion air is supplied to the fire through a draft tube at the base of the firebox; a sliding draft door adjusts air volume. The top of the heater is equipped with two flat areas for holding pots and kettles. Very high temperature, flame-proof paint coats the stove.

All models have a blower and shroud assembly available as an option.

*The Fire-View stove tucks neatly into a fireplace.*

**Fisher Stoves, Inc.**
**River Road**
**Bow, New Hampshire 03301**
**(603) 228-1353**

Fisher manufactures three sizes of airtight box stoves (*Baby Bear, Mama Bear & Papa Bear*) and two stove/fireplace combinations (*Grandma Bear, Grandpa Bear*). These chunky-looking stoves are constructed of 1/4-inch and 5/16-inch steel plate welded together, lined with firebrick and triple-sealed, cast iron doors. The two-level design provides a secondary combustion chamber for more efficient burning and two cooking surfaces for two cooking temperatures. The four larger models have twin spin-draft controls and the smallest model, *Baby Bear*, has one. Moderate-size ash aprons are standard on all models, and you can hook up to the flue from either side or back.

The fireplace models, *Grandma Bear* and *Grandpa Bear*, have double, swing open doors a lock-in spark protector for when you want to see the fire. All stoves are guaranteed for 25 years for materials and workmanship.

**Free Flow Stove Works.** *Wonder;* see description under Small Stoves.

**Garrison Stove Works**
**Box 412**
**Claremont, New Hampshire 03743**
**(603) 542-8761**

The *Garrison*, an octagonal-shaped stove with two swing-out front doors, is designed to fit the majority of American hearths and to vent into American fireplaces. The sides, top, base and internal baffles are made of quarter inch hot rolled steel, the doors and draft controls are high phosphorus cast iron and the firebox is lined with firebrick.

Air enters through draft controls high on two angled sides and is preheated as it travels down through a 20-inch channel and into the firebox. The resulting air flow means logs burn from both ends toward the middle, from bottom to top and from back to front. Heat is directed toward the front of the stove, keeping the doors free of creosote and the temperature 200° warmer than the back of the stove. When reloading, you push hot coals back into the stove instead of raking them forward.

A spark guard screen and heat shield are included at no additional cost. A soapstone griddle and cast iron warming plate that fit on top of the 3.55-square-foot cooking surface are options.

**HDI Importers
Schoolhouse Farm
Etna, New Hampshire 03750
(603) 643-3771**

HDI imports the *Berliner*, a high-quality European heater that uses the finest design, materials, and workmanship to make it last a lifetime. It is a cast iron inner stove with firebrick lining and cast iron grate surrounded by a ceramic tile cabinet. *Model 6.14R* has an automatic draft regulator to control the amount of air supplied to the wood or coal fire. *Model 6.14* has a manual draft and is best suited for burning only wood. Both models disperse heat through means of the warm air convection channels as well as by radiation. The fuel feed door and the ash door are lined with brass trim. The doors, protective sill and the top are all enameled deep brown to contrast with the amber glaze of the ceramic tiles. The ashes are shaken into the ash drawer by means of a handle outside the stove which rotates the grate inside. There is a built-in damper at the pipe collar. The unit weighs 375 pounds.

**Hinckley Foundry and Marine
13 Water Street
Newmarket, New Hampshire 03857
(603) 659-5804 or 3629**

Hinckley's *Box Stove* and Hinckley's *Super Heater* both exhibit the remarkably clean lined, functional aesthetics of Shaker design. They are a rare blend of quality materials and craftsmanship. All of the stove parts, except for the legs, bolts and baffles are sand castings of machine-grade gray iron, bronze, or aluminum alloy. The one-piece, ⅜-inch thick, five-sided firebox has a grainy surface texture that increases the radiant heating surface. Aluminum is used for the heat exchanger on the Super Heater and bronze for the hinge assembly.

Each stove is hand built; doors are individually fitted with gaskets and mounted; legs are hand forged. A unique safety latch feature keeps the door shut. The firebox holds 50 pounds of wood in 24- to 26-inch lengths. The *Box Stove* weighs 245 pounds; the *Super Heater* model, 275 pounds.

**Hydraform Products Corp.
P.O. Box 2409
Rochester, New Hampshire 03867
(603) 332-6128**

Several of the claims made for these stoves—the *Smaller Eagle* and *Larger Eagle*—run contrary to accepted wood burning theory. We don't think the manufacturer is deceptive so much as he is confusing. For example a great emphasis is placed on the "full refractory firebox" and the stoves' ability to burn green wood "better than others burn dry wood." It is certainly true that 165 pounds of refractory material in a stove weighing 500 pounds will be able to generate the very, very high firebox temperatures capable of burning green wood. However, the fact remains that a great deal of energy is spent driving the water out of green wood before it can burn and that energy is not heating up your home.

These are very large stoves. The cast slabs of refractory are on five sides of the firebox; the stove itself is a large heat sink—definitely not a parlor stove—with 28 square feet of radiating area. It has a secondary baffled chamber above the refractory. The swing-down fuel door has a "tip-on roller" for loading logs as large as 32 inches long and 12 inches in diameter.

**J and J Enterprises.** *Frontier M-28-8*; see description under Small Stoves.

**Kickapoo Stove Works, Ltd.
Box 127-2J
La Farge, Wisconsin
(608) 625-4430**

The Kickapoo Stove Works makes four sizes of stoves, all of similar design, and a fireplace/stove combination. Each is constructed of an airtight steel hull in a modified diamond shape. That is, it is widest at the center and tapers off to a blunt end. The stoves stand on short legs; the furnace model sits on the floor. All have cast iron doors, gasketed door frames, recessed flue, manual draft, a grate, ash pan and ash compartment and a solid cast refractory "firepot."

The firepot is a five-sided refractory structure (four sides and bottom) backed and edged by steel and welded into place. The cast iron grate is in the center of the bottom slab and allows the ashes to fall into the ashpan. The draft is located on the ash compartment door and controls the volume of air flowing upward through the grate.

The main difference among the *Cabin, Standard* and *Furnace* models is size. The *Cabin*, at 235 pounds, takes a 20-inch log; the *Standard* is 258 pounds and takes a 24-inch log. The *Starlor* and the *Parlor Furnace* are variations on the *Standard*.

The *Boxer* weighs 330 pounds and takes a 22-inch log. It has a steel baffle, twin spin draft controls, and an optional spark screen.

The *Furnace* models incorporate the basic design features in a unit meant to supplement your present forced air system. In addition, there are a series of metal heat exchangers located between the outer surface of the fire chamber and the 24 gauge sheet metal shroud. A thermostatically controlled blower and filter unit are optional.

The *Fireplace/Stove* model is constructed of 10-gauge steel, reinforced with stiffening refractory lined angle irons. The refractory lined combustion chamber is vented by a 7-inch recessed flue and handles a log 18 inches long. The unit stands 50 inches high, tapering from a wide sturdy base to a flat-topped food warming surface. When you remove the spark screen, and swing up the cast iron loading door, you convert the fireplace to an airtight stove.

*The Kickapoo* Boxer *model.*

**Kristia Associates.** *Jotul 118* and *606*; see descriptions under Small Stoves.

**Locke Stove Company.** *Model W-24*; see description under Small Stoves.

**Martin Industries.** *Automatic Wood Heater 6601; Wood King 2600-3*; see descriptions under Small Stoves.

**The Merry Music Box.** *Styria Reliable*; see description under Small Stoves.

**Mohawk Industries Inc.**
**173 Howland Ave.**
**Adams, Massachusetts 01220**
**(413) 743-3648**

The *Tempwood* is a fully welded, airtight, downdraft stove constructed of ⅛-inch steel that will operate 12 to 14 hours on a burn. It gives off moderate heat, depending on outside temperature and the size and insulation of the area you are heating. It has a firebrick lining and an 11-inch diameter, cast iron, removable top plate in the center of the stove top where fuel is added and ashes removed. Two top vents lead air down, across and under the fuel bed. Gases rise off the fire and are forced downward by the thrust of air between the two downdraft vents. Baffle plates serve the same purpose in other stoves. The smoke vent is on the top.

# Thermo-Control

**National Stove Works**
**Howe Caverns Road**
**Cobleskill, New York 12043**
**(518) 296-8517**

This company makes five different *Thermo-Control* wood stoves of continuous seam, welded, ¼-inch rolled steel construction with lustrous black finish, heat resistant to 1,200 degrees. Unlike some companies whose models differ only in size, *Thermo-Control* stoves seem to be designed to meet different heating situations.

If you like to see the fire, you can get the *Franklin* model shipped fully assembled, complete with grate and fire screen. It has tight-fitting doors with graduated locking system.

*Model 100* of the same materials and construction but with firebrick lining, handles 22-inch logs and weighs about 200 pounds. It has manual draft control on the door.

The *Thermo-Control 200, 300* and *500* all have firebrick lined bottoms, an interior preheat chamber, and baffle systems for efficient burning. All have airtight, downdraft design and automatic thermostat control. *Model 200* weighs about 170 pounds. *Model 300* comes with a backing plate in one of three standard sizes that you attach to your existing fireplace. Special sizes can be manufactured on request.

Capable of a 24-hour burn, the *Thermo-Control 500* weighs 390 pounds and will heat an entire home. Two variations on this model can be hooked into your present heating system if it is hot water or hot air.

**New Hampshire Wood Stoves, Inc.**
**P.O. Box 310**
**Plymouth, New Hampshire 03264**
**(603) 536-3388**

Thoughtfully designed, the *Home Warmers I* and *II* are airtight steel and cast iron stoves that are safe and easy to operate and efficient to use. The door, with New Hampshire's Old Man of the Mountain relief design, is made of cast iron and gasketed. The rest of the stove is steel—¼-inch plate steel bottom, ³⁄₁₆-inch top and horizontal baffles, and ⅛-inch side baffles. There are *three* horizontal baffles in the stove. Combustion air is drawn through a thermostatically controlled draft, up the front door, across the top and down in front of the top firebox baffle where it is mixed with heated flue gases. This sounds very complicated, but it makes sense because it uses one air intake for both primary and secondary burning.

The three baffles, in addition to causing air turbulance for thorough burning of the fuel, act as heat exchangers, resulting in very low stovepipe temperatures: most of the heat stays in the room.

The *Home Warmer I* takes a 29-inch log and a 6-inch rear-vented flue; the *Home Warmer II* takes a 23-inch log and a 6-inch rear flue.

**Quaker Stove Company**
**200 W. 5th Street**
**Landsdale, Pennsylvania 19446**
**(215) 362-2019**

The airtight Quaker stove is constructed of a combination of cast iron and steel. The door, face plate and legs are cast iron and of unique appearance, designed by C. and L. Rennels. The top surface is ¼-inch plate steel and the rest of the stove is ⁵⁄₁₆-inch plate steel. The firebrick-lined firebox has a top baffle for efficient burning. Air is preheated in a chamber inside the door, which has two side-by-side spin draft controls. Both door and face plate are fitted with asbestos gaskets. Flue connection is on top, but you can request it elsewhere. The stove is made in three sizes, *Fawn, Doe* and *Buck*. The deluxe model in each size has a window in the door to let you see the fire.

*The Quaker deluxe.*

225

**Scandinavian Stoves Inc.** *Lange #6203BR, Lange #6303, Lange #6302A* and *Lange #6302K;* see Small Stoves for descriptions.

**Self-Sufficiency Products.** *Gibraltar IV;* see description under Small Stoves.

**Shenandoah Manufacturing Company, Inc.** *Model #R65;* see description under Small Stoves.

**Sierra Stoves**
**One Appletree Square**
**Minneapolis, Minnesota 55420**
**(612) 854-0276**

Sierra is a Minnesota firm offering two airtight, ¼-inch and 5⁄16-inch steel plate, firebrick lined stoves similar to Fisher, but without the two-level design or cast iron door. Both Sierra *Models 150* and *300* have two spin draft controls, moderate-sized ash aprons, gravity door lock and come with lifetime guarantee on workmanship.

**Solis Energy Works**
**Box 262A RD #1**
**New Hope, Pennsylvania 18938**
**(215) 297-8550**

A one-piece, 5⁄16-inch cast iron, box stove, the *Solis 6* is designed in the Shaker tradition, cast and assembled to very close tolerances. The door is hand-fitted with an asbestos gasket and has a mica window that stays clean during normal burning cycles, allowing you to see the fire. The stove has separate controls for the primary and secondary air, each with its own preheating baffle that directs the air to two distinct regions of the firebox. The horizontal baffle is not a flat plate, but a long trough attached to the top of the stove. Flue connection is on top.

The stove bottom is designed to accommodate a hard firebrick surface (not included). There is a large apron in front to catch ashes and to warm cold feet. The door latch is handled by a turned hardwood knob that is cool to the touch. Legs and door latch are hand forged.

**Southport Stoves**
**248 Tolland Street**
**East Hartford, Connecticut 06108**
**(203) 289-6079**

If you live in an area where you can buy anthracite coal economically and have a place to store it, you should probably look into coal-burning stoves. A ton of coal will heat a home in Connecticut for 6 to 8 months, depending on the severity of the winter.

The Surdiac Company of Belgium has been manufacturing coal stoves and combination fireplace/stoves for many years. They are airtight and have been rated up to 89 percent efficient. These long-burning stoves (100 hours on 25 pounds of anthracite—try that in your wood stove!) have precision thermostats, top-loading interior storage bins that gravity-feed the fire below, and a shaker for dropping ashes into a clean-out pan. The firebox is made of the finest cast iron with all parts that receive intense heat made of a special mixture of iron and stainless steel to prevent burnout. The top has been polished for a cook surface. The exterior cabinet is enamelled steel, inside and out. The glass doors are made of Pyrex glass in strips to allow each section of the door to expand at its own rate. They will not become dirty when burning coal and 25 percent of the heat of the unit is radiated through the glass.

A heat exchanger covers the back of each stove with cleanout plates on each side at the bottom for easy maintenance. The combustion air enters the stove from the lower back, making it easy to rig an outside feed. These stoves have a low smoke vent at the back and can be vented into a masonry or a manufacturer's all-purpose chimney.

The *Gotha 511* is dark gray with glass door and relief reproductions of Flemish paintings. Other models (*MCK 508, MCK 512* and *MCK 516*) come in black or beige enamel.

Southport also distributes the *Mørso 2BO* and *Mørso 1B;* see Small Stoves for details.

**Spalt Associates Corporation, Importers**
**275 Circuit Street**
**Hanover, Massachusetts 02339**

Spalt sells both traditional American styles and Scandinavian-style stoves. They are all imported, but from where? Clue: *Model 33* is purported to be a masterpiece of Danish design and Asian workmanship.

The *Quincy Adams* (*Model H190*) parlor stove weighs about 225 pounds and is constructed of cast iron with nickel-plated trim. It has front and side loading doors, accepts a 21-inch log and takes a 6-inch stove pipe.

The *Ben Franklin Heater* (*Model H126* and *H130*) is all cast iron construction with flat black finish. Two accordian-hinge doors have sliding draft controls. Standard equipment includes an all-purpose cast iron grate and a cast iron boot with damper that can be mounted on top or back according to your needs.

The *Cohasset Boxwood* (*Model H73*), is a traditional cast iron box stove. It has two 6-inch lids on a swing top, large feed door, a stable 24-inch leg spread, sliding hearth plate for draft control and a large ash apron. It weighs 132 pounds and takes a top-mounted 6-inch stove pipe.

The *Plymouth* (*Model H80*) is a similar box stove, but larger and with more beautiful designs in the castings. In appearance it is a copy of an early stove made by Atlantic. It has an 8-inch lid on a swing top, and a 7-inch flue collar.

The newest *Viking, Model 63* is in the Scandinavian tradition. It has an internal baffle system, double cast lining on sidewalls and floor, a by-pass damper for quick starts and two vertically aligned draft controls for primary and secondary air. It weighs 264 pounds and handles a 24-inch log. *Viking Model 22* is a medium-weight (170 pounds), airtight cast iron stove with firebrick-lined sides. It has a spin draft control on the door, a small ash apron, rear mounted flue connection and handles a 17-inch log.

*Model 33* is similar, except that it has a heat exchanger mounted on top. The flue can be connected in the rear or out either side. It accepts a 26-inch log.

Finally, *Model 44* is a fireplace/stove with a large swing-down front door that can be left open for viewing the fire or closed up to convert the unit into a very large, airtight heater. The lower walls are lined with firebrick.

**Thulman Eastern Corp.** *Reginald 102;* see description under Small Stoves.

**Timberline Stove.** *Timberline T-24* and *Timberline T-SF;* see description under Small Stoves.

**Torrid Air**
**Torrid Manufacturing Co., Inc.**
**1248 Poplar Pl. So.**
**Seattle, Washington 98144**
**(206) EA4-2754**

A Franklin type of stove constructed of 5/16-inch steel plate, *The Triumph* includes the unusual feature of a 7-gallon water tank with towel bar. The tank is unlined but can be removed for cleaning, presumedly when it isn't either hot or full. The two swing-open doors have translucent, replaceable mica windows and a screen is provided for when you want to see the fire. The firebox is firebrick lined and there is a draft control on each door.

**United States Stove Company**
**South Pittsburg, Tennessee 37380**

The *Wonderwood 2600* is a 210-pound, welded steel stove with firebrick lining and cast iron grates. It has gasketed doors for airtightness and a thermostat for automatic control of the draft. An optional 2-speed blower discharges at floor level. You can use logs up to 24 inches long and it takes a 6-inch flue pipe.

*Model 2601* is the same as the *2600* except that it has cast iron feed and ash doors and improved cast iron grates for more complete combustion.

**Vermont Castings, Inc.**
**Box 126 Prince Street**
**Randolph, Vermont 05060**
**(802) 728-3355**

The *Defiant* is the first all–cast iron efficient wood heater to be produced in America. It is thermostatically controlled so you can preset the heat level and the stove will maintain an even temperature for hours. You can load stove from the side when using the thermostat or from the double, swing-open front doors when you use it as a fireplace. The swing doors are removable and a screen is provided.

This is a massive heater with a baffled firebox and the longest flame path of any stove made. A damper-controlled, internal system uses preheated primary and secondary air to help ignite the volatile gases for efficient burning. There is a cast iron cooking griddle, and the whole stove reflects the classically simple lines of 19th-century American architecture. A smaller model by Vermont Castings of slightly different design is called the *Vigilant*.

*Vermont Castings'* Defiant *(left) and* Vigilant.

**Vermont Iron Stove Works**
**Bobbin Mill**
**Box 252B**
**Warren, Vermont 05674**
**(802) 496-2617**

*The Elm* is a ¼-inch thick steel cylinder-type box stove with a cast iron front and back secured by four 3/8-inch solid brass rods. The firebox is firebrick lined. On the door an Elm tree is silhouetted against the heat-resistant glass window. The door handle and draft control knob are hardwood. Flue connection is on top.

You can opt for a cast iron cooking surface that bolts to the top of the stove and a combination oven and heat exchanger. An unusual-looking and beautiful heater.

The Elm *in action.*

**Vermont Woodstove Co.**
**P.O. Box 1016**
**Bennington, Vermont 05201**
**(802) 442-8197**

One of the most unusual designs we've seen, the *Down Drafter I* is a conventional-looking stove made of ¼-, ³⁄₁₆- and ⅛-inch steel plate with cast iron loading door and separate ash removal door. Inside are two side-by-side, V-shaped grates with cast iron baffles suspended vertically above them. The grates are made of cast iron and firebrick. Progressively burning coals are funneled to the bottom of these V's. The firebox is sealed above so that combustible air enters below the grates, passing through them and through the coal bed. Not only does this insure combustion of the volatile gases, but it results in the fire burning *away* from the wood instead of up through it.

The *DDI* weighs 500 pounds, has a built-in heat exchange chamber and thermostatically controlled blower that circulates room air through the chamber and out the front. Manifold kits are available for connecting the stove to existing duct work, as are hot water coils for connecting to home systems. The *DDII* weighs 250 pounds and is built without the heat exchange chamber or blower.

The *Canadian Stepstove* is a steel-plate box stove with heat exchanger chamber on top as the "step." The firebox is firebrick lined; a baffle separates the firebox from the heating chamber where the flue pipe connects. The cast iron fuel door is fully gasketed for airtight seal and contains a chamber for preheating the intake air. You adjust the air volume by means of twin spin draft controls on the door. The stove weighs 350 pounds and takes a 24-inch log.

**Victorian Wood Stoves.** *Ulefos 865*; see description under Small Stoves.

**Warm Glow Products, Inc.**
**625 Century S. W.**
**Grand Rapids, Michigan 49503**
**(616) 774-2909**

Two units are manufactured by Warm Glow: the *Maxi II*, an airtight box stove and the *Maxi I*, a combination fireplace/stove. Both are made of cast iron with firebrick-lined fireboxes and interior baffles for efficient burning. Each has a spin draft control, interior baffles for efficient burning, and a dull black, textured enamel finish. The *Maxi I* can be vented out the back or from either side.

The fireplace/stove model is somewhat like the *Jøtul #4* in appearance with a single door that stores under the firebox. No screen is included.

**Washington Stove Works.** *Olympic Franklin #26, #30*, and *Olympic Crest*; see descriptions under Small Stoves.

**Wood Heat**
**Route 212 Pleasant Valley**
**Quakertown, Pennsylvania 18951**
**(215) 346-7894**

The *Pleasant Valley* stove is steel plate, welded box construction with firebrick lining on bottom, sides and rear (firebrick included). The door frame and door are cast iron. The frame is sealed to the stove and the door sealed to the frame with heat-proof rope gasket. A liner plate covers the inside of the door to prevent warpage by over-heating, directs the stream of air over the base of the fire and prevents embers from popping out through the draft control.

You can move the horizontal baffle forward and back with a stove rake for quick starts or more efficient burning. The stove has a rather small ash apron and is painted with 2000° matte black paint. Options are top or rear flue connection and long or short legs.

**Yankee Wood Stoves.** *Model 28* and *28CR*; see Small Stoves for descriptions.

## Medium Stoves Compared

| Manufacturer | Stove | Wood Length | Flue Size | Flue Location | Materials | Price |
|---|---|---|---|---|---|---|
| All Nighter Stove Works, Inc. | Tiny Mo' | 16″ | 6″ | Back | ¼″ and 5/16″ plate steel | $340 |
| | Little Mo' | 20″ | 6″ | Back | ¼″ and 5/16″ plate steel | $390 |
| | Mid Mo' | 24″ | 6″ | Rear | ¼″ and 5/16″ plate steel | $445 |
| American Way | Washington Parlor Stove AW-1 | 24″ | 6″ | Back | Cast iron, mica-backed windows, polished chrome | $249 |
| | Jefferson Delux AW-4 | 28″ | 6″ | Back | Cast iron, polished chrome | $250 |
| Ashley Products Division | Columbian 25-HF | 22″ | | Top | Steel | $210 |
| Atlanta Stove Works, Inc. | Model #24 Woodsman | 26″ | 6″ | Back | Cast iron | $486 |
| | Model #241 Huntsman | 24″ | 6″ | Back | Steel | $505 |
| Birmingham Stove and Range Co. | Nordic | 26″ | | Back | Cast iron | $400 |
| | Majik 122-A | 22″ | 6″ | Top | Cast iron, refractory lining, blue steel jacket | $199 |

## Medium Stoves Compared *(Continued)*

| Manufacturer | Stove | Wood Length | Flue Size | Flue Location | Materials | Price |
|---|---|---|---|---|---|---|
| Bow and Arrow Stove Co. | Petit Godin #3721 | 20″ | 4″ | Back | Steel, cast iron | $425 |
| | Trolla 107 | 24″ | 5″ | Top/back | Cast iron | |
| Cawley/LeMay Stove Co., Inc. | Model 600 | 24″-27″ | 5″ | Back | Cast iron | $560 |
| Fire-View Distributors | Fire-View #270 | 24″ | 7″ | Top/back | 12 ga. steel for firebox, ³⁄₁₆″ for end portions | |
| Fisher Stoves Inc. | Baby Bear | 18″ | 6″ | Back | ¼″ and ⁵⁄₁₆″ plate steel | $335 |
| Free Flow Stove Works | Wonder | 27″ | | Back | ¼″ steel | $600 |
| Garrison Stove Works | Garrison Two | 24″ | 6″ | Back | ¼″ steel, cast iron, firebrick | $395 |
| | Garrison One | 24″ | 8″ | Back | ¼″ steel, cast iron, firebrick | $495 |
| HDI Importers | Berliner 6.14 | | 5″ or 6″ | Back | Cast iron, firebrick, ceramic tile, brass trim | |
| | Berliner 6.14R | | 5″ or 6″ | Back | Cast iron, firebrick, ceramic tile, brass trim | |
| Hinckley Foundry and Marine | Hinckley's box stove | 26″ | 6″ | Top | Cast iron, bronze | |
| Hydraform Products Corp. | Smaller Eagle | 24″ | | Back | Steel, refractory | $495 |
| J and J Enterprises | Frontier M-28-8 | 22″ | 8″ | Top/back | ¼″ and ⁵⁄₁₆″ steel | $499 |
| Kickapoo Stove Works Ltd. | Cabin Model | 20″ | 6″ | Top | 12 ga. steel, cast iron | $416 |
| | Standard | 24″ | 6″ | Top | 12 ga. steel, cast iron, refractory | $424 |
| Kristia Associates | Jøtul No. 118 | 24″ | 5″ | Side/back | Cast iron | $500 |
| | Jøtul No. 606 | 12″ | 5″ | Side/back | Cast iron | $480 |
| Locke Stove Company | W-24 | 24″ | | | Steel, firebrick | |
| Martin Industries | 6601 Automatic Wood Heater | 24″ | | Top | Cast iron, steel | |
| | Wood King 2600-3 | | | Top | | |

229

# Medium Stoves Compared *(Continued)*

| Manufacturer | Stove | Wood Length | Flue Size | Flue Location | Materials | Price |
|---|---|---|---|---|---|---|
| The Merry Music Box | Styria "Reliable" | | | Back | | $1,055 |
| Mohawk Industries | Tempwood V | 12″-14″ | 5″ | Back | ¼″ and ¼″ steel | $219 |
| National Stove Works | Thermo-Control Model 100 | 18″ | 6″ | Top | ¼″ steel, firebrick | $209 |
| | Thermo-Control Model 200 | 18″ | 6″ | Top | ¼″ and ³⁄₁₆″ steel, firebrick | $249 |
| | Thermo-Control Model 300 (fireplace heater) | 18″ | | | ¼″ and ³⁄₁₆″ steel, firebrick | $279 |
| New Hampshire Wood Stoves, Inc. | Home Warmer II | 23″ | 6″ | Back | ⅛″ and ¼″ steel | $399 |
| Quaker Stove Co. | Fawn | 15″ | 6″ | Top | Cast iron, ¼″ and ⁵⁄₁₆″ steel, firebrick | $389 |
| Scandinavian Stoves Inc. | Lange #6203BR | | 5″ | Top | Cast iron | $415 |
| | Lange #6303 | | 5″ | Side | Cast iron | $415 |
| | Lange #6302A | | 5″ | Top | Cast iron | $530 |
| | Lange #6302K | | 5″ | Top | Cast iron | |
| Self Sufficiency Products | Gibraltar IV | 28″ | 6″ | Back | ³⁄₁₆″ and ¼″ steel | $439 |
| Shenandoah Mfg. Co., Inc. | Model #R65 | 18″ | | Top | Steel | $204 |
| Sierra Stoves | Sierra #150 | 22″ | 6″ | Back | ¼″ and ⁵⁄₁₆″ steel | |
| Solis Energy Works | Solis 6 | 24″ | 5″ | Top | Cast iron, mica window | $525 |
| Southport Stoves | Gotha 511 | Coal in 3 sizes | 5″ | Back | Cast iron, stainless steel, enamelled steel, Pyrex glass | $950 |
| | MCK 512 MCK 516 | ″ | 5″ | Back | ″ | $786 $860 |
| | MCK 508 | ″ | 5″ | Back | ″ | $685 |
| | Morsø 2BO | 20″ | 4¾″ | Top | Cast iron | $450 |
| | Morsø 1B | 22″ | 4¾″ | Top | Cast iron | $450 |
| Spalt Associates Corp., Importers | Cohasset Boxwood Heater | 23″ | 6″ | Top | Cast iron | $ 90 |
| | Quincy Adams Parlor Stove | 21″ | 6″ | Top | Cast iron, nickel plated trim | $209 |

## Medium Stoves Compared *(Continued)*

| Manufacturer | Stove | Wood Length | Flue Size | Flue Location | Materials | Price |
|---|---|---|---|---|---|---|
| Spalt | Viking 33 | 26″ | 5″ | Rear or sides | Cast iron | $349 |
| | Viking 63 | 24″ | 5″ | Top | Cast iron | $434 |
| Thulman Eastern Corp. | Reginald 102 | 24″ | 5″ | Top/ back/ sides | Cast iron | $419 |
| Timberline Stoves | Timberline T-24 | 24″ | | Top/ sides/ back | ¼″ steel | |
| | Timberline T-SF | 20″ | | Top/ sides/ back | ¼″ steel | |
| Torrid Mfg. Co., Inc. | Triumph | 24″ | 8″ | Top | ⁵⁄₁₆″ steel, mica windows, firebrick lined | |
| United States Stove Co. | Wonderwood 2600 | 24″ | 6″ | | Steel, fire- brick lining, cast iron grates | |
| | Wonderwood 2601 | 24″ | 6″ | | Steel, cast iron, firebrick | |
| Vermont Castings, Inc. | Vigilant | 18″ | 8″ | Top/ back | Cast iron | $500 |
| Vermont Iron Stove Works | The Elm | 24″ | 6″ | Back | ¼″ steel | $350 |
| Vermont Woodstove Co. | DownDrafter II | 18″ | 6″ | Back | Steel plate stainless steel | $329 |
| | Canadian Stepstove | 24″ | 6″ | Back | ¼″ and ⁵⁄₁₆″ steel | $395 |
| Victorian Woodstoves | Ulefos 865 | 23″ | 5″ | Rear | Cast iron | $445 |
| Warmglow Products, Inc. | Maxi-Heat II | 24″ | 7″ | Sides/ back | Cast iron | |
| Washington Stove Works | Olympic Franklin #26 | 26″ | 8″ | Top | Cast iron | $365 |
| | Olympic Franklin #30 | 30″ | 10″ | Top | Cast iron | $435 |
| | Olympic Crest | | 8″ | Top | Cast iron | $669 |
| Wood Heat | Pleasant Valley Stove | 30″ | 6″ | Top | Steel plate, cast iron, firebrick | |
| Yankee Wood Stoves | Model 28 | 12″ | 5″ | Top | 18 ga. steel drum, cast iron | $ 68 |
| | Model 28CR | 24″ | 5″ | Top | 18 ga. steel drum, cast iron | $ 75 |

# Large Stoves

**All Nighter Stove Works, Inc.** *Big Mo*; see description under Small Stoves.

**The American Way.** *Franklin Cabinet Stove*; see description under Small Stoves.

*The Autocrat* Americana 76FH.

**Autocrat Corporation**
**New Athens, Illinois 62264**
**(619) 475-2121**

Two styles of Franklin fireplaces are made by Autocrat. One is the traditional Franklin *Model 76FH*, tightly welded inside with airtight doors and automatic thermostat. You can use it as a free-standing fireplace with the doors open (or removed) and the spark screen locked in place. The firebox has cast iron linings to allow air to flow around all sides of the fire. It comes with a built-in, contoured cast iron log grate and takes up to a 25-inch log.

With the doors in place and the thermostat set, the stove will hold a fire up to twelve hours. Louvers on the top and sides direct a flow of hot air. Ash doors lead to full-width ash pan. Firedoors, ash doors and ash pan close tightly with cam-locking latches that you can remove and store in a cool place. The fire doors or screen can be hung in brackets at the back of the stove when not in use.

A reducer and double-wall pipe are furnished to reach an 8-foot ceiling. The first section of outside pipe has grills that serve as a heat exchanger. Middle section of pipe includes a barometric draft control to offset weather conditions that would affect the draft.

The cabinet and pipe are finished with heat-resistant flat black enamel; polished cast brass ornaments give it a classic design.

An optional blower accessory turns on when the stove is hot and off when it cools. It draws air from the hottest part of the unit, forces it through space between outside and inside of the first section of pipe and out into the room through the heat exchanger grill. The contemporary style Franklin, the *Americana 2000*, is a free-standing fireplace with cast iron doors and thermostatically controlled combustion. This model comes in three colors: red (*R2000FH*), black (*B2000FH*) and almond (*M2000FH*). As with the traditional Franklin, you can remove the doors, lock in the spark screen and detach the handles. The same cast iron grates, linings, full-width ash pan and double-wall stove pipe features are included, as well as the barometric draft control. The blower is optional on the contemporary models also.

**Birmingham Stove and Range Co.** *Ponderosa*; see description under Small Stoves.

**C & D Distributors, Inc.**
**P.O. Box 766**
**Old Saybrook, Connecticut 06475**
**(203) 388-5665**

The *Better 'n Ben's* stove is designed to convert your fireplace into an efficient heater. The combined stove and cover panel is fastened over the front of the fireplace without masonry alterations. The stove, constructed of 11-gauge, low-carbon steel, uses the existing fireplace flue. The back cover panel and the heat deflector angled above the stove create additional heat radiation surfaces. A sliding draft control is located under the fuel door and a damper is located at the back of the stove. The firebox has an internal baffle for efficient burning. A screen for viewing the fire is available as an option.

232

**Comforter Stove Works
Box 175
Lochmere, New Hampshire 03252
(603) 524-0909**

The *Comforter* is a thoughtfully designed and well-made cast iron parlor stove that also happens to be beautiful. It is constructed of ¼-inch castings with selected stress points made of ¼-inch malleable iron, a special heat-treated cast iron that will never crack or warp. Air-tightness is achieved with asbestos cement–sealed interlock seams and an asbestos gasket on the door.

A special chamber draws air around a heated damper, then directs and superheats it with channeling heat fins to first- second-, and third-stage air portals for efficient combustion. The interior of the firebox is baffled to provide a longer flame path and again, efficient burning.

The hinged damper control is at the front of the stove. The stove is loaded from a side door, takes up to a 21-inch log and weighs 250 pounds. Coal can be burned as an option.

**Fire-View Distributors.** *Fire-View 360*; see description under Medium Stoves.

**Fisher Stoves, Inc.** *Grandpa Bear, Grandma Bear* and *Papa Bear*; see descriptions under Medium Stoves.

*Fisher Stoves'* Papa Bear, *showing refractory lining.*

**Free Flow Stove Works.** *Furnace*; see description under Small Stoves.

**Hinckley Foundry and Marine.** *Superheater*; see Medium Stoves.

**Hydraform Products Corp.** *Larger Eagle*; see description under Medium Stoves.

**J and J Enterprises.** *Frontier XL-32-8* and *L-30-8*; see description under Small Stoves.

**Kickapoo Stove Works, Ltd.** *Models BX, BBR-S* and *Fireplace/Stove*; see descriptions under Medium Stoves.

**Kristia Associates.** *Jøtul No. 4 Combi-fire*; see Small Stoves for description.

**The Merry Music Box.** Styria *Imperial*; see description under Small Stoves.

**Mohawk Industries.** *Tempwood II*; see description under Medium Stoves.

**National Stove Works.** *Thermo-Control Model 500*; see description under Medium Stoves.

**New Hampshire Stoves, Inc.** *Home Warmer I*; see description under Medium Stoves.

**Quaker Stove Co.** *Buck* and *Doe* models; see descriptions under Medium Stoves.

**Ram Forge Stoves
Brooks, Maine 04921
(207) 722-3379**

The *RAM* is a ¼-inch welded steel airtight stove that weighs about 300 pounds. It looks like the standard box stove except that the top third of the sides slopes inward. A horizontal baffle forces the draft into an S pattern for a more efficient burn. The stove accepts a 28-inch log, has a spin-draft control on the door and a good sized but unrimmed ash apron. The 5-inch flue connection is in the rear.

The *RAM* is also available with hand-painted earthenware tiles fitted in steel tracks on the top and sides of the stove. The 32 tiles provide an additional 50 pounds of thermal mass to radiate heat longer.

The *RAM* wood sauna stove, available in limited supply, is also welded from heavy steel plate and completely airtight, drawing its draft from the outside. It comes complete with rocks and instructions and weighs about 190 pounds.

*RAM tile stove—colorful and efficient.*

**Riteway Manufacturing Co.**
**Division of Sarco Corporation**
**P.O. Box 6**
**Harrisburg, Virginia 22801**
**(703) 434-7090**

In the forty-odd years that the Riteway people have been selling stoves, they have earned the reputation of being serious and dedicated to wood heat safety and efficiency. They make two radiant heaters: the *Riteway 2000*, rated at 50,000 Btu/hr., and the *Riteway 37*, rated at 73,000 Btu/hr., which will also burn coal. Both come with bimetallic thermostat, magnetic damper, poker and ash pan. Cabinets are available in two-tone mahogany and gold or black and gold for an additional sum.

    *Model 2000* has a firebox capacity of 4 cu. ft. and accepts a 24-inch log. It has firebox lining and grates of aluminized steel. Preheated primary air travels below the grate, upward behind the liners and into the combustion chambers. Volatile wood gases are forced back through the fire and into the cast iron secondary combustion chamber and then out the flue.

    *Model 37* operates in a similar manner except that it uses cast iron grates and firebrick firebox lining and can therefore burn coal. Its firebox capacity is 7½ cu. ft. and it also takes a 24-inch log.

*Riteway Model 37.*

**Scandinavian Stoves, Inc.** *Lange #6302K*; see description under Small Stoves.

**Shenandoah Manufacturing Co.** *Model #R-75*; see description under Small Stoves.

**Sierra Stoves.** *Sierra #300*; see description under Medium Stoves.

**Southeastern Vermont Community Action**
**Box 477**
**Saxton's River, Vermont 05154**
**(802) 869-2772**

Production of the SEVCA stove began as a project by Southeastern Vermont Community Action, a private, non-profit corporation whose purpose is to assist low-income folks. It is made from recycled propane cylinders that are both durable (³⁄₁₆ inch) and less expensive than new materials. The cylindrical shape offers greater heat resistance than a rectangular steel stove, which makes the SEVCA stove comparable to cast iron in durability without the threat of cracking.

    This airtight stove consists of three compartments: the firebox, secondary combustion chamber and heat exchanger. It has a primary air inlet in the door and a secondary inlet on the back of the bottom. This baffled stove is so well designed (it has a flame path of 8 feet), it puts out an incredible amount of heat for its 260 pounds. A smaller unit has been developed for parlor stove situations and a hot water coil is available for the large stove, which heats 52 gallons of water to 140° in about 5 hours. This is a highly efficient, well-made stove; about the only disadvantage is that its appearance may disappoint those of you who expect beauty with efficiency.

**Southport Stoves, Inc.**
**248 Tolland Street**
**East Hartford,**
    **Connecticut 06108**

**morsø**

The Belgian *Efel* is an airtight, controlled-draft stove and fireplace combination that burns wood or coal and is extremely versatile. It circulates heat by drawing air between the inner firebox and the iron-grated top. For extreme radiant heat you can raise the porcelainized exterior hood and expose the cast iron firebox hood. The exterior hood then reflects the heat radiated from the firebox hood, a flat surface you also can use to cook on. While the exterior hood is up you can open the pyrex glass door and raise it up against the cast iron firebox. By lowering the exterior hood you have an open fireplace.

    The cabinet, constructed of porcelainized steel inside and out, comes in blue, beige, gray, brown, red or green. The frame of the glass door, the grate, draft controls, log rail, back plate, left end plate and hood of the firebox are all cast iron. Fuel is loaded from the right side. Air feeds through the front draft controls and is drawn down under the grate and up through the burning coals. The *Efel* has an asbestos-sealed ash pan beneath the grate. The glass in the door is cut into 1½ inch strips to allow it to expand at its own rate without breaking. The glass doors radiate a great deal of heat because the heat flow pattern is toward the glass, upward along the front hood and back to the venting smoke pipe.

    The firebox is 22 inches wide by 9 inches deep, by 16½ inches high. The 8-inch flue must be vented as such if it is to be used with the glass door open. If it is to be used only as an airtight stove, however, the flue size can be reduced to 6 inches. When burning as an airtight stove with draft very low and the damper in the collar in a closed position, the glass door will become darkened from the smoke and creosote. It can be cleaned by placing the door upward against the case iron hood, spraying it with oven cleaner, and wiping clean immediately.

    Southport also distributes the *Morsø 1B0* and *Morsø 1125*; see descriptions under Small Stoves.

**Spalt Associates Corporation, Importers.** *Ben Franklin Heater, H126* and *H130, Plymouth Boxwood Heater* and *Viking 44* (fireplace/stove); see descriptions under Medium Stoves.

**The Stoveworks™**
**Box 172**
**Marlboro, Vermont 05344**
**(802) 257-7364**

A lot of thinking has gone into the design of the three stoves offered by The Stoveworks™; not only that, they are willing to think some more about your special problems and custom-build a stove to meet your needs.

*The Independence*™ is a ³⁄₁₆-inch rolled steel stove of baffled, Scandinavian design modified by wood-burning expert Larry Gay for American technical advances. It has an 11½-inch square door and takes 28-inch logs.

*The Independence Jr.*™ is the same stove with about half the firebox volume. Both have primary and secondary draft controls, flue connection on side, top or rear, ash apron with one-inch lip and can be fitted with 120-pound soapstone slabs either factory-installed or as a kit. A factory-installed hot water coil is also available that consists of 3/4-inch copper tubing mounted inside the firebox and protected by a steel liner.

The unusual and innovative *Culvert Queen* combines downdraft design with a corrugated cylindrical firebox to mix incoming air with gases distilled from the wood. The corrugations also increase the radiating surface area and break up the air flow around the stove, which otherwise would have an insulating effect. The natural strength of corrugated steel eliminates the need for internal reinforcing rods.

**Timberline Stoves.** Timberline *T-33* and *T-LF*; see description. under Small Stoves.

**Vermont Castings, Inc.** *Defiant*; see descriptions under Medium Stoves.

*Stoveworks'* Independence Jr. *with soapstone slabs.*

**Vermont Woodstove Co.** *DownDrafter I*; see description under Medium Stoves.

**Victorian Woodstoves.** *Ulefos 172*; see description under Small Stoves.

**Warmglow Products, Inc.** *Maxi-Heat I*; see description under Medium Stoves.

## Large Stoves Compared

| Manufacturer | Stove | Wood Length | Flue Size | Flue Location | Materials | Price |
|---|---|---|---|---|---|---|
| All Nighter Stove Works, Inc. | Big Mo' | 30″ | 6″ | Back | ¼″ and ⁵⁄₁₆″ plate steel | $ 530 |
| The American Way | Franklin Cabinet Stove AW-7 | 24″ | 8″ | Top | Cast iron | $ 299 |
| | Franklin Cabinet Stove AW-8 | 24″ | 10″ | Top | Cast iron | $ 360 |
| Autocrat Corporation | Americana Model 76 FH (fireplace/stove) | 25″ | 8″ | Top | Steel, cast iron | $ 749 |
| | Americana 2000 | 25″ | 8″ | Top | Steel, cast iron | $ 749 |

## Large Stoves Compared *(Continued)*

| Manufacturer | Stove | Wood Length | Flue Size | Flue Location | Materials | Price |
|---|---|---|---|---|---|---|
| Birmingham Stove and Range Co. | Ponderosa | 24" | | Back | ¼" to ¹⁹⁄₆₄" boiler plate, firebrick | $ 450 |
| C & D Distributors, Inc. | Better 'n Ben's (fireplace heater) | 18" | 6" | Back | 11-gauge black iron | |
| Comforter Stove Works | Comforter | 21" | 6" | Back | Cast iron, malleable iron | $ 498 |
| Fire-View Distributors | Fire-View #360 | 36" | 7" | Top/back | 12 gauge steel for firebox, ³⁄₁₆" for end portions | |
| Fisher Stoves, Inc. | Grandpa Bear | 24" | 8" | Top | ¼" and ⁵⁄₁₆" plate steel | $ 530 |
| | Grandma Bear | 18" | 8" | Top | ¼" and ⁵⁄₁₆" plate steel | $ 495 |
| | Papa Bear | 30" | 6" | Back | ¼" and ⁵⁄₁₆" plate steel | $ 455 |
| Free Flow Stove Works | Furnace | 30" | | Back | ¼" steel | $ 720 |
| Hinckley Foundry and Marine | Superheater | 26" | | Top | ³⁄" sand-cast gray iron, bronze, aluminum alloy | |
| Hydraform Products Corp. | Larger Eagle | 32" | 6" | Back | ³⁄₁₆" steel | $ 545 |
| J and J Enterprises | Frontier XL-32-8 | 26" | 8" | Top/back | ¼" steel | |
| | Frontier L-30-8 | 24" | 8" | Top/back | ¼" steel | |
| Kickapoo Stove Works, Ltd. | Boxer (BX) | 24" | 6" | Top | ³⁄₁₆" steel, cast iron | $ 499 |
| | Starlor (BBR-S) | 22" | 6" | Top | ³⁄₁₆" steel, cast iron | $ 340 |
| | Kickapoo Fireplace/Stove | 18" | 7" | Back | 10 ga. steel | $ 541 |
| Kristia Associates | Jøtul No. 4 Combi-fire (Fireplace/stove) | 20" | 7" | Top or back | Cast iron | $ 685 |
| The Merry Music Box | Styria "Imperial" | | | Back | | $1,500 |
| Mohawk Industries | Tempwood II | 16"-18" | 6" | Back | ⅛" and ¼" steel | $ 279 |
| National Stove Works | Thermo-Control 500 | | 8" | Top | ¼" and ³⁄₁₆" steel | $ 454 |

## Large Stoves Compared *(Continued)*

| Manufacturer | Stove | Wood Length | Flue Size | Flue Location | Materials | Price |
|---|---|---|---|---|---|---|
| New Hampshire Stoves, Inc. | Home Warmer I | 29″ | 6″ | Back | ⅛″ and ¼″ steel, cast iron | $ 449 |
| Quaker Stove Co. | Buck | 28″ | 6″ | Top | ¼″ and ⁵⁄₁₆″ plate steel | $ 499 |
| | Doe | 25″ | 6″ | Top | ¼″ and ⁵⁄₁₆″ plate steel | $ 449 |
| Ram Forge Stoves | Ram Wood Stove | 28″ | 5″ | Back | ¼″ steel | |
| | Ram Tile Stove | 28″ | 5″ | Back | ¼″ steel, ceramic tile | |
| Riteway Manufacturing Co. | Riteway #2000 | 24″ | 6″ | Side | 14 ga. steel | $ 369 |
| | Riteway #37 | 24″ | 6″ | Side | 10 and 14 ga. steel | $ 395 |
| Scandinavian Stoves, Inc. | Lange #6302K | | 5″ | Side | Cast iron | $ 695 |
| Shenandoah Mfg. Co. | Model #R-75 | | 6″ | Top | 11 and 18 ga. steel | $ 215 |
| Sierra Stoves | Sierra #300 | 30″ | 6″ | Back | ¼″ and ⁵⁄₁₆″ steel | |
| Southeastern Vermont Community Action | SEVCA | 18″ | 8″ | Top/back | ³⁄₁₆″ steel | $ 340 |
| Southport Stoves | Efel | 21″ | 8″ | Back | Steel, cast iron, glass | $ 625 |
| | Morsø #1125 | 18″ | 8″ | Top/back | Cast iron | $ 790 |
| | Morsø #1BO | 22″ | 4¾″ | Top | Cast iron | $ 810 |
| Spalt Associates Corp., Importers | Ben Franklin Heater H126 | 23″ | 8″ | Top or back | Cast iron | $ 209 |
| | Ben Franklin Heater H130 | 27″ | 10″ | Top or back | Cast iron | $ 229 |
| | Plymouth Boxwood Heater | 26″ | 7″ | Top | Cast iron | $ 229 |
| | Viking 44 (fireplace/stove) | 26″ | 7″ | Back | Cast iron, firebrick | $ 455 |
| The Stoveworks | Culvert Queen | 15″ | 6″ | Top | Steel | $ 245 |
| | Independence | 30″ | 6″ | Top/back | ³⁄₁₆″ steel | $ 370 $90 soapstone $50 hot water coil |
| Timberline Stoves | Timberline T-33 | 30″ | | | | |
| | Timberline T-LF | 24″ | | | | |

## Large Stoves Compared *(Continued)*

| Manufacturer | Stove | Wood Length | Flue Size | Flue Location | Materials | Price |
|---|---|---|---|---|---|---|
| Vermont Castings, Inc. | Defiant | 24″ | 8″ | Top/ back | Cast iron | $ 600 |
| Vermont Woodstove Co. | DownDrafter I | | 8″ | Back | Steeplate stainless steel | $ 549 |
| Victorian Woodstoves | Ulefos No. 172 | 20″ | 5″ | Top | Cast iron | $ 850 |
| Warmglow Products, Inc. | Maxi-Heat I | | 7″ | Top/ back | Cast iron | |

# Circulator Stoves

**Ashley Products Division.** *C-60 Imperial*; see description under Medium Stoves.

**Atlanta Stove Works, Inc.** *Homesteader 240*; see description under Small Stoves.

**Autocrat Corporation
New Athens, Illinois 62264
(618) 475–2121**

Autocrat makes two thermostatically controlled wood heaters, both encased in contemporary brown and gold heat-resistant enamel finished cabinets. The smaller heater, *Model 6724,* has an 18-gauge steel combustion chamber electrically welded airtight. It is then lined with sections of cast iron 8¼ inches high, perforated and ventilated. The wood rests on a two-piece ribbed cast iron grate, also perforated to allow ashes to fall through to an ash pan. Ashes are then removed through an ash door. Both the ash door and the cast iron feed door are on the side of the stove and are airtight. A thermostatic draft control is at the rear. The cast iron flue collar accepts a 6-inch pipe. The stove comes with two joints of 6-inch blued steel flue pipe, one of which has a built in flue damper.

*Model FF76* is very similar except that it loads from the front, has a three-piece cast iron grate, a hinged smoke curtain and a cast iron flue baffle. It takes a 24-inch log and weighs 245 pounds.

You can install an optional thermostatic blower on either model for more even heat distribution. It's automatic because it turns on when the stove is hot and off when it's cool.

**Birmingham Stove and Range Company.** *Knight 124* and *Knight 524*; see Small Stoves for descriptions.

**Bow and Arrow Stove Co.** *Trolla No. 530*; see description under Small Stoves.

**Contractor Equipment
  Manufacturers Inc.
P.O. Box 290
Ashland, Ohio 44805
(419) 289–2224**

The unique feature of the *Cemi Independence (Model No. HMF-1)* is a pair of ¼-inch thick 2- by 4-inch steel air ducts passing through the firebox. The air ducts become super-heated, attract cool air from the floor and discharge hot air from the top.

*Model No. HMF-2* is identical except that it supplements this natural convection with twin electric blowers that circulate air at a rate of 210 cfm and a cost of 3 cents a day for 24-hour operation.

Both models are welded ¼-inch steel plate with firebrick-lined firebox and cast aluminum doors. The fire door has two side-by-side spin-draft controls and is double sealed with an asbestos gasket and a beaded edge. An ash apron is standard and the flue connection is in the rear. The stove is designed with two level, varying-temperature cooking surfaces.

## The Defiance Company
## Chassell, Michigan 49916
## (906) 523-4232

The *Volcano* and *Volcano II* are heavy (435 and 485 pounds, respectively) airtight welded steel stoves. Preheated air is distributed between the firebox and a baffled second chamber for primary and secondary burning.

Cool air near the floor is fan-forced through a heat exchanging air jacket surrounding the primary firebox and leading through the secondary firebox. The war air is then released into the room or into your hot air system. The larger model has an ash drawer.

Two accessories offered are the deflector ($69), a means of directing the warm air to the area where it is most needed; and the humidifier ($89), which adds moisture to the air.

## Greenbriar Products
## 100 W. Jefferson Street
## Spring Green, Wisconsin 53588

Thoughtfully engineered (when you include some optional accessories) the *Greenbriar* is a pleasing alternate to other combination fireplace/stoves we have reviewed in this book. Its arched, semi-circular shape contains a 40-inch firechamber of 14 gauge steel with firebrick or refractory mix hearth. A spark screen, 8-inch flue pipe to reach a 9-foot ceiling and adjustable flue damper are standard equipment.

Options such as a steel or pyrex glass door with adjustable draft, outside air intake vent with adjustable damper and hot water coil heat exchanger could turn this fireplace into a very efficient heater. The coil will heat 30 gallons of water from 50° to 120° in one hour and is rated at 18,000 Btu/hr. The outside combustion air intake is thermostatically controlled.

## Nashua Doubleheat Woodstoves
## Heathdelle Sales Associates, Inc.
## Laconia, New Hampshire 03246

If your house consists of many small rooms, you may have problems getting heat from your wood stove distributed evenly. Nashua makes three sizes of wood heater that both radiate heat as an ordinary stove does and circulate warm air by means of a powerful blower mounted at the rear of the stove. The blower picks up cooler, floor level air and forces it through a sealed steel manifold within the firebox. Each model recycles air equal to 20 times its own size every 60 seconds, for about the same amount of electricity as is used by an ordinary light bulb.

The stoves are constructed of ¼-inch-steel plate and have an airtight, fully lined firebox of 3000° firebrick. Each model has a horizontal baffle to achieve near total combustion in a front to rear burn. The smaller two models have two side by side spin draft controls on the door. The largest model, *N-30* has three, under the door. An optional firescreen with safety locking mechanism is available if you want to use the stove as a fireplace.

The *N-18* and *N-24* have rear flue connections at heights under normal fireplace hearth openings. You can adapt the stove blowers to fit into your existing forced air duct system. The manufacturer also claims that the large steel mass of the stove remains so cool in the summer that by turning on the blower you will actually help to cool your home.

## Hydroheat Division of Ridgway Steel
## P.O. Box 382
## Ridgway, Pennsylvania 15853
## (814) 776-1323 or 6156

To solve the problem of getting the heat from your wood stove all through the house, the makers of the *Hydrostove* have come up with the idea of circulating water through the stove. You hook up the water line with your existing forced air or hot water system.

The stove itself is the two level, baffled design constructed of ³⁄₁₆-inch low carbon steel (stove top ¼-inch low carbon steel) with cast iron door, door frame, damper and legs. Grooved baffle design around the door and frame, between all steel-to-iron surfaces and an asbestos gasket around the door assure airtightness.

Basket type water circulating grates capture heat from the coals and an upper heat exchanger absorbs heat from the gases as they travel to the flue. The water-circulating grates protect the top and upper side-walls of the stove and ½-inch asbestos board protects the floor and lower side walls. The stove takes up to a 26-inch log and can deliver 50,000 Btu/hr into your heating system. Of course, the installation of this stove is more complicated than just hooking it up to a chimney; but the returns may be well worth the trouble.

## KNT, Inc.
## P.O. Box 25
## Haywsville, Ohio 44838

The *Impression 5* is another compromise between an inefficient open fireplace and an efficient, but relatively unappealing wood stove. It is a circulating heater with steel, double-wall construction that has specially designed ducts which draw cool air from the floor, heat it and circulate warm air back into the room. The bottom of the firebox is lined with firebrick and the unit has a standing grate through which ashes fall to the ash retainer below. You can choose between using the heavy wire screen door or solid, slip in door that extends the burning efficiency. KNT also offers a glass door kit as an accessory. A forced air, thermostat controlled blower is also optional. A heavy aluminum plate in the top that retains heat and radiates it into the room, can be used as a cooking surface. The stove also comes with a swing-out grill "for those cozy winter barbecues" (a practice we hesitate to recommend) and a heat shield suspended on the inner back wall. You have a choice of colors in ceramic finish or flat black. Accepts 24-inch logs and uses an 8-inch stove pipe.

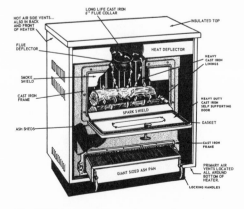

*The KNT* Impression, *cutaway view.*

**Locke Stove Company**
**114 West 11th Street**
**Kansas City, Missouri 64105**

If you want to heat with wood but aren't into the rustic look, the *Warm Morning Model 701* deserves your attention. It's a steel heater with a cast iron grate on the bottom, firebrick halfway up the sides, and cast iron liner plates on the upper sides and end of the firebox. Openings in the firebrick liner sections bring in primary air from the automatic draft regulator and distribute it evenly in the combustion zone. You control secondary air by a sliding draft. The loading door and ash door are cast iron with asbestos seals for airtight fit. You can slide out the ash drawer for cleaning. A cast iron chute drops down when you open the fuel door to contain any ash that might spill out.

The whole thing is contained in a contemporary cabinet in a dark brown porcelain enamel finish. This heater takes a 26-inch log and weighs about 275 pounds. You can also choose a 3-speed blower that projects the heated air through a fan-shaped outlet under the heater cabinet.

**Martin Industries.** *Wood Circulator 8801-B*; see description under Small Stoves.

**Monarch Stoves**
**Division of Malleable Iron Range Co.**
**Beaver Dam, Wisconsin 53916**

In addition to its line of cook ranges, Monarch makes several airtight wood heaters. *Model CR24D* is a wood or coal burning, circulating heater. It is constructed with a heavy gauge steel cabinet, base and combustion chamber. The firebox, grate bed, door and flue collar are cast iron. The removeable ash pan has a cast iron frame and locking handles. A cast iron flue deflector prevents heat loss through the chimney. The top is insulated. A shelf-type front loading door that holds fuel while loading, measures 21¼ inches wide. The heater is equipped with spark and smoke shields, and automatic draft control. A blower kit is optional. The unit weighs about 260 pounds.

*Model CR24E*, a 16-gauge steel welded seam heater with firebrick lining also burns either wood or coal. Encased in a contemporary enamel finish cabinet with louvered, lift-up top, this end loading stove also has the automatic draft control feature. The steel fuel door and liner as well as the ash drawer are gasketed and lock for an airtight seal. This heater weighs about 230 pounds, accepts a 21-inch log and requires a 6-inch stove pipe. A flue damper should be installed approximately 4 feet off the floor near the first pipe joint. A blower kit and shaker grate are available as options.

*Model CR24F* is essentially the same heater as the CR24E except that it is loaded from the front and has a cast iron flue baffle and flue collar.

**Riteway Manufacturing Co.** *Wood Heater #2000* and *Model #37*; see description under Large Stoves.

**Shenandoah Manufacturing Co.** *Model R-76* and *Model R-76L*; see description under Small Stoves.

**Southport Stoves.** *Efel*; see description under Large Stoves.

**Washington Stove Works.** *Norwester #38* and *Norwester #40*; see description under Small Stoves.

## Circulator Stoves Compared

Circulators allow the heat to pass between an exterior cabinet and the radiant heater.

| Manufacturer | Stove | Wood Length | Flue Size | Flue Location | Materials | Price |
|---|---|---|---|---|---|---|
| Ashley Products Division | C-60 Imperial | 24″ | 6″ | Back | Steel | $375 |
| Atlanta Stove Works, Inc. | Homesteader 240 | | 6″ | Back | Cast iron; bonderized enamel cabinet | $385 |
| Autocrat Corporation | Model #6724 | 24″ | 6″ | Back | Cast iron and 18 ga. steel with enamel cabinet | $335 |
| | Model #FF 76 | 25″ | 6″ | Back | Cast iron and 18 ga. steel with enamel cabinet | $410 |

## Circulator Stoves Compared (Continued)

| Manufacturer | Stove | Wood Length | Flue Size | Flue Location | Materials | Price |
|---|---|---|---|---|---|---|
| Birmingham Stove and Range Co. | Knight 124 | 24" | 6" | Back | Steel, cast iron enameled cabinet | $359 |
| | Knight 524 | 24" | 6" | Back | Steel, cast iron, firebrick, enameled cabinet | $419 |
| Bow and Arrow Stove Co. | Trolla No. 530 | | 5" | Back | Enamel cabinet, firebrick lined, cast iron | |
| Contractor Equipment Manufacturers | Cemi Independence HMF-1 and HMF-2 | 25" | | | Steel, firebrick, aluminum | |
| Defiance Company | Volcano | 24" | | Top | Steel | $595 |
| | Volcano II | 24" | | Top | Steel | $695 |
| Greenbriar Products, Inc. | The Greenbriar (fireplace/stove) | 40" | 8" | Top | 14 ga. steel | $320 |
| Heathdelle Sales Associates, Inc. | Nashua #18 | 18" | 6" | Back | ¼" steel | $525 |
| | Nashua #24 | 24" | 6" | Back | ¼" steel | $750 |
| | Nashua #30 | 30" | 8" | Back | ¼" steel | $895 |
| Hydroheat Division of Ridgway Steel | Hydrostove | 26" | | Back | ¼" and ³⁄₁₆" steel, cast iron | |
| KNT, Inc. | The Impression | 24" | 8" | Top | Firebrick and ⅛" steel | $360 to $500 |
| Locke Stove Company | Warm Morning Model 701 | 26" | 6" | Back | Porcelain enamel cabinet; cast iron liner plates with firebrick lining | |
| Martin Industries | Wood Circulator #8801-B | 25" | 6" | Back | Cast iron and 18 ga. steel with porcelain enamel cabinet | |
| Monarch Kitchen Appliances | Model CR24D | | 6" | Back | Steel with cast iron linings; enamel cabinet | |
| | Model CR24E | | 6" | Back | 16 ga. steel; firebrick lined; enamel cabinet | |

## Circulator Stoves Compared *(Continued)*

| Manufacturer | Stove | Wood Length | Flue Size | Flue Location | Materials | Price |
|---|---|---|---|---|---|---|
| | Model CR24F | | 6″ | Back | 16 ga. steel; enamel cabinet | |
| Riteway Manufacturing Co. | Wood Heater #2000 | 24″ | 6″ | | 14 ga. steel | $369 |
| | Model #37 | 24″ | 6″ | Back | 14 ga. steel | $395 |
| Shenandoah Mfg. Co. | Model R-76 | | 6″ | Back | Porcelain cabinet | $338 |
| | Model #R-76L | | 6″ | Back | Porcelain cabinet | $255 |
| Southport Stoves | Efel | | 8″ | Back | Cast iron; porcelain cabinet | |
| Washington Stove Works | Norwester #38 | | 6″ | | Enamel cabinet | $486 |
| | Norwester #40 | | 6″ | | Enamel cabinet | $330 |

# Furnaces

**Tasso Kedler
Hjallesegade 45
DK-5260 Hjallese
Denmark**

**Alternative Energy Associates
Browns Trace
Jericho, Vermont 95465
(802) 899-3649**

The *Tasso*, distributed by Alternative Energy Associates, is a woodburning boiler of sectional cast iron construction made in Denmark. It can be used alone or in combination with an oil or gas-fired boiler in any conventional hot water heating system. Available in four sizes ranging from 126,000 Btu/hr to 180,000 Btu/hr, it comes with cast iron grates, enameled and insulated steel jacket, cast iron doors and an automatic draft regulator.

Because the boiler firebox is surrounded by water, the firebox walls remain at a relatively cool 200° F. This means that you must use well-seasoned hard wood with this unit. Using wood with greater than 20 percent moisture content will result in poor burning and excessive creosote buildup.

**Gustav Ospelt Hovalwerk AG
FL 9490 Vaduz
Liechtenstein**

**Sole agent in U.S.:
AROTEK Corp.
1703 East Main Street
Torrington, Connecticut 06790
(203) 489-0214**

*Hoval* boilers are distributed in the United States by AROTEK Corporation. They are the Mercedes Benz of boilers—beautiful, functional and built to last. Developed and produced in Liechtenstein by one of the world's leading boiler manufacturers, the *Hoval* combination boiler has been in continuous use for the past 25 years in Europe. Whether used in combination with gas or oil, it has separate combustion chambers and flue passes and a sealed combustion system. A bottom-burn design and special inclined grate result in long-burning solid fuel (wood or coal) fire since combustion air does not pass up through the fuel to accelerate combustion unnecessarily. The oil or gas efficiency is a remarkable 86 to 88 percent.

It comes with a stainless steel domestic hot water tank of double-shell design; boiler water flows completely around it when the domestic water temperature drops. This insures a 20-minute recovery for hot water and a longer tank life by preventing hot spots from forming in the stainless steel. A special circulating pump limits the temperature in the domestic water tank to 140° F, inhibiting the buildup of lime deposits within the tank.

A special three-way mixing valve preheats the water returning to the boiler, eliminating thermal shock that causes metal fatigue and electrolysis. The boiler control panel is mounted at the front where the water temperatures of the boiler and the hot water heater are continually shown on separate gauges.

Unfortunately, the boiler must be burned hot. That is, it is sized about 10 to 15 percent below the calculated heat loss, since during extremely low temperatures it can be overfired without problems. (The manufacturer recommends using oil or gas during mild weather.) Only seasoned hard wood should be used: in the opinion of the manufacturer this is wood seasoned 1½ to—2 years with a moisture content below 20 percent.

The boiler must be cleaned once a month. At the end of the heating season it must be thoroughly cleaned and sprayed with oil-graphite mixture. The automatic draft regulator has to be set between 167°–194° F., but in no case below 167° F. These measures are designed to insure the boiler is operated safely and with maximum life expectancy.

### Bellway Manufacturing
### Perley C. Bell, Sales and Service
### Grafton, Vermont 05146
### (802) 843-2432

Bellway is a small Vermont firm manufacturing wood-burning furnaces and boilers to order and selling direct. They can be used alone or in series with your present system. Made of heavy steel and welded construction, wood is fed to the firebox in a gravity system for two-stage burning. All units are available with hot water coils and automatic, nonelectric humidifiers plus nonelectric thermostats if desired.

The smallest model, #F50, generates 50,000 Btu and takes 24-inch logs; the 75,000-Btu model #F75 takes 36-inch logs and the 125,000 Btu model (#F125) takes 48-inch. Poker, ash shovel and shaker handle are included.

### Carlson Mech. Contractors, Inc.
### Heating and Boiler Mfg. Division
### P.O. Box 242
### Prentice, Wisconsin 54556
### (715) 564-2481 or 428-3481

Carlson makes a solid fuel boiler (*Model SF-1*) that is meant to be used in conjunction with your present boiler system, utilizing existing pump and controls. It is constructed of welded steel plate and tubing: the firebox uses ¼-inch steel plate and the ash drawer is 16 gauge steel. It delivers 170,000 Btu and uses 20-inch wood. Combination and forced air units are also available from these people, though we have no information on them.

### Charmaster Products, Inc.
### 2307 Highway No. 2 West
### Grand Rapids, Minnesota 55744
### (218) 326-6786

Charmaster manufactures several woodburning furnaces ranging from a simple gravity system to a unique furnace/fireplace combination.

The basic *Charmaster* woodburning unit is available for the rock-bottom initial investment. Next up in the line is the same furnace with a blower, fan-limit switch, automatic draft control and Honeywell thermostat. This unit may be installed in conjunction with your present gas, oil or electric furnace.

Charmaster also makes combination wood/oil or wood/gas furnaces that include blower, fan-limit switch, automatic draft control, relay and two thermostats. Fireboxes on these are constructed of ¾-inch steel plate and measure 30 inches long by 22½ inches wide. The heat exchanger is fabricated of 14 gauge steel.

The *Charmaster II* is a fireplace built into a fully automatic wood/oil or wood/gas furnace. The furnace door is located behind the fireplace wall, in a completely separate room, so the fire need not be tended from the room the fireplace is in. The fireplace comes with brass-bound bi-fold doors of heat-resistant glass. Of course, you finish off the fireplace in the style of your choice.

Charmaster II.

### Combo Furnace Co.
### Division of Northern Heating and Sheet Metal
### 1707 W. 4th Street
### Grand Rapids, Minnesota 55744
### (218) 326-6668

Combo manufactures wood-only furnaces and boilers that will accept oil burners at a later time; combination wood and oil furnaces and boilers; and a forced-air, wood-only add-on furnace. In the combination units, wood and oil are burned in the same combustion chamber and the oil burner will ignite wood. When the wood fire is hot, the oil burner shuts off. The wood can be completely independent of the oil and is regulated by an automatic draft control. The firebox is made of 12 and 7 gauge steel and lined with *serra felt*, a long-lasting material lighter than firebrick that is used in the nose cones of jets.

The furnaces have fan and limit control switches and the boilers have high-limit aquastats adjustable from 50 to 300 psi, pop off valves, circulating pump, expansion tank and switching relay. Both come with cast iron grates and liners for burning coal and are equipped with hookups for domestic hot water and creosote clean-out access. *Model W12-23-0* and *WO-12-23-1* forced air furnaces generate 84,000 to 95,000 Btu/hr. Boilers *WB-22-10* and *WOB-22-11* generate 84,000 to 126,000 Btu/hr.

**Dual-Fuel Products, Inc.**
**2775 Pittsburgh Ave.**
**Cleveland, Ohio 44115**

The *Newmac* wood and oil combination furnace burns each fuel in a separate combustion chamber and switches between them automatically. The wood fire box is brick and stainless steel lined and handles a 24-inch log. Because no grates are used, wood is burned to a fine powder. The system also uses two heat exchangers and two blowers. It comes equipped with a Carlin oil flame retention burner.

The *Newmac* furnaces come in four sizes: *CL-115* at 113,000 Btu; *CL-140* at 137,000 Btu; *CL-155* at 149,000 Btu and the *CL-170* at 168,000 Btu.

**Duo-Matic**
**450 W. 169th Street**
**South Holland, Illinois 60473**
**(312) 596-7700**

Duo-Matic makes three kinds of furnaces: the *CWO Series* that burns oil, gas/wood, coal; the *DWO Series* that burns oil, gas/wood and the *DWF Series* that burns wood and is designed to be connected to your own oil or gas furnace and existing ductwork.

The combination furnaces have two combustion chambers and automatic thermostatically controlled switchover to oil (or gas) heat. An electrical device closes the wood furnace damper when the oil (or gas) furnace comes on. The wood or coal burning firebox is lined with firebrick or alloy stainless steel. The *CWO Series* has heavy cast iron grates. A high capacity twin blower circulates air through spun glass disposable filters and then into the duckwork.

The gas or oil flame retention burner cannot be fouled by soot from the wood or coal. Its refractory combustion chamber has been tested to 2600° F. Its heat exchanger is constructed of electronically welded heavy gauge steel.

The *CWO Series* comes in four capacities: 112,000 Btu through 170,000 Btu. The *DWO Series* comes in three sizes 114,000 Btu, 137,000 Btu and 148,000 Btu. The *DWF* is estimated at 100,000 Btu capacity and has a 20½ by 18¾ inch firebox.

*Duo-Matic DWO combination furnace.*

**Energy Options, Inc.**
**P.O. Box 303**
**Green Bay, Wisconsin 54305**
**(414) 435-5544 or 435-8471**

The *Red Ox* wood-fired boiler is designed to be used alone or in tandem with your present boiler. Its airtight construction includes cast iron doors and frame, a baffled firebox of 3/16-inch steel and an outer shell of 16 gauge and 3/16-inch steel. The high-pressure/temperature seamless boiler pipe coil has been tested to 2500 psi. Primary and secondary air are operated by dual solenoid-controlled dampers but you can override them manually. The firebox accepts 30-inch logs or coal, and ash is removed from an ash pan.

*Model 231* with a 3.83 gallon capacity generates 130,000 Btu per hour; *Model 221* has a 5.51 gallon capacity and generates 140,000 Btu per hour; and *Model 211* with a 9.79 gallon capacity generates 150,000 Btu per hour. A hot water saver tank and domestic hot water coil are optional.

**Enwell Corporation**
**750 Careswell Street**
**Marshfield, Massachusetts 02050**
**(617) 837-0638**

The *Spaulding Concept Furnace* is an extremely interesting idea—one that raises as many questions as it answers.

To begin with, it uses the downdraft principle. A one-piece cast ceramic refractory firebox tapers to a variable height burning plate. Preheated air is supplied for both primary and secondary burning. Exhaust gases then travel upward through the heat exchanger and out the chimney, assisted by a variable speed blower.

The manufacturer claims the unit will burn unsplit wood up to 30 inches long, chips, bark, sawdust, household trash, recycled municipal waste, rubber, and used engine oil(!) interchangeably and efficiently. Its output is thermostatically controlled in three modes from 20,000 to 1000,000 Btu per hour and it has a failsafe automatic shutdown in the event of power failure or overheating. According to the manufacturer, the controlled forced draft maintains negative pressure within the furnace, increasing efficiency and eliminating the need for a conventional chimney.

**The G & S Mill**
**Otis Street**
**Northborough, Massachusetts 01532**
**(617) 393-9266**

The G&S Mill manufactures six models of wood-burning furnaces that produce from 187,000 to 1,548,000 Btu per hour of heat and weigh between 2,600 and 10,000 pounds. Obviously they are for those who wish to make a "heavy" commitment to wood heat. These furnaces operate on a three-zone combustion system. The primary stage completely burns the solid portion of the wood; the secondary stage burns the volatile gases; the final stage provides for afterburn by reigniting the smoke.

Force drafting of the preheated combustion air in all three stages provides for significantly higher firebox temperatures.

Besides the heat exchanger, the 1½-ton mass of the furnace acts as a heat reservoir to dissipate heat over a long time span. Although the furnace depends upon electricity to operate the tubeaxial fans for force drafting and force cooling, it will still provide residual heat in the event of power failure. It can be installed alone or in connection with an existing forced air system.

The firebox is constructed of ½-inch welded steel; the heat exchanger is ⅜-inch thick welded steel with more than 100 square feet of surface area. Constant electric ignition for volatile gases is an option. The furnace is sold with blowers, controls, four thermometers, instruction, fire and clean-out tools, pretested, skid mounted.

*The G&S Mill furnace, designed for large buildings, not for homeowners.*

## Jordahl Industries Inc.
## P.O. Box 407
## Osseo, Wisconsin 54758
## (715) 597–3101

The *Ltd Limited*, manufactured by Jordahl Industries Inc., is designed to be a supplement to your present gas or oil forced air heating system. It uses the same duct work and chimney and its blower activates the blower of your present furnace, which then circulates the warm air through the house.

When the temperature between the jacket and the firebox reaches 150° F., the blower engages and transfers the wood heat to the primary furnace blower until the fire dies and the interlining temperature drops below 120° F. Then the *Ltd Limited* blower shuts down.

This unit comes in three sizes ranging from about 80,000 Btu to 140,000 Btu. All three have firebrick-lined firebox, heavy cast iron grates, cast iron door, spin draft control, ash pan and thermostatically controlled blower. The small, medium and large sizes accept 18-inch, 24-inch, and 26-inch logs, respectively.

## Kerr Controls Ltd.
## P.O. Box 744
## Truro, Nova Scotia B2N 5G1
## (902) 895–1663

All Kerr products are manufactured and tested in the Atlantic Provinces by craftsmen who guarantee their work. The *Scotsman* is a wood burning furnace that can be used in conjunction with an oil furnace or alone as a gravity or forced air furnace. The airtight cylindrical firebox is constructed of 1/8-inch plate steel, 36 inches long by 23 inches in diameter. Preheated air is fed into the rear of the firebox, stimulating the combustion of unburned gases travelling up into a secondary heat exchanger above it that is made of 14 gauge rolled steel. An automatic thermostat and limit control are set in series with a damper motor to regulate the fire. The furnace jacket is lined with 1 inch of reinforced foil backed insulation and finished in urethane enamel.

Further up the Kerr line are the *DWO* and *CWO* series, wood/oil and coal/wood/oil burning furnaces. These are forced-air systems with two separate combustion chambers. A special electronic device closes the wood furnace damper when the oil furnace side is operating to maximize the oil burner efficiency. Both have heat exchangers and ⅓ hp (¾ hp in the *CWO-170*) twin blowers. Models in the *DWO* series are available from 114,000 to 148,000 Btu/hr. Models in the *CWO* series are available from 112,000 to 170,000 Btu/hr.

Finally, Kerr offers the *Titan*, a wood-fired boiler. It has an airtight, firebrick-lined combustion chamber and it preheats both primary and secondary combustion air. The heat exchanger is made from ¼-inch plate and seamless boiler tubes. It can be installed independently or in conjunction with your present boiler.

## Longwood Furnace Corp.
## Gallatin, Missouri 64640

The *Longwood* is a true dual-fuel furnace in the sense that it burns both wood and oil or gas at the same time. The oil or gas burner is not used just to start the wood burning; it is the primary control over the wood in this no-draft, charcoal method developed by Longwood.

With the thermostat set, the burner runs periodically as the thermostat calls for heat. In the absence of a draft, the wood is converted to charcoal. Thereafter, as the thermostat calls for heat, the burner ignites and forces the charcoal bed to generate combustible gases. Overheating, a common wood furnace problem, is prevented with this system because the charcoal bed is not drafted and because the thermostat contains a heat anticipator that deactivates the burner before the full thermostat setting is reached.

The furnace may be operated manually with wood during electrical failure by drafting it through the ash pit door, so long as prudent judgment and care are exercised. This is because without the blower and limit controls, rapid overheating could damage the furnace.

The *Longwood* has a 14-gauge stainless steel combustion chamber inside a ⅜-inch steel heat exchanger. The heat reclaimer consists of 35 heat tubes over which hot flue gases must pass. A thermostatically controlled blower forces fresh air through the tubes and reclaims as much as 30,000 Btu.

The Longwood *Dualfuel* is just as efficient as a conventional furnace when operated on gas or oil alone.

*Longwood* Dualfuel *furnace.*

**Lynndale Heating System**
**1309 North Hills Blvd.—Suite 207**
**Crossroads Business Park**
**North Little Rock, Arkansas 72116**
**Sales Office: (501) 758-9602**

The Lynndale central heating system is a single-fuel (wood) system that can work alone or with other power resources. It uses two separate combustion chambers within a single firebrick-lined firebox, one for primary and one for secondary combustion. Primary combustion is forced air, electronically controlled, designed to generate heat a little at a time to prevent wasted combustion and excessive heat.

Secondary combustion increases burning efficiency by inducing oxygen into a separate combustion chamber to burn volatile gases. The whole system is thermostatically controlled and you can automatically switch from one heat source to another. Domestic hot water heating is an option.

**Marathon Heater Co., Inc.**
**Box 265, R.D. 2**
**Marathon, New York 13803**

the **Logwood**

The *Logwood*, made by the Marathon Heater Company, is a combination oil and wood furnace or boiler that uses the same firebox to burn both fuels. It is thermostatically regulated for both fuels and switches between them automatically. The oil burner is protected from wood fire by a gate that opens when the thermostat calls for heat.

The boiler has hot water intake and outlet, a pressure relief valve and pressure temperature gauge. The furnace can be operated on a gravity basis or as a forced air system. Domestic hot water coils are standard in either boiler or furnace.

The firebox firewall is refractory lined. At the bottom are cast iron tubular grates. Air travels through these grates becoming preheated before entering at the rear of the firebox. This extremely hot air assists in keeping the wood gases above ignition temperature, resulting in thorough burning and less smoke and creosote. The firebox wall of the *Logwood* is filled with water and acts as a heat exchanger. A control damper decreases the exchange area by 40 percent, allowing you to keep stack temperatures considerably higher during low firing times or when you are forced to burn green wood.

**Minnesota Energy Savers Inc.**
**305 Main**
**La Crescent, Minnesota 55947**
**(507) 895-6284**

The *Lumberjack* is essentially an extra-large wood stove surrounded by a baffled plenum and is meant to be hooked into existing forced air ductwork and vented out a class A chimney. Its double-walled construction begins with a ³⁄₁₆-inch continuous welded plate steel firebox that is firebrick lined and uses cast iron grates. A horizontal baffle of ³⁄₁₆-inch plate steel insures the burning of secondary gases. It has a cast iron fuel door and an ash drawer with draft control.

The plenum or exterior jacket is constructed of 12 gauge steel and it has two horizontal baffles and a 465 cfm blower. The entire unit is rated at 55,000 Btu.

**Monarch Kitchen Appliances**
**Malleable Iron Range Company**
**Beaver Dam, Wisconsin 53916**
**(414) 887-8131**

The Monarch *Add-A-Furnace* is meant to be installed beside your existing forced air furnace with connections to its plenum and to a suitable chimney. A thermostatically controlled blower (standard on models *AF124* and *AF224*, optional on *AF324*) on the rear of the unit automatically switches on when the temperature in the hot air passage at the top reaches 160° to 180° F. It blows the heated air into the plenum of the primary furnace. Sensing heat delivered by the *Add-A-Furnace*, the forced air furnace blower comes on and moves the heated air into the existing ductwork. When the wood fire dies down, the blower turns off and your primary furnace functions in an ordinary manner.

The *Add-A-Furnace* is available in three sizes (Model *AF124*, maximum 35,000 Btu per hour, 50 pounds of wood; *Model AF224*, maximum 50,000 Btu per hour, 80 pounds of wood; and *Model AF324*, 75,000 Btu per hour, 100 pounds of wood capacity). The two smaller units have 3 extra-heavy cast iron grates. The large unit has the same grate bed plus linings. Large and intermediate models have thermostatically controlled primary and secondary air dampers. All three have heavy-gauge steel fireboxes with continuously welded construction and airtight heavy steel fire doors with high-temperature seals.

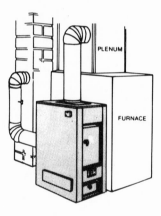

*Monarch Add-a-Furnace installed with an existing forced air furnace.*

**Passat**
**Highland Court**
**Gloucester, Massachusetts 01930**
**(617) 283-0025**

Passat, a Danish firm, makes a wide range of solid fuel and oil burners that work separately or in combination. All are constructed of corrosion-resistant Cor-Ten steel, have 2 inches of insulation and a galvanized outer hood.

The *HO-30* wood burning model has a maximum capacity of 108,000 Btu and takes logs up to 3 feet long. Models *HOLO-20* and *HOLO-45* are hot air furnaces for solid fuel and oil with automatic switchover. The output for the *HOLO-20* is 88,000 Btu and with oil is 100,000 Btu.

In addition, Passat makes a fireplace/stove combination that has two heating coils mounted in it. They can be coupled or work separately and heat up to 52 gallons of water per hour. The unit has two swing-open glass doors in front and optional flue connection in back or on top. It is rated at about 24,000 Btu per hour for hot air and 36,000 Btu per hour for the hot water coils.

**Powrmatic, Inc.**
**Member Stamm**
  **International Group**
**Finksburg, Maryland 21048**
**(301) 833-9100**

Powrmatic manufactures several solid fuel furnaces that operate alone or in combination with oil or gas. The wood-only furnace generates 150,000 Btu per hour and uses a ⅓ hp, 10-inch blower to distribute it. It is an airtight, firebrick-lined firebox without grates that accepts 23-inch logs and burns them completely to a fine ash. The furnace is thermostatically controlled, has positive draft control, and can be fired when the power is off.

The *Powrmatic* wood or coal forced air furnace is essentially the same as the wood furnace except that heavy cast iron grates are supplied for burning coal. Either of these two furnaces can be used in combination with an existing other full furnace.

The wood/oil or gas combination furnace burns the two fuels in separate combustion chambers and switches between them automatically. It has the same firebrick-lined solid fuel firebox that takes a 23-inch log and the same draft and thermostatic controls as the wood furnace. It uses two 10-inch blowers. This furnace comes in four sizes ranging from 112,000 Btu to 170,000 Btu per hour. A wood/coal/gas or oil combination is also available.

**Ram Forge**
**Brooks, Maine 04921**
**(207) 722-3379**

The *RAM Furnace* is designed for installation either as a sole heat source or as a wood burning companion to an existing gas or oil fired hot air system, sharing common ductwork. It you already have hot water heat, the *RAM Boiler* is the companion unit to choose. It is the basic heavy-duty firebox surrounded by an ASME (American Society of Mechanical Engineers) code-approved boiler jacket. It has three 1¼ IP flow tappings, one for a pressure relief valve and two for water flow. An insulated jacket is offered as an option.

You can install the furnace yourself, but you should have a licensed plumbing and heating contractor install the boiler.

The furnace is constructed of ¼-inch welded steel plate and has 30 fins on the firebox sides that add an extra 7 square feet of radiant surface area. It is supplied with a sturdy 24-gauge galvanized steel plenum.

Both the furnace and boiler are available with thermostatic controls that automatically switch on a fan (in the case of the furnace) or a circulating pump (in conjunction with the boiler). When the fire goes out and heat is required, thermostats switch on the oil-fired unit. While you certainly could rely on convection to heat with the furnace, the boiler should always have a circulator pump for safety.

The furnace and boiler fireboxes are shaped similarly to RAM wood stoves, are baffled and have a single door with spin draft control for both loading fuel and removing ashes. Both products are sold with a 25-year warranty against burnout or warpage.

**Riteway Manufacturing Co.**
**Division of Sarco Corporation**
**P.O. Box 6**
**Harrisburg, Virginia 22801**
**(703) 434-7090**

Riteway wood-fired furnaces and boilers can optionally burn bottled gas, natural gas or oil in the same combustion chamber as the wood. The wood is burned on the same complete combustion principle employed in Riteway stoves. An ash pit blower controlled by room thermostat creates a pre-heated forced-air draft in the combustion chamber for the primary burn. A heavy cast iron gas combustion flue is located completely inside the combustion chamber and is supplied with pre-heated secondary air to burn volatile gases. A barometrically controlled damper operates a by-pass air flue to permit a continual flow of dry warm air to mix with flue gases and prevent condensation in the chimney.

A special stainless steel damper operated by the heavy duty solenoid isolates the optional oil or gas burner from the combustion chamber when it is not in use. Other safety features are a time delay relay that holds the damper open 8–10 seconds after the fuel pump stops and a micro safety switch that keeps the burner from firing unless the damper is open.

Furnaces are equipped with a complete set of thermostatic controls, barometric damper, draft inducer, forced-draft and warm air circulation blowers, filters, galvanized steel casing and heat exchanger. They come in four sizes ranging from 125,000 Btu/hr. to 350,000 Btu/hr.

Hot water boilers are equipped with combination temperature, pressure and altitude gauge, dual controls including pressure relief valve, draft inducer, barometric draft regulator and complete thermostatic controls. They range in size from 125,000 Btu/hr. to 350,000 Btu/hr.

---

## CONVECTION FIREPLACE HEATER

If you really want to use your fireplace to the utmost, there is a new device on the market that effectively converts an ordinary fireplace into an efficient circulating air heater.

The device uses natural heat convection principles and, with an auxiliary blower, is capable of producing up to ten times greater net heat output than a standard fireplace! Yet it is very easy to install, requiring only the setting of two anchors into the hearth to seal the glass door front against the face of your fireplace.

In addition to being attractive and providing safety when burning in your fireplace, the glass doors prevent much of the loss of heated air up the chimney. This also works to keep other rooms in the house warmer because the need for replacement is reduced and less cold air is drawn into the home from the outside.

Other benefits of the fireplace heaters include improved draft control, easier fire starting, more efficient burning of wood and other combustible fuels—including household wastes—and curing of smoky fireplace conditions.

## Sam Daniels Company
## Box 868
## Montpelier, Vermont 05602
## (802) 223-2801

The Sam Daniels Company has been building furnaces in Vermont for more than 60 years. Models range in heating capacity from 100,000 Btu to 400,000 Btu and in complexity from gravity flow to wood/oil forced air combination furnaces. The firebox and two heat exchanger drums suspended above are made of 12 gauge steel, electronically welded. The grate, feed door, draft door (located in the feed door) and lining plates are cast iron and cast iron collars are used between the firebox and heat exchangers. A second draft opening is in the ash pit door. The plenum is constructed of 26 gauge galvanized steel and knocks down completely.

The forced air system consists of furnace with low-velocity, high-volume fan that filters air through 3 large 16-by-25-inch filters that are 1 inch thick. Temperature is automatically controlled by thermostat.

The combination furnaces are built with two separate fireboxes for wood and oil one behind the other in the same casing. They come with damper motor, fan and limit switches. The fireboxes can be vented separately or the oil exhaust can be vented into the wood exhaust and then both vented out a single flue.

## Solar Wood Energy Corporation
## Fall Road
## East Lebanon, Maine 04027
## (207) 457-1219

The *Northeaster* is a wood-burning forced-air furnace that also produces domestic hot water in sufficient quantities to meet the average family's needs. *Model 101-B* generates 100,000 Btu and *Model 224-B* has a 125,000 Btu capacity. Both furnaces have ⅛-inch cold rolled steel fireboxes of welded construction with ⅛-inch stainless steel replaceable firebox liners and cast iron grates. The heat exchanger is constructed of 11 and 14 gauge steel and the shroud of 22 gauge galvanized steel. The primary, preheated draft is regulated by a bimetallic thermostat controlled by furnace temperature. The secondary air is manually adjusted. A third stage burns combustible gases inside the heat exchanger. The ⅓ hp, four-speed blower is thermostatically controlled but has a manual override for summer cooling.

## Tekton Corporation
## Conway, Massachusetts 01341
## (413) 369-4367

HS Tarm boilers, manufactured in Denmark and imported by Tekton Corporation, come in two types. The *MB-Solo* series is an add-on unit you may use to supplement an existing oil- or gas-fired central hot water heating system. The *OT* series is a combination boiler that burns wood and oil or gas in separate combustion chambers. In addition there are three center tappings for the optional installation of electric heating elements.

In either type the firebox employs a base-burning arrangement for maximum efficiency in solid fuel combustion. Smoke leaves at the lower rear of the firebox where volatile gases are drawn over the fire's hot coals. Additional air to aid in the combustion of these gases is provided by the air inlet in the upper door of the firebox and the secondary air dial on the right side of the boiler. This secondary air dial meters air to a manifold at the bottom rear of the firebox. The manifold preheats and injects this air into the hot gases leaving the firebox, enabling secondary combustion of otherwise unburned compounds in these gases.

The *MB-Solo* is available equipped to burn wood or coal, as a back up to your present boiler. Or it can be supplied as an oil or gas fired boiler that is easily converted to solid fuel operation should the need arise. If you plan to use oil or gas for quite a while, a burner plate is used in place of the upper firing door, and a conversion plate is substituted for the grates. Where quick changeover between solid fuel and oil or gas is desired, the boiler can be supplied with a special door in place of the upper firing door. The "double-swing door" is a doorframe with a solid fuel firing door hinged to the left. By swinging one door out and the other in, either type of fuel may be used on a moment's notice.

The *MB-Solo* boilers are manufactured for use with standard American systems and are supplied with automatic draft regulator, cast iron grates, cleaning tools, insulated jacket with baked enamel finish, ASME pressure relief valve for the boiler and over heat control.

In both the *Solo* and *OT* series the firebox is surrounded by water and the walls are maintained at a relatively cool temperature. This precludes the use of any but very dry wood. A flap-like damper in the *OT* series controls the relative amount of smoke leaving the top and bottom of the firebox. The damper is operated through the cleaning door in the center of the boiler. When the damper is in the vertical position, much of the smoke will be drawn out at the base. An oil or gas burner works well with the damper in the vertical or an intermediate position. Equipped with a flame retention type oil burner, this boiler will operate at an efficiency of up to 84 percent.

*OT* boilers have a tankless system for the production of domestic hot water. They can supply ample hot water for large homes with several bathrooms. The tankless coil is ¾" copper tubing and can convert the entire output of the boiler to hot domestic water. All *OT* boilers are supplied with automatic draft regulator for the wood fire, cast iron grates, cleaning tools, touch up paint, built-in glass lined tank for domestic hot water, insulated jacket with baked enamel finish, ASME pressure relief valve for boiler, ASME pressure and temperature relief valve for hot water tank and over heat control.

## Wood Energy Systems Corp.
## Box 2
## Searsmont, Maine 04973

The *Wesco* furnace made by Wood Energy Systems is designed to be installed in conjunction with an existing oil or gas hot air furnace. The unit includes the furnace, galvanized sheet metal plenum with steel base, and the cutouts for the door and smoke pipe. The airtight firebox is constructed of ¼-inch steel plate and has a welded steel feed door with spin draft control. It has a sliding steel horizontal baffle that can be pulled forward for rapid combustion and slid back for more efficient burning.

The circulating hot water boiler preheats water before it reaches the existing hot water circulating furnace. It heats cool water from the bottom of the oil or gas boiler and returns hot water to the top, keeping a reserve of hot water for delivery by existing circulators on demand of the thermostat.

Both furnace and boiler are rated in the 60,000 to 70,000 Btu range.

# Furnaces Compared

| Manufacturer | Furnace | Wood Length | Flue Size | Materials | Btu/hour | Price |
|---|---|---|---|---|---|---|
| Alternative Energy Associates | Tasso A3-9 | 22″ | 6″ | Cast iron, enamel cabinet | 144,000 | |
| Arotek Corporation Add-on Unit | Hoval Boiler HK 30 | 18″ | 8″ | Firebrick lined | 80,000-120,000 | $1,840 |
| | Hoval Boiler HK 45 | 18″ | 9″ | Firebrick lined | 128,000-180,000 | $2,125 |
| | Hoval Boiler HK 60 | 18″ | 9″ | Firebrick lined | 188,000-240,000 | $2,595 |
| | Hoval Boiler HK 75 | 26″ | 9″ | Firebrick lined | 248,000-300,000 | $2,925 |
| Bellway Manufacturing | Model #F50 | 24″ | 6″ | Firebrick lined; steel cabinet | 50,000 | |
| | Model #F75 | 36″ | 7″ | Firebrick lined; steel cabinet | 75,000 | |
| | Model #F125 | 48″ | 8″ | Firebrick lined; steel cabinet | 125,000 | |
| Carlson Mech. Contractors, Inc. | Solid Fuel Boiler Model SF-1 | 20″ | 8″ | ¼″ steel | 170,000 | |
| Charmaster Products, Inc. | Charmaster Wood/Oil | 30″ | | Steel plate; 3/16″ firebox; 20 ga. steel cabinet | | |
| | Charmaster Wood/Gas | 30″ | | Steel plate; 3/16″ firebox; 20 ga. steel cabinet | | |
| Combo Furnace Co. | Forced Air Furnace No. W12-23-0 or No. WO12-23-1 | | 8″ | 12 and 7 ga. firebox; 12 ga. heat exchanger; 22 ga. casing | 84,000 95,000 | $ 970–$1,250 |
| | Forced Air Furnace W12-22-8 or No. WO12-22-9 | | 9″ | 12 and 7 ga. firebox; 12 ga. heat exchanger; 22 ga. casing | 140,000 175,000 | $1,220–$1,500 |
| | Model No. WB 22-10 or WOB-22-11 Hot Water Boiler | | 8″ | 12 and 7 ga. firebox; 12 ga. heat exchanger; 22 ga. casing | 84,000 126,000 | $1,295–$1,595 |
| Dual Fuel Products | Newmac Oil-Wood Furnace #CL-115 | 24″ | 8″ | Stainless steel firebox liner | 113,000 | $1,540 |
| | Newmac Oil-Wood Furnace #CL-140 | 24″ | 8″ | Stainless steel firebox liner | 137,000 | $1,540 |
| | Newmac Oil-Wood Furnace #CL-155 | 24″ | 8″ | Stainless steel firebox liner | 149,000 | $1,540 |
| | Newmac Oil-Wood Furnace #CL-170 | 24″ | 8″ | Stainless steel firebox liner | 168,000 | $1,580 |

## Furnaces Compared *(Continued)*

| Manufacturer | Furnace | Wood Length | Flue Size | Materials | Btu/hour | Price |
|---|---|---|---|---|---|---|
| Duo-matic | Duo-matic Combination Furnace | 24″ | 8″ | Steel with firebrick | | |
| Energy Options | Red Ox Model #231 | 30″ | 8″ | Steel, cast iron, boiler pipe | 130,000 | $1,045 |
| | Red Ox Model 221 | 30″ | 8″ | Steel, cast iron, boiler pipe | 140,000 | |
| | Red Ox Model 211 | 30″ | 8″ | Steel, cast iron, boiler pipe | 150,000 | |
| Enwell Corporation | Spaulding Concept Furnace | 30″ | 5″ | | 20,000–100,000 | |
| G & S Mill | Model. 5 | 30″ | 6″ | ½″ steel fire chamber; ⅜″ steel heat exchanger | 187,652 | $4,500 |
| | Model 1 | 54″ | 8″ | ½″ steel | 377,927 | $4,800 |
| | Model 2 | 54″ | 8″ | ½″ steel | 595,335 | $7,050 |
| | Model 3 | 54″ | 10″ | ½″ steel | 860,000 | $8,745 |
| Jordahl Industries Inc. | Ltd Limited 1000 Series | 18″ | 6″ | Firebrick lined | 75,000–85,000 | |
| | Ltd Limited 2000 Series | 24″ | 8″ | Firebrick lined | 120,000–130,000 | |
| | Ltd Limited 3000 Series | 26″ | 8″ | Firebrick lined | 130,000–150,000 | |
| Kerr Controls Ltd. | Scotsman Wood Furnace | 36″ | 7″ | ⅛″ plate steel | 140,000 | $ 450 |
| | Titan Boiler | | 7″ | Firebrick lined | | |
| | DWO Series | | 7″ | Stainless steel | 114,000–148,000 | |
| | CWO Series | | 8″ | | 112,000–170,000 | |
| Longwood Furnace Corporation | Longwood Dualfuel | 60″ | 6″ | Aluminum jacket; stainless steel 14 ga. firebox | 150,000 | |
| Lynndale Manufacturing Co. | Furnace #810 | 30″ | 7″ | 24 ga. sheet metal jacket; firebrick lined | 125,000 | |
| | Furnace #910 | 30″ | 7″ | 24 ga. sheet metal jacket; firebrick lined | 200,000 | |
| | Furnace #1007 | | 10″ | | | |
| Marathon Heater Company, Inc. | Logwood Lo-Profile | 24″ | 7″ | ⅛″ and ³⁄₁₆″ ga. steel | 120,000 | $1,265 |

| Manufacturer | Furnace | Wood Length | Flue Size | Materials | Btu/hour | Price |
|---|---|---|---|---|---|---|
| Marathon Heater Company, Inc. | Logwood Standard | 36″ | 8″ | ⅛″ and ³⁄₁₆″ ga. steel | 245,000 | $1,765 |
| | Logwood Standard | 48″ | 9″ | ⅛″ and ³⁄₁₆″ ga. steel | 327,600 | $2,030 |
| | Logwood Wood-burning Boiler Model 16″ | | 8″ | | 80,000 | $2,180 |
| | Logwood Wood-burning Boiler Model 24″ | | 8″ | | 125,000 | $2,325 |
| | Logwood Wood-burning Boiler Model 36″ | | 8″ | | 200,000 | $2,635 |
| | Logwood Wood-burning Boiler Model 48″ | | 9″ | | 300,000 | $2,855 |
| Minnesota Energy Savers Inc. | Lumberjack Add-on Wood Furnace | 28″ | 8″ | 12 ga. steel; firebox of ³⁄₁₆″ steel and firebrick lined | 55,000 | $ 650 |
| Monarch Kitchen Appliances | Model AF 124 Add-a-Furnace | 24″ | 6″ | 12 ga. steel | 35,000 | |
| | Model AF 224 | 24″ | 6″ | 12 ga. steel | 50,000 | |
| | Model AF 324 | | 6″ | | 75,000 | |
| Passat | HO-20 | 36″ | 6.3″ | COR-TEN steel | 72,000 | $ 975 |
| | HO-30 | 36″ | 7.9″ | COR-TEN steel | 108,000 | $1,295 |
| | HO-45 | 55″ | 7.9″ | COR-TEN steel | 152,000 | $1,575 |
| | HOL-20 | 36″ | 6.3″ | COR-TEN steel | 88,000 | $1,575 |
| | HOL-45 | 55″ | 6.3″ | COR-TEN steel | 200,000 | $2,800 |
| | HOLO-20 | 36″ | 7.9″ | COR-TEN steel | 88,000 | $2,898 |
| | HOLO-45 | 55″ | 7.9″ | COR-TEN steel | 200,000 | $4,195 |
| Powrmatic | Model OW-110 Combination Furnace | 24″ | 8″ | Firebrick-lined firebox | 112,000 | |
| | Model OW-140 Combination Furnace | 24″ | 8″ | Firebrick-lined firebox | 140,000 | |
| | Model OW-150 Combination Furnace | 24″ | 8″ | Firebrick-lined firebox | 150,000 | |
| | Model OW-170 Combination Furnace | 24″ | 8″ | Firebrick-lined firebox | 170,000 | |
| Ram Forge | Wood Furnace | 28″ | 5″ | 24 ga. steel | 75,000 | |

# Furnaces Compared (Continued)

| Manufacturer | Furnace | Wood Length | Flue Size | Materials | Btu/hour | Price |
|---|---|---|---|---|---|---|
| Riteway Manufacturing Company | Furnace LF30 | 24" | 8" | Steel with fire-brick lining | 160,000 | $2,281 |
| | Furnace LF50 | 36" | 8" | Steel with fire-brick lining | 215,000 | $2,468 |
| | Furnace LF70 | 48" | 10" | Steel with fire-brick lining | 350,000 | $3,229 |
| | Boiler LB30 | 24" | 8" | Steel with fire-brick lining | 160,000 | $3,612 |
| | Boiler LB50 | 36" | 8" | Steel casing | 200,000 | $3,768 |
| | Boiler LB70 | 48" | 10" | Steel casing | 350,000 | $4,108 |
| Sam Daniels Company | Chunk Furnace R30W | 30" | 8" | 26 ga. steel with stainless steel firebox | 100,000 | |
| | Furnace R36W | 36" | 8" | Stainless steel firebox | 128,000 | |
| | Furnace R42W | 42" | 8" | | 157,000 | |
| | Furnace R48W | 48" | 9" | | 225,000 | |
| | Furnace R1-60W | 60" | 9" | | 300,000 | |
| | R2-60W | 60" | 10" | | 400,000 | |
| Solar Wood Energy Corp. | Northeaster 101B | 16" | 7" | 1/8" steel with steel liners | 100,000 | |
| | Northeaster 224-B | 24" | 7" | 1/8" steel with steel liners | 125,000 | |
| Tekton Corp. | MB 30 | 15" | 8 × 8" | 5/16" plate steel | 72,000 | $1,377 |
| | MB 40 | 15" | 8 × 8" | 5/16" plate steel | 100,000 | $1,526 |
| | MB 55 | 27" | 8 × 12" | 5/16" plate steel | 140,000 | $1,736 |
| | MB 75 | 27" | 8 × 12" | 5/16" plate steel | 180,000 | $1,961 |
| | OT 28S | 15" | 8 × 8" | 5/16" plate steel | 72,000 | $1,940 |
| | OT 35S | 21" | 8 × 8" | 5/16" plate steel | 112,000 | $2,120 |
| | OT 50S | 21" | 8 × 8" | 5/16" plate steel | 140,000 | $2,360 |
| | OT 70S | 30" | 8 × 12" | 5/16" plate steel | 196,000 | $2,776 |
| Wood Energy Systems Corp. | Wesco Boiler | 24" | | 24 ga. galvanized steel; firebox of 1/4" plate | 70,000 | $ 725 |

### Atlanta Stove Works, Inc.
### Atlanta, Georgia 31307

Atlanta presently has only one cookstove in production, *Model 15–36*, but it has been proven over several generations of use. It comes in two styles: with or without the dual warming ovens. The stove is made of solid cast iron and will operate on wood or coal. Well-engineered dampers and draft controls help you to hold temperatures and the 35½-inch by 21½-inch cast iron cooking surface and 15- by 14- by 11-inch oven allow you to maintain a steady, even heat.

The stove measures 29½ inches to the cooking surface which has four 8-inch and two 5½-inch covers. The firebox accepts a 15-inch log without the end liners in place and requires a 7-inch flue pipe. There is no oven thermometer. Shipping weight is 285 pounds with the warming ovens, 254 without.

## The Atlanta Stove Works, Inc.

### Birmingham Stove and Range Co.
### P.O. Box 2647
### Birmingham, Alabama 35202

The *Red Mountain "T"* cooking range has been in production since 1936. It burns wood or coal, has cast iron oven plates, three draft controls and optional dual warming ovens. The oven is 15- by 14- by 11-inches and it is 29½-inches to the cooking surface. The stove weighs 285 with the warming ovens.

### Enterprise Sales
### R.F.D. #2
### Apple Creek, Ohio 44606

*Model 52DYT* is an ordinary-size kitchen range designed for cooking and baking with coal or wood. It may not look as romantic as an old Atlantic Queen, but it's bound to be a lot easier to work with. The inside body is made of steel, welded, riveted and bolted. The outside panels and high shelves are finished with baked-on porcelain enamel available in either black or white.

The firebox, equipped with cast iron grate and linings, is 16 inches long, 8 inches wide and 10 inches deep and capable of holding a fire for 12 hours. The door panels are insulated so you can stand up close to a hot range.

The oven is porcelain enamel inside for better heat penetration and easier cleaning. It is 16 inches wide, 18 inches deep and 11½ inches high. A 6¾ gallon copper reservoir is located at the opposite end from the firebox. Weight is 385 pounds.

Essentially the same as the *52DYT, Model 52DY* does not have the water reservoir. It does have a glass window in the oven door. It is 32 inches long, 31 inches wide and 32½ inches high with a net weight of 340 pounds. When you buy this model with the deluxe backguard in chrome, white and wood grain finish complete with installed electric clock, you have *Model 52DYA*.

### Lyons Supply Company, Inc.
### 49 Beech Street
### Manchester, New Hampshire 03105

Two versions of the cookstove are made by Trolla and distributed through Lyons Supply. (There may be a distributor closer to your area.) *Trolla No. 354*, the larger of the two can be operated with coal or wood. Damper controls are on the right; the firebox is on the left with the ash pan immediately underneath. This range has two cooking rings, 12½ inches in diameter, and a 7- by 13- by 13-inch oven. The stove top is porcelain enamel finish. A nickel plated towel bar accents the front edge. Extra long legs are available to boost the cook surface to 32 inches from 24¾ inches.

The smaller model, *No. 325*, has no oven. The two lids are 9½ inches in diameter and the firebox is located in the center of the range between them. It is a good choice for boat or camp and comes with pre-drilled ⅜-inch holes in the legs to allow for fastening it to the deck. Extra long legs are available.

Both stoves come in dull stove-black finish. *Model 354* weighs 220 pounds; *Model 325* weighs 92½ pounds.

### Martin Industries
### P.O. Box 128
### Florence, Alabama 35630

The *8-16 Perfection* cookstove is the perfect back up alliance for a family that does not wish to rely on only one type of fuel. It is a small, cast iron stove with four round cooking lids, a warming shelf and a 15- by 15-inch oven. The top surface, including a small towel bar measures 22 inches by 29 inches and is 25¼ inches high. The stove has a heavy basket grate, extra heavy ribbed fireback and ribbed covers and top oven plate. A soot rake and cover lifter are included with each stove. Shipping weight is 202 pounds.

### The Merry Music Box
### 20 McKown Street
### Boothbay Harbor, Maine 04538
### (207) 633-2210

Styria ranges are hand-built by an Austrian family business and distributed in the United States by The Merry Music Box. They make three models, ranging in weight from 611 pounds (*Model No. 106*) to 1100 pounds (*Model No. 130*). The stove is designed with a central steel cooking surface (36 inches by 24 inches on the large model, 30 inches by 21 inches on the smaller models) surrounded by a stainless steel "warming border" handy for simmer-cooking. A towel rack extends 2 inches beyond the warming border.

The firebox has a 5-inch by 7½-inch opening on all models and is 20 inches deep on the larger two, 18½ inches on the smaller. The oven opening is 17 inches by 9 inches with a 29-, 24- and 23-inch depth on the large, medium and small models, respectively. All three models have water resevoirs—6½ gallon capacity on the large and medium stoves, 4½ gallons on the small.

## Monarch Kitchen Appliances
## Malleable Iron Range Company
## 715 North Spring Street
## Beaver Dam, Wisconsin 53916

Monarch ranges are made by a division of the Malleable Iron Range Company. In addition to its coal/wood-operated range, *Model R9CW*, Monarch makes three other combination fuel ranges. *Model 6LEH* is an electric range with built in wood/coal heater section. It has four infinite control plug-in surface units in addition to the quick-to-heat-up Malleable iron cook top. The firebox is 36 inches wide by 26⅛ inches deep and stands 47½ inches high. The porcelain enamel-lined oven is 20 inches wide, 17 inches high and 19⅞ inches deep with a removeable bottom panel for easy cleaning at the sink.

Model *HF36HW* is a gas range with wood/coal heater section. You use gas for cooking, broiling and baking; wood or coal for heating and auxiliary cooking. The firebox and oven dimensions are the same as the electric combination range, *Model 6LEH*.

*Model CE119Y* combination electric coal/wood range lets you bake or roast with coal or wood and automatically holds the temperature with electricity. A patented damper closes the flue when baking and roasting with electricity.

Finally, *Model R9CW* is a coal- or wood-only range with a firebox 43 inches wide, 25 inches deep and 47¾ inches high. It has the same cast iron duplex grates as the combination fuel models. Comes with a four-gallon water reservoir on the right side. All models described have white porcelain finish.

*Tirolia cooking range, imported by Old Country Appliances.*

## Old Country Appliances
## P.O. Box 330
## Vacaville, California 95688

Old Country Appliances is the sole U.S. importer for Tirolia ranges. Tirolia makes five models of cooking ranges, three of them (the *D5N, D7N* and the *D9N*) with adjustable firebox volumes to vary the amount of fuel burned according to the season. The overall impression is of a well-built, technically advanced piece of equipment. All have firebrick-lined fireboxes. The mid-range model, the *D5N Innsbruck*, is approximately 29 inches wide, 23 inches deep and 33½ inches high with three possible flue pipe connections. Its oven opening is about 12 inches by 8½ inches and 21 inches deep. The approximate space heating ability is rated at 3500 cubic feet. It weighs 355 pounds.

Each of the models is completely airtight with asbestos gaskets under the solid steel range top, and around the firebox and ashbox doors. All models have the "Bavarian Double Draft" system, which allows rapid starting. This means the fire can be drafted directly to the flue or drafted across the bottom of the cook surface, down around the oven, back up and out the flue.

Three models, the *D6, D7N* and the *D9N*, have water reservoirs, the largest having a 4¾ gallon capacity.

## Pioneer Lamps and Stoves
## 71 Yesler Way
## Seattle, Washington 98104

If you are looking for an authentic, old-fashioned-looking cookstove without the hassles of a used antique, the *Victor Jr. Kitchen Range* may be the stove for you. Designed in 1911, this beauty comes with a nondecorative sand-cast finish. Nickel, brass or copper trim can be custom plated by your local plater.

The firebox is 9 inches deep, 18½ inches long and 7 inches wide and has one piece, replaceable firebox liners. The 15½- by 15½- by 10-inch oven is cast iron and the "Kindle/Bake" damper is used to vent the fire either directly to the flue or to pull it over, around and under the oven before doubling back to the flue. Cast iron walls between the cooktop and oven force heat to pass under the entire cooktop.

The overall dimensions of the stove, which also operates on coal, are 28 inches deep by 40 inches wide and 30 inches high to the cook surface. It weighs 274 pounds and has a 7-inch flue opening. The warming oven and water reservoir are optional and increase the weight to a total of 320 pounds.

The *Findlay Oval*, "the Rolls Royce of cook ranges," is not only a handsome beast, its performance has been endorsed by the Ontario Mennonites, who have declared it the "best range ever built."

The original 1908 *Oval* design was modified in 1924 and again in 1976; it is now considered to have a 60-year, full-duty service span. The adjustable firebrick firebox measures 9 inches by 22 inches by 12 inches high and the ceramic porcelain-lined oven is 18 inches by 20 inches. The cooktop is 24 inches by 39 inches plus 9 more inches for the reservoir. The stove comes standard with ceramic-porcelain paneling and pure nickel-plated trim. Options are the 32-quart, pure copper reservoir and the warming oven which bring the weight up to 400 pounds. *Ovals* can be put on the road in as little as two weeks after ordering in the off-season (January through July) but take up to two months when ordered between August and December.

254

**S/A Import Division**
**730 Midtown Plaza**
**Syracuse, New York 13210**

S/A Import Division is one of the importers of *Stanley* ranges. They are made by Waterford Ironfounders, Ltd. of Ireland, where the use of solid fuel is still common. The fireboxes are airtight on all three models and accept standard 16-inch cord wood. The only differences between the models is firebox size (0.42 cubic feet for *Models 8B* and *8W*; 1.06 cubic feet for *Model MK-1*) and the exterior finish—matte black or white porcelain with black accents. All models measure 28 3/8 inches high, 35 3/8 inches wide and 21 3/4 inches deep. The cast iron oven's dimensions are 15 3/4 inches wide, 13 inches high and 15 inches deep. You can choose flush-to-the-floor styling or colonial legs. A 21-inch high back-splash, 12-inch warming shelf and a water heater are each optional. The water heater can be connected to your existing storage and distribution system.

*Stanley* Mark I *cooking range.*

**Scandinavian Stoves, Inc.**
**Box 72**
**Alstead, New Hampshire 03602**

Scandinavian Stoves, Inc. is the importer of *Lange* stoves whose *Model 911W* is a small, cast iron cook range. This wood-operated stove has a large firebox with removeable grate, tight construction and two spin draft controls. The firebox can be vented directly to the flue for quick starts. The stove has two cooklids, a 7 1/2- by 11- by 16-inch oven and a towel rail around three edges. It is 33 1/4 inches to the cooking surface. Shipping weight is 375 pounds.

**Washington Stove Works**
**P.O. Box 687**
**Everett, Washington 98201**

*Olympics* are wood- and oil-operated cooking ranges. *Model 18-W* has white procelain enamel finish with polished iron top and lids. It measures 32 inches wide, 22 inches deep and 32 inches high to the cook top. The oven interior is enameled and measures 18 inches deep and wide and 13 inches high. Only the oven door is insulated. The firebox is 16 inches deep, 8 inches wide and 8 1/2 inches high. Optional extras are full-width warmer shelf, factory-installed copper coils, an extra large firebox with heavy iron grates and lining, sliding draft and oven door thermometer. Shipping weight is 320 pounds.

*Model 8-15* is a lighter-weight model in matte black finish. It has a slightly larger firebox with heavy iron grates and lining. Tight-fitting feed door and ash door are standard. Optional extras are the warming shelf and factory-installed copper coils. Shipping weight is 245 pounds.

*Model B-18* is a full-sized range with polished tops, full width towel rack and commercial griddle. Lids and centers are reinforced to prevent warping and cracking. Two center posts give the top central support, assuring a flat surface over the years. The wide, shallow fire box is equipped to burn either wood or coal. Linings are sectional to avoid burn out. Ovens are keystone rust-resistant steel with heavy cast iron braces. The body is one piece, 20-gauge Wellsville polished steel, double-wall construction, insulated with asbestos. The firebox is pre-tapped for hot water coils. The stove has a 12-month guarantee against defects in materials assembly.

## Cookstoves Compared

The following stoves are designed primarily for cooking.

| Manufacturer | Stove | Height to Cooking Surface | Firebox Size | Size of Oven | Weight/Materials | Price |
|---|---|---|---|---|---|---|
| Atlanta Stove Works, Inc. | #15–36 | 29 1/2 " | 15" L | 15" × 14" × 11" | 285 Cast iron body | $ 597 |
| Birmingham Stove and Range Co. | Red Mountain "T" | 29 1/2 " | | 15" × 14" × 11" | 285 Cast iron | $ 449 |
| Enterprise Sales | Model 52DYT | 31 1/2 " | 16" × 8" × 10" | 16" × 18" × 11 1/2" | Steel, cast iron, copper | $ 475 |

# Cookstoves Compared *(Continued)*

| Manufacturer | Stove | Height to Cooking Surface | Firebox Size | Size of Oven | Weight/Materials | Price |
|---|---|---|---|---|---|---|
| Enterprise Sales | Model 52DY | 32½" | 16" × 8" × 10" | 16" × 18" × 11½" | Steel, cast iron, glass | $ 415 |
| Lyons Supply Company, Inc. | Trolla No. 354 | 25" | 6" × 6" × 12" | 7" × 13" × 13" | 220 Cast iron | |
| | Trolla No. 325 | 15¾" | 16" × 9" | None | 92½ Cast iron | |
| Martin Industries | 8-16 Perfection | 25¼" | | 15" × 15" | 202 Cast iron | |
| The Merry Music Box | Styria 106 | 34" | 5" × 7½" × 18½" | 9" × 14" × 23" | 611 Enamel finish; firebrick lining | $2,300 |
| | Styria 119 | 34" | 20" L | 9" × 14" × 24" | 800 Enamel finish; firebrick lining | $2,100 |
| | Styria 130 | 34" | 5" × 7½" × 20" | 9" × 14" × 29" | 1040 Enamel finish; firebrick lining | $2,300 |
| Monarch Kitchen Appliances | Model CE 119Y-1 | 34⅝" | 8" × 17½" | 15¾" × 19" × 21" | 537 s.w. Porcelain enamel finish | |
| | Model R 9 CW | 34⅝" | 8" × 17½" | 19" × 15¾" × 21" | 513 s.w. Porcelain enamel finish | |
| | Model 6 LEH | 36" | 7" × 17" | 20" × 17" × 19⅞" | Porcelain enamel finish | |
| Old Country Appliances | SD4 Thriftmaster | 29" | 6½" × 12" | 10" × 17" × 8" | 245 Iron, steel, firebrick | $ 434 |
| | D6 Alpine | 31½" | 8" × 14" | 10" × 19" × 8½" | 310 Iron, steel, firebrick | $ 688 |
| | D5N Innsbruck | 33½" | 11½" × 16" | 12" × 21" × 8" | 355 Steel, iron, firebrick | $ 834 |
| | D7N Salzburg | 33½" | 11½" × 15½" | 12" × 21" × 8" | Iron, steel, firebrick | $ 898 |
| | D9N Vienna | 33½" | 14" × 16½" | 15½" × 21" × 9½" | Iron, steel, firebrick | $1,087 |
| Pioneer Lamp & Stove Co. | Victory Jr. 1911 Wood/Coal Range | 57" | 7" × 9" × 18½" | 15½" × 15½" × 10½" | 325 Cast iron | $ 495 to $ 595 |
| | Findlay Oval | | 9" × 22" × 12" | 18" × 20" | 400 Cast iron, firebrick, ceramic porcelain paneling, nickel trim | $1,295 |
| S/A Imports Division | Stanley 8B & MK1 | 28⅜" | | 13" × 15¾" × 15" | Enamel finish; cast iron oven | $ 986 |
| | Stanley 8W | 28 ⅜" | | 13" × 15¾" × 15" | Enamel finish; cast iron oven | $ 750 |
| Scandinavian Stoves, Inc. | Lange Model 911W | 33¼" | 17½" L | 7½" × 11" × 16" | 375 s.w. Cast iron body | |

| Manufacturer | Stove | Height to Cooking Surface | Firebox Size | Size of Oven | Weight/Materials | Price |
|---|---|---|---|---|---|---|
| Washington Stove Works | Olympic 18 W | 32″ | 8½″ × 8″ × 16″ | 13″ × 18″ × 18″ | 320 s.w. Porcelain enamel finish; cast iron firebox lining | $ 640 |
| | Olympic 8-15 | 30¾″ | 8¾″ × 8″ × 19¾″ | 10″ × 18″ × 15″ | 245 s.w. Matte black finish; firebox lining | $ 360 |
| | Olympic B-18-1 Home Range | 31½″ | 8″ × 8¾″ × 21″ | 11¼″ × 17¼″ × 18½″ | 490 s.w. Steel body; cast iron lining | $1,085 |

# Index

The Index is in two parts. *Part I* refers to the descriptive text of all the chapters. *Part II* refers to the Catalog section at the end of each chapter and is divided into five sections accordingly, i.e., Energy Conservation, Solar Energy, Wind Power, Water Power, and Wood Heat.

## I

# II

## ENERGY CONSERVATION CATALOG

## SOLAR ENERGY CATALOG